Introduction to
OCEANOGRAPHY

Introduction to OCEANOGRAPHY

David A. Ross

Woods Hole Oceanographic Institution

APPLETON-CENTURY-CROFTS
Educational Division
MEREDITH CORPORATION New York

Acknowledgments for Chapter Title Photographs

All photographs from Monkmeyer Press Photo Service
and the following photographers: Chapter 1 J. Cron;
Chapter 2 Palmer; Chapter 3 Grant White; Chapter 4
Foote; Chapter 5 Fritz Henle; Chapter 6 Proi; Chapter
8 Fritz Henle; Chapter 9 Fritz Henle.

to Edith

PREFACE

In this book I have attempted to describe and explain oceanography in a manner that is understandable to nonscientists. I have tried to avoid the common tendency to make oceanography sound more glamorous than it really is. Submersibles, undersea treasures, and mysterious animals, exciting as they are, constitute only a small part of oceanography. Oceanography is the application of all science to the study of the ocean: I have tried to make clear the role of the separate scientific disciplines and to show their interrelationships in the study of the marine environment. I have also discussed the uses of technology and instrumentation, and I have sketched the historical development of oceanography. No one can ignore the economic potential of the ocean or the hazards of marine pollution. I have given space to both.

When I started to teach a course in Introductory Oceanography at a nearby community college, I found, to my surprise, that no suitable text was available. The continuing need for an elementary book in oceanography compelled me to undertake the task of writing one.

I have had the aid and cooperation of many gifted persons, especially my colleagues at the Woods Hole Oceanographic Institution. Richard T. Barber, Egon T. Degens, Kenneth O. Emery, Howard L. Sanders, and Bruce A. Warren read sections of the book. Their comments and criticisms were most helpful. Others gave freely of their time and ideas, in particular Melbourne R. Carriker, Louis A. Hobson, Robert H. Meade, John S. Schlee, Susan Schlee, Mary Sears, John M. Teal, and Elazar Uchupi. Many persons provided graphic and background material, among them William M. Dunkle, Jr., Charles D. Hollister, Ned Hooper, Charles S. Innis, Frank Medeiros, John D. Milliman, Peter J. Oldham, Johanna Reinhardt, John L. Schilling, and Donald P. Souza. I should like to thank all of them.

Numerous persons have permitted me to use their unpublished and published material, which I have acknowledged appropriately in the text.

Betty Frank, Heide Frantz, Louise Langley, Susan Jonas, and Anne Collins helped me with the preparation of the manuscript. Peter Fenner of the American Geological Institute and Joseph Ewing of Appleton-Century-Crofts had the unfortunate job of reading the many drafts of this book. Their persistent and critical review is greatly appreciated. Finally, I should like to thank my wife, Edith, who encouraged me when I needed encouragement, who helped me when I needed help, and who left me alone when I needed privacy.

D. A. R.

Woods Hole, Massachusetts

CONTENTS

Introduction to OCEANOGRAPHY

Chapter 1

INTRODUCTION

WHAT IS OCEANOGRAPHY?

What is oceanography? What is this new science that is so important to our country and to the human race? Many definitions are possible; a simple one is, **the application of all science to the phenomena of the ocean.** The key word in this definition is "all," for to be a good oceanographer one should know something about most fields of science and their influence on the ocean. To make this point clearer let me quote a definition of oceanography given by one of the pioneers of this science, Henry Bryant Bigelow.[1]

OCEANOGRAPHY has been aptly defined as the study of the world below the surface of the sea; it should include the contact zone between sea and atmosphere. According to present-day acceptance it has to do with all the characteristics of the bottom and margins of the sea, of the sea water, and of the inhabitants of the latter. Thus widely combining geophysics, geochemistry, and biology, it is inclusive, as is, of course, characteristic of any "young" science; and modern oceanography is in its youth. But in this case it is not so much immaturity that is responsible for the fact that these several sub-sciences are still grouped together, but rather the realization that physics, chemistry, and biology of the sea water are not only important **per se,** but that in most of the basic problems of the sea all three of these subdivisions have a part. And with every advance in our knowledge of the sea making this interdependence more and more apparent, it is not likely that we shall soon see any general abandonment of this concept of oceanography as a mother science, the branches of which, though necessarily attacked by different disciplines, are intertwined too closely to be torn apart. Every oceanic biologist should, therefore, be grounded in the principles of geophysics and geochemistry; every chemical or physical oceanographer in some of the oceanic aspects of biology.

This definition, which was first given in 1929, is still applicable today. From it we can see that oceanography is not a single science but rather a combination of various sciences. Most oceanographers have divided oceanography into four main parts: (1) chemical oceanography; (2) biological oceanography; (3) physical oceanography; and (4) marine geology and geophysics.

The chemical oceanographer is concerned with chemical reactions that occur both in the ocean and on the sea floor. The biological oceanographer studies the occurrence and distribution of life in the ocean. Physical reactions, such as changes and motion of sea water, are included in the realm of the physical oceanographer. The marine geologist, or geological oceanographer, studies the sediments and topography of the ocean floor. The deeper structure of the ocean floor and its physical properties are the domain of the marine geophysicist.

[1] Bigelow, H. B. *Oceanography: Its Scope, Problems, and Economic Importance.* Boston: Houghton Mifflin Co., 1931.

Although these divisions seem to break oceanography up into neat little niches, in practice it is otherwise. For example, a marine geologist taking a sample of the sediment at the bottom of the equatorial Pacific would obtain a sediment composed mainly of shells of dead microscopic organisms; thus, he is looking at a biological deposit. The organisms do not live on the bottom, but in the surface waters more than 2 miles above the bottom. If samples were taken of the ocean bottom north or south of the equator the number of shells would decrease considerably. This is because a unique physical condition exists in the region of the equator, where the right combination of currents and winds keeps the water agitated and mixed. The mixing, in turn, influences the chemistry of the water; nutrients which are necessary for the life cycle of the organisms are brought to the surface waters where they can be used. Thus deposits on the sea floor are intimately influenced by the chemistry, physics, and biology of the water above.

This example suggests that perhaps the different divisions of oceanography are artificial and unnecessary. For as Bigelow said, an oceanographer should be versed in all of these fields. Oceanography has advanced so rapidly, however, that it is nearly impossible for a scientist to be expert in all its aspects. Consequently, most oceanographers specialize in one or two of the divisions I listed earlier. In this book I treat each division in a separate chapter. But the reader should always remember that the divisions are not rigid and that the different aspects are closely related.

Now that we have a definition of oceanography we can consider some general questions about the science. One question is why does one study oceanography. Clearly the ocean is an environment that is hostile to man and that does not easily yield its secrets. This very secrecy, this lure and romance of the sea, has drawn many persons to oceanography. Equally enticing is the knowledge that water covers about 72 percent of the world: man has always been interested in his environment and the depths of the ocean are no exception. The discoveries of men like Beebe and Cousteau, who have explored the depths of the ocean, have fascinated many people.

To the trained scientist the ocean may have the answer to some of man's important questions and problems. Within the sediment layers on the ocean floor are recorded the geological and, in fossils, the biological history of the earth. Life on earth undoubtedly began in the ocean a few billion years ago, and since that time evolution has produced the vast quantities and varieties of life now found in the ocean. This abundance of life has been an important source of food for man for many centuries and holds the promise of solving some of today's food problems. Biological products of the sea such as pearls or the shells of dead organisms have varied uses—the shells, for example, are especially valuable as building materials..The ocean is also an important source of commercially valuable chemical resources, including iodine, bromine, potassium, magnesium, manganese, and other elements. Desalinization of ocean water is yielding increasingly important amounts of fresh water in arid areas of the world. Sea floor mineral accumulations, like phosphorite, manganese, sand, and gravel, are valuable commodities that may become more fully exploited in the future. Accumulations of oil and gas below the sea floor have already become important natural resources. The ocean also plays an important, but incompletely understood, role in influencing the weather and climatic patterns of the earth.

The ocean is necessary to commerce, communication, and national defense. Much of the trade between countries is carried by ships over the ocean, and beneath the ocean are transoceanic cables linking the communication networks of many of the world's countries. The seas have been a battlefield for most of man's history, and much of the oceanic research today is in part concerned with national defense. Finally, the ocean is important for recreation; the sports of fishing, boating, waterskiing, and SCUBA diving, as well as swimming, attract ever greater numbers of persons each year. This underscores one of the major problems facing man—pollution. One can only hope we will control and prevent the pollution of the ocean before these activities become things of the past.

Today's oceanographer enters the field by one of two routes: either through formal training in oceanography or from an associated scientific field. Because oceanography is usually taught as a graduate course of study, an aspiring oceanographer would do best to get himself or herself a sound training in the basic sciences as an undergraduate and then to specialize in an aspect of oceanography in graduate school. Among the best oceanographers are those who specialized in a basic science and then developed an interest in the application of that science to the ocean.

There are many universities and research laboratories where good training in oceanography is available. The three largest institutions are Scripps Institution of Oceanography, Woods Hole Oceanographic Institution, and Lamont-Doherty Geological Observatory. Scripps (Figure 1-1) in La Jolla, California, became affiliated with the University of California in 1912. It has grown since that time to become the largest oceanographic institution in the United States. Woods Hole (Figure 1-2), in Woods Hole, Massachusetts, was chartered in 1930 as a private, nonprofit research institution and has recently developed a degree-granting educational program. Lamont-Doherty, in Palisades, New York, was founded in 1949, and is part of Columbia University. These large institutions and others such as those associated with the Univer-

Figure 1-1 The Scripps Institution of Oceanography, in La Jolla, California (foreground). In the left background is the San Diego campus of the University of California. (Photograph courtesy of Scripps Institution of Oceanography.)

sity of Miami, University of Rhode Island, Texas A and M, Oregon State University, and the University of Washington usually emphasize deep-sea research. In smaller institutions, research is generally directed toward more local, nearshore problems.

It has been estimated that only 1,000 people in the United States would qualify as trained marine scientists, or about 1 for every 200,000 persons, a very small percentage indeed, especially when one considers that most of the earth's surface is covered by water.

Oceanographers possessing a bachelor's degree in one of the associated sciences usually first work as laboratory or research assistants. Scientists with more advanced training or experience may have teaching or research positions. Whatever their training, most marine scientists spend part of their time at sea. Generally, oceanographic cruises last from a few days to several months. Most of the time at sea is spent acquiring data, sometimes under adverse conditions.

Figure 1-2 The Woods Hole Oceanographic Institution (center of picture). Part of the Marine Biological Laboratory can be seen in the upper part of the photo. The research vessel CHAIN and the catamaran LULU, carrying the submersible ALVIN, can be seen in the picture. (Photograph courtesy of Woods Hole Oceanographic Institution.)

Oceanographers are employed by universities and research laboratories, as well as by the Federal Government. The Federal Government has several agencies engaged in oceanographic work: the Bureau of Commercial Fisheries; the Naval Oceanographic Office; the Environmental Science Services Administration; and the United States Geological Survey, to name a few. The outlook for future employment in the field of oceanography is considered to be good. In the United States, an annual oceanographic industry of over 15 billion dollars is anticipated by 1975. The Federal Government, recognizing the increasing importance of oceanography, has established several long-range programs, such as the International Oceanographic Decade which started in 1970. There are also plans to increase the size of the U.S. fleet of oceanographic research vessels.

Before we turn, in following chapters, to the origin of the ocean, the history of oceanography, and oceanographic instrumentation, I will mention some terms and statistics commonly used in oceanography.

Terms and Statistics

Oceanographers, for various reasons, use a confusing mixture of terms when discussing the ocean. The metric system, adopted by most scientists, is only sometimes used in oceanography. The metric system is based on multiples of ten. The smallest unit we shall be concerned with is a micron (μ); 1,000 microns equal 1 millimeter (mm), 10 millimeters equal 1 centimeter (cm), 100 centimeters equal 1 meter (m), and 1,000 meters equal 1 kilometer (km). A kilometer is about 0.6 miles (Tables 1-1 and 1-2).

Depth is measured either in fathoms or in meters. A fathom is 6 feet (ft), or approximately the length of line a man can hold between his outspread hands. One hundred fathoms equal 183 meters.

TABLE 1-1   METRIC-ENGLISH EQUIVALENTS

	Metric			English		
	Centimeters	**Meters**	**Kilometers**	**Inches**	**Feet**	**Miles**
cm	1	1/100	1/100,000	0.3937	—	—
m	100	1	1/1,000	39.37	3.28	—
km	100,000	1,000	1	—	3,280	0.624
in	2.54	—	—	1	1/12	—
ft	30.48	0.3048	—	12	1	1/5,280
mile	—	1,609	1.609	—	5,280	1

1 square kilometer = 0.386 square mile
1 cubic kilometer = 0.238 cubic mile

Grams	**Kilograms**	**Ounces**	**Pounds**
1	1/1,000	0.035	—
1,000	1	—	2.20
28.35	—	1	1/16
453.54	0.453	16	1

TABLE 1-2   CONVERSION OF VARIOUS UNITS USED IN OCEANOGRAPHY

To Convert	**Into**	**Multiply by**
centimeters	inches	0.3937
meters	feet	3.28
meters	centimeters	100.0
meters	fathoms	0.546
kilometers	miles	0.624
kilometers	meters	1000.0
grams	ounces (avdp)	0.035
kilograms	pounds	2.2
degrees C	degrees F	($^\circ$C $\times$ 9/5) + 32

Velocity is usually measured in knots; one knot equals one nautical mile (6,000 feet) per hour. The commonly used metric equivalent of one knot is approximately 50 centimeters per second.

Temperature is measured in degrees centigrade (C). 0° C equals 32° Fahrenheit (F) (the freezing point of water), 20° C equals 68° F (room temperature), and 100° C equals 212° F (boiling point of water).

The average area and volume of different parts of the ocean have recently been calculated by H. W. Menard and S. M. Smith (Table 1-3). The total volume of the ocean is about $1,350 \times 10^6$ (1,350 million) cubic kilometers (km^3) or about 318×10^6 cubic miles.

The average depth of the ocean is 3,729 meters which is equal to 2,036 fathoms, 12,216 feet, or 2.3 miles.

TABLE 1-3 AREA, VOLUME, AND MEAN DEPTH OF THE OCEAN (DATA FROM MENARD AND SMITH, 1966)

Ocean and Adjacent Seas	Area (10^6 km^2)	Volume (10^6 km^3)	Mean Depth (m)
Pacific	181.344	714.410	3940
Atlantic	94.314	337.210	3575
Indian	74.118	284.608	3840
Arctic	12.257	13.702	1117
Totals and mean depth	362.033	1349.929	3729

The distribution of elevation over the world is shown in Figure 1-3. This type of representation is called the hypsographic or hypsometric curve. The curve shows the amount of the earth's surface above any given elevation or depth. Two important facts are evident from Figure 1-3:

1. Two elevations dominate, one about 100 meters, the other at about —5,000 meters.
2. There is a sharp intermediate zone between these two elevations.

The two elevations clearly indicate two different parts of the earth's crust: the sea floor, and the portion of land at or above sea level. Note that if all the water were removed from the ocean, this major difference would still exist. The sharp intermediate zone corresponds to the transition area between the continental and the oceanic regions. This part of the curve is represented in the ocean by the continental slope.

Most of the earth is covered by water: about 72 percent. Perhaps our planet should have been called "Water"!

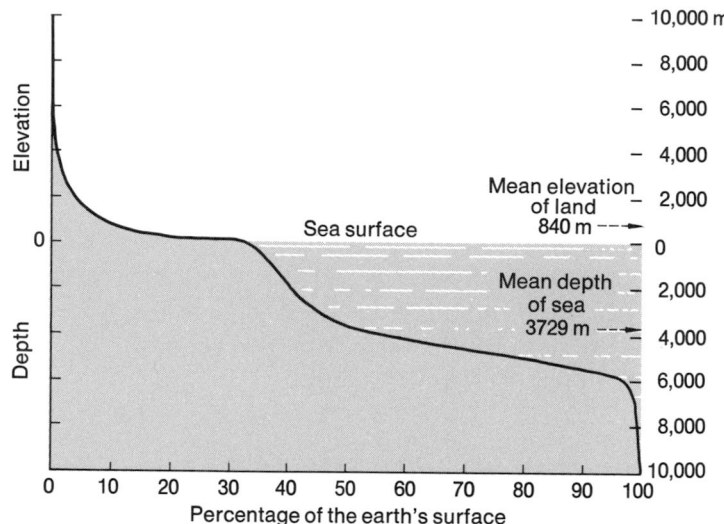

Figure 1-3 Hypsographic curve showing the percentage area of the earth's surface above a given elevation or depth.

SUGGESTED FURTHER READING

Bigelow, H. B. *Oceanography: Its Scope, Problems, and Economic Importance.* Boston: Houghton Mifflin, 1931.

Menard, H. W., and Smith, S. M. "Hypsometry of Ocean Basin Provinces." *Journal of Geophysical Research* **71** (1966): 4305–4325.

Sverdrup, H. U., Johnson, M. W., and Fleming, R. H. *The Oceans: Their Physics, Chemistry, and General Biology.* New York: Prentice-Hall, 1942.

Chapter 2
THE ORIGIN OF
THE EARTH,
THE OCEAN,
AND LIFE

Evidence about the origin of the earth generally indicates that it formed 4.5 or 5 billion years ago. Because this evidence comes mainly from the abundance and distribution of radioactive elements, a brief discussion of the use of these elements for age-dating is necessary before we consider the origin and evolution of the earth and ocean.

THE USE OF RADIOACTIVE ELEMENTS FOR AGE-DATING

Atoms of elements may occur in several forms called **isotopes;** the relatively rare isotopes differ from normal forms only in their atomic weight, and in other respects have chemical properties similar to the more common form of the element. The slight differences in atomic weight are mainly evident as small changes of boiling point, freezing point, and rates of diffusion, and they can therefore be used to study some oceanographic processes. Some isotopes are radioactive and can change, or decay, by losing part of their atomic structure to a different isotope or element. For example, Carbon occurs in three forms: Carbon-12, Carbon-13, and Carbon-14. The numbers 12, 13, 14 indicate the different atomic weights of the element. These three forms are chemically similar; however, Carbon-14 is radioactive and will decay to Nitrogen-14. The original radioactive isotope is known as the parent and the resulting form or forms (which, if radioactive, will also decay or change) are called the daughters. The rate at which radioactive isotopes decay, or the **half-life**[1] of the parent element, is constant for each isotope (Table 2-1). The half-life indicates how long it takes for half

TABLE 2-1   SOME IMPORTANT RADIOACTIVE ISOTOPES AND THEIR HALF-LIVES

Parent	Stable Daughter	Half-Life in Years
Thorium-232	Lead-208	14×10^9
Uranium-238	Lead-206	4.5×10^9
Potassium-40	Argon-40	1.3×10^9
Uranium-235	Lead-207	0.7×10^9
Carbon-14	Nitrogen-14	5,570

of the original quantity of radioactive material to decay into another isotope. For example, if the ratio of Potassium-40 to Argon-40 in a rock is 1, the age of the rock is 1.3 billion years, because that figure is the half-life of Potassium-40 or the amount of time for half of the Potassium-40 to decay. If the ratio were 3, the age of the rock would be 2.6 billion years (three-fourths of the original Potassium-40 will have been converted to Argon-40).

[1] Words in boldface type are defined in the Glossary of Oceanographic Terms.

Therefore, by measuring the relative amounts of the parent and daughter, we can determine the age of a rock. Actually, the age obtained only indicates when the rock last solidified. The reliability of this technique is based on two assumptions:

1. No daughter isotope was originally present.
2. There has been no addition of parent or daughter isotope during the aging of the rock.

It is usually difficult to test these assumptions, but if more than one parent-daughter pair is used, they can provide an independent check on each other. In other words, two different radioactive isotopes could only produce similar results if the assumptions were correct, or if they were incorrect in exactly the right proportions—an unlikely situation.

The oldest dated rocks are 3.5 billion years old. Because this date indicates when those rocks last solidified, it establishes a minimum age for the earth. Another indication of the earth's age is obtained from an analysis of the relative abundance of radioactive isotopes on earth and in meteorites. This method is similar to that used for rocks (a measure or estimate is made of the ratio of parent and daughter isotopes), and it indicates that the earth probably was in a solid state 4.5 to 5 billion years ago.

Isotopes that have long half-lives are best suited for evaluation of the age of the earth, because sufficient amounts of the parent will be present and measurable after billions of years. Isotopes with relatively short half-lives, like Carbon-14, are useful for measuring recent events of shorter duration, such as dating marine sediments.

ORIGIN OF THE EARTH

Before we discuss the origin of the earth, some consideration should be given to the origin of the universe, a subject of profound questions and little data. For example—Where did the matter that forms the universe come from and when was it formed?

The so-called big-bang hypothesis assumes that the universe has been expanding since an initial explosion. The best evidence that the universe is expanding is the shift towards the red end of the spectral lines observed from distant galaxies. This phenomenon, called the Doppler shift, results from one body moving toward or away from another body. If the body is moving away it will appear to be emitting light of lower frequency (longer wavelength) or having a red shift. The degree of this shift can be used to calculate the movement of the bodies away from the earth. Although the big-bang hypothesis accounts for the expanding universe it does not explain the origin of matter or describe what the universe looked like before the explosion.

An alternative, the cyclic hypothesis, does not assume a single origin of the universe, but does assume the eventual end of the expansion of the universe, at which time the universe will start to contract, owing to gravitational forces, and will come together in a huge, high temperature mass. An explosion will then occur, sending the matter back out to space, whereupon the entire process will be repeated. Although this hypothesis answers some of the previously mentioned questions it offers no explanation of where the matter that forms the universe came from. Clearly more data are needed before definite conclusions can be made concerning the origin of the universe.

More data *are* available for the earth and scientists generally agree on some aspects of its history, such as its age. However, the exact method of its formation is still debatable. Discussion has centered on two main hypotheses: the fragmentation hypothesis and the condensation hypothesis. The fragmentation hypothesis suggests that the planets of our solar system were torn from the sun when the sun collided with, or came very close to, another star, and that the sun and the planets were formed at different times. This hypothesis is in disagreement with the abundance of radioactive elements of the sun and the earth, which indicates a simultaneous formation of the planets and the sun.

The condensation hypothesis suggests that all parts of our solar system were formed about the same time by the compaction of a cloud of cosmic dust and gas. Most of this material formed our sun; a smaller amount formed a diffuse cloud, or nebula, around it. Eventually the nebula flattened into a disk-like shape, and in doing so it increased in density. This increase in density created an unstable condition and the nebula broke into several small clouds. These clouds were the protoplanets, which developed into the present planets. The protoplanets were originally cold and gaseous, but after losing their gases, they became heated by radioactivity and compression until they became molten. Eventually, 4.5 or 5 billion years ago, the earth solidified, but its core remained in a molten state. The condensation hypothesis, although it also has some complications, is presently favored over the fragmentation theory.

The original, or primordial, atmosphere of the earth, composed of gases that are not now common, was lost. The present atmosphere developed over long periods of geological time from gases emanating from the earth and, after plant life developed, from oxygen released by plants during photosynthesis.

ORIGIN OF THE MOON

There are two main hypotheses about the origin of the moon. The first is that the moon was torn from the earth, presumably from the Pacific

Ocean basin. The second, the condensation hypothesis, is generally more widely accepted by scientists. This hypothesis suggests that the moon formed at the same time as the earth from the condensation of cosmic gas and dust. Recent theoretical studies indicate that the moon was considerably closer to the earth in the geological past (see the section on tidal friction in Chapter 7). Preliminary analysis of rocks obtained from the moon's surface suggests a composition somewhat similar to basalt, a common volcanic rock on earth. These two observations, though not definitive, suggest a close connection between the earth and moon.

ORIGIN OF THE OCEAN

The origin of the ocean presents two problems: where did the water come from, and how did it get its present composition.

According to the three hypotheses that have developed, the vast quantities of water that today constitute the ocean may have arisen (1) from the primordial atmosphere of the earth, (2) from the decomposition of volcanic rock, (3) from incremental addition of water throughout geological time.

Proponents of the first hypothesis suggest that the primordial atmosphere condensed all at one time to form the ocean. If this really happened, one would expect the postulated original components of this atmosphere to be present in the ocean in higher quantities than have been observed. The so-called rare gases, such as neon and argon, are present in quantities millions to hundreds of millions of times less than expected if the first hypothesis is correct. Neon has an atomic weight of 20, that of water vapor or H_2O is 18; thus, if the atmosphere was unable to maintain its neon content, it seems unreasonable to expect it to have held on to large quantities of water vapor. One possible reason that the original atmosphere was lost is that gravity was not as strong as it is now. The present atmosphere of the earth in fact can hold no more than about 13,000 km^3 of water, whereas the volume of water in the ocean is over 1 billion km^3.

Advocates of the second hypothesis suggest that when the earth consolidated, much of the original water was chemically bound into volcanic rock and subsequently has been removed by decomposition of these rocks to form the ocean. Experimental and field evidence indicates that volcanic rocks contain only about 5 percent water, and even if all the water in the volcanic rocks of the earth's crust were removed, it would amount to less than 50 percent of the water in the ocean. Thus it seems obvious that most of the water of the ocean did not come from the weathering of rocks. Nevertheless, many **cations** (atoms or molecules with a positive charge) in sea water, such as sodium, magnesium, calcium, and zinc, could have come from these rocks.

The third hypothesis for the origin of the water, that of incremental addition throughout geological time, is generally the most accepted. This hypothesis proposes that ocean water was slowly, but not necessarily uniformly or continuously, added over geological time. The source of the water is volcanic activity, hot springs, and the heating of igneous rocks. In addition to water, **anions** (atoms or molecules with a negative charge) such as chloride and sulfide are released by volcanic activity.

In the preceding discussion I have simplified a complex subject. Even so, present evidence suggests volcanic activity as the source of the water and the anions, and it suggests that cations come mainly from the decomposition of igneous rocks.

Little is known about the early history of the ocean. Fossils approximately 2 billion years old, and apparently of marine origin, indicate that the ocean (although not necessarily the same as the present ocean) existed that long ago. The similarity of later fossils to present-day living forms suggests that the composition of sea water has changed little in the last 600 million years. One of the major objectives of oceanographers is to trace the early history of the earth, both chemically and biologically.

The relative amounts of the various elements in the ocean are determined by numerous chemical and physical processes that control and regulate the chemical composition of sea water. These processes take place mainly at the interfaces or boundaries of the ocean. These are: (1) the water-atmosphere interface; (2) the water-biosphere interface; and (3) the water-sediment interface. I will discuss the importance of these in the following chapters.

ORIGIN OF LIFE

The origin of life has concerned man since the beginning of his history. For many centuries it was believed that life arose by spontaneous generation. In 1862, Pasteur showed that spontaneous generation was not a reality. S. L. Miller, in 1963, listed some of the hypotheses concerning the origin of life:

1. Life arose from a supernatural event.
2. Life came from outer space.
3. Life arose from a very improbable event.
4. Life arose from favorable conditions existing in the ocean of the primeval earth.

The fourth hypothesis is accepted today by most scientists who have studied the problem. Laboratory experiments have shown that if an electrical discharge (simulating lightning) strikes a mixture of water, ammonia, and methane (compounds that were common to the primeval earth), it will create amino acids and other organic compounds of biological importance. These compounds are not truly life, especially since they are not capable of reproduction.

Some scientists have speculated that at one time early in the earth's history its surface was covered with an "organic soup" or, in other words, waters that were rich in nonbiologically produced organic molecules. The method whereby organisms formed from these molecules is unknown. Once formed, however, the organisms used some of the organic molecules as a source of food. Eventually green plants developed, needing only carbon dioxide, water, and sunlight to produce food by photosynthesis. These plants release oxygen during the photosynthetic process; the availability of oxygen and the plants as a food supply led to the development of animals.

Once living matter was available, evolution by natural selection could produce complex plants and animals from simple one-celled organisms. This process, of course, took many millions of years. Before I conclude this section, a brief discussion of geological history is appropriate.

Geological History

There is a natural tendency to think that the earth is static, that the conditions we see today have prevailed for millions of years. In some respects this view is correct. For the ocean, however, one has to think in terms of a more dynamic situation; we have observed daily, monthly, and yearly changes. Sea level has risen and fallen hundreds of feet within the last several thousand years, a phenomenon caused by changes in the earth's climate and ocean temperature. The earth's magnetic field has changed numerous times within the last several million years, and the relative position of continents and oceans has changed within the last hundred million years. Knowledge of these events comes from detailed study of geological history as it is preserved in the sediments and rocks of the ocean, and from study of the subtle changes in the biology and evolution of plants and animals.

Geologists have divided the age of the earth into four Eras; the Eras have been subdivided into Periods and even smaller units of time, called Epochs. The geological time scale and some important associated events are shown in Figure 2-1 and Table 2-2.

Geologically, little is known about the early history of the ocean. The ocean and simple marine life probably existed in Pre-Cambrian

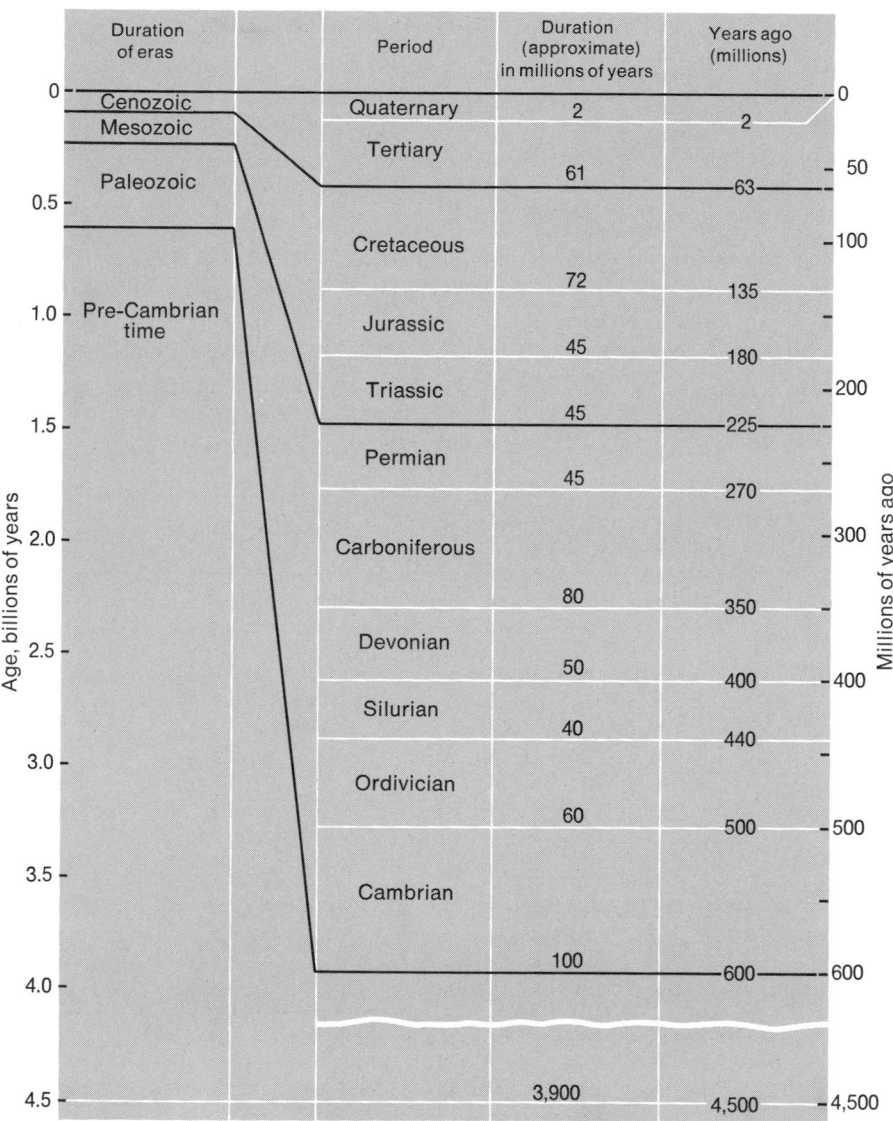

Duration of eras		Period	Duration (approximate) in millions of years	Years ago (millions)
Cenozoic		Quaternary	2	2
Mesozoic		Tertiary	61	63
Paleozoic				
		Cretaceous	72	135
Pre-Cambrian time		Jurassic	45	180
		Triassic	45	225
		Permian	45	270
		Carboniferous	80	350
		Devonian	50	400
		Silurian	40	440
		Ordivician	60	500
		Cambrian	100	600
			3,900	4,500

Age, billions of years (left axis: 0, 0.5, 1.0, 1.5, 2.0, 2.5, 3.0, 3.5, 4.0, 4.5)

Millions of years ago (right axis: 0, 50, 100, 200, 300, 400, 500, 600, 4,500)

Figure 2-1   The geological time scale.

times. By the Cambrian or Ordovician Period the ocean may have been chemically similar to the present ocean. The geography and climate of the earth, however, went through several changes during the Paleozoic and earlier Eras. Shallow seas covered most of the earth during a large part of geological history. Many areas that are now much higher than sea level were below it in the past. Large climate changes resulting in extensive glaciation occurred in the Pre-Cambrian, Permian, and more recently in Quaternary times.

TABLE 2-2 GEOLOGICAL TIME SCALE AND SOME MAJOR EVENTS

Era	Period	Events	Began Millions of Years Ago
Cenozoic	Quaternary	Age of Man. Four major glacial advances (see Table 2-3).	2
	Tertiary	Increase in mammals. Appearance of primates. Mountain building in Europe and Asia.	63
Mesozoic	Cretaceous	Extinction of dinosaurs. Increase in flowering plants and reptiles.	135
	Jurassic	Birds. Mammals. Dominance of dinosaurs. Mountain building in Western North America.	180
	Triassic	Beginning of dinosaurs and primitive mammals.	225
Paleozoic	Permian	Reptiles spread and develop. Evaporate deposits. Mountain building in United States. Glaciation in Southern Hemisphere.	270
	Carboniferous	Abundant amphibians. Reptiles appear. Mountain building in United States.	350
	Devonian	Age of fishes. First amphibians. First abundant forests of land.	400
	Silurian	First land plants. Mountain building in Europe.	440
	Ordovician	First fishes and vertebrates.	500
	Cambrian	Age of marine invertebrates.	600
Pre-Cambrian Time		Beginning of life, at least five times longer than all geological time following.	

Studies of the magnetism of old rocks, and thereby of the earth's magnetic field at the time these rocks were formed, suggest gradual movement of the magnetic poles during parts of geological time. There is also growing evidence that the continents, rather than being individual pieces of land as they are now, were once connected and actually formed only one or two large continents. At some time in the past, probably near Cretaceous time, the continents split apart and slowly started drifting toward their present position. This hypothesis, termed continental drift, is very popular among scientists today. A recent extension of this hypothesis, called sea-floor spreading, uses the magnetic properties of the ocean floor to detail its present movement (see Chapter 8 for a detailed discussion of this interesting hypothesis).

The Quaternary glaciation in the **Pleistocene** Epoch was very significant for many features of the ocean. In North America, the Pleistocene glaciation consisted of four major advances and withdrawals (interglacial stages) of glaciers over the continents (Table 2-3). The

TABLE 2-3 DIVISIONS OF THE CENOZOIC WITH SPECIAL EMPHASIS ON THE PLEISTOCENE

Era	Period	Epoch	Millions of Years Ago	Divisions of the Pleistocene
Cenozoic	Quaternary	Holocene	0.01	Wisconsin Glacial
		Pleistocene	1–2	Sangamon Interglacial
	Tertiary	Pliocene	7	Illinoian Glacial
		Miocene	25	Yarmouth Interglacial
		Oligocene	36	Kansan Glacial
		Eocene	58	Aftonian Interglacial
		Paleocene	63	Nebraskan Glacial

periods of glaciation had two distinct effects on the ocean: they lowered sea level by as much as 100 m or more, and they changed the temperature of the surface water by several degrees.

The amount sea level was lowered during the most recent Wisconsin glaciation has been studied by obtaining Carbon-14 dates of deposits that formed at or near sea level. The deposits include peat and shells of animals that live in shallow water. Many of the deposits are now found underwater. By dating this material and noting the depth at which it was found, it is possible to reconstruct a curve of recent sea-level changes (Figure 2-2). The data show that about 15,000 years before present (B.P.), sea level was more than 100 m lower than today. Additional evidence of recent raising of sea level comes from discovery of elephants' teeth on what are now the submerged parts of the continental shelf (Figure 2-3). Geologically this means that the now-submerged continental shelf was exposed to the eroding forces of waves and tides as sea level rose during the 15,000-year interval to its present position (Figure 2-4). Before the rise in sea level, rivers crossed the shelf and deposited much of their sediment into the deeper parts of the ocean. After 15,000 B.P., sea level rose relatively rapidly until about 7,000 B.P., when it reached a level of roughly 10 m below present sea level. Since 7,000 B.P., sea level has risen slowly and irregularly.

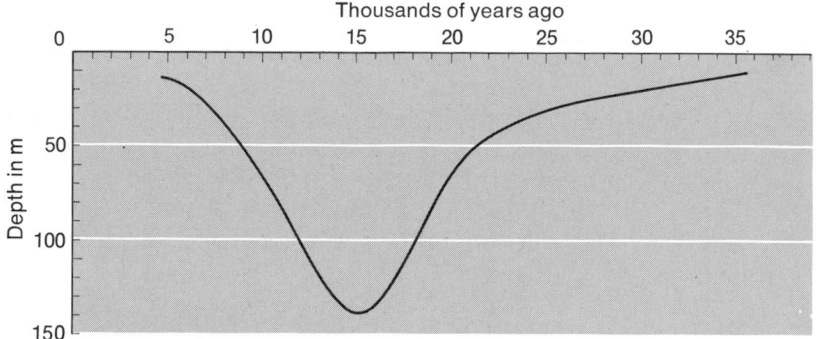

Figure 2-2

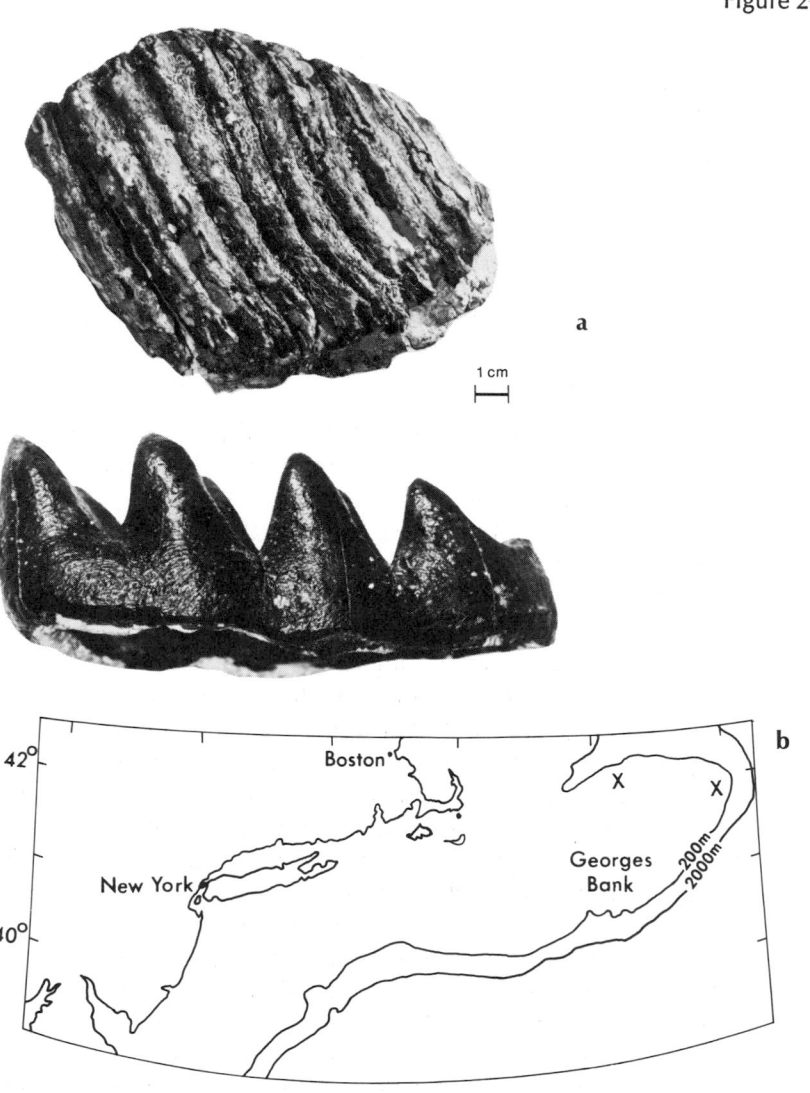

1 cm

a

b

New York

Boston

Georges
Bank

200m
2000m

42°

40°

X   X

Figure 2-3

Figure 2-2   Recent changes in sea level. Some possible small-scale fluctuations in the last 5,000 years are not shown. (Data mainly from Curray [1961, 1965], Shepard [1963], and Milliman and Emery [1968].)

Figure 2-3   (a) Elephants' teeth collected from the continental shelf. Both teeth were obtained from a depth of about 80 m near Georges Bank. (b) Xs on insert show where teeth were found. (From Whitmore and others, *Science*, Fig. 1, **156** [June, 1967]: 1477–1481; Copyright 1967 by the American Association for the Advancement of Science.)

Figure 2-4   Shorelines of 15,000 years ago (lowest level of the sea during the Wisconsin glacial stage) and 11,000 years ago. The present shoreline and the future one (if all ice were to melt) are also indicated. The insert shows the changing position of sea level with time as determined from radiocarbon ages of shallow-water shells and peat deposits. (Data from K. O. Emery.)

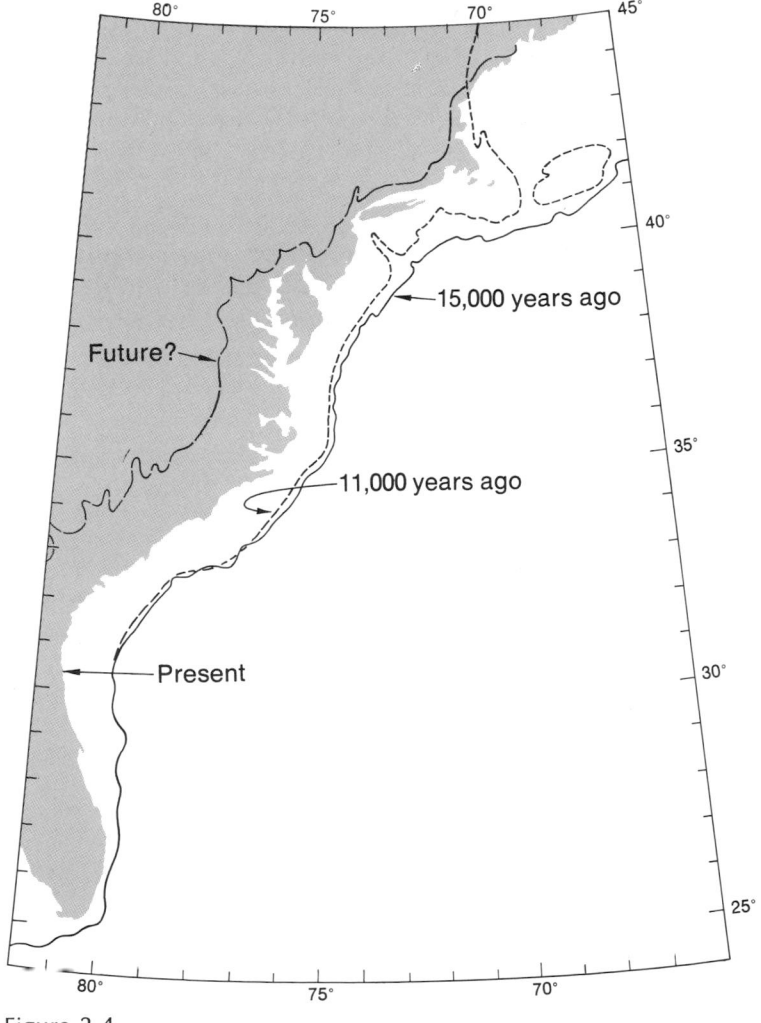

Figure 2-4

It is questionable whether we are completely out of the period of glaciation. Sufficient ice remains on land so that a major warming of the earth would produce a rise in sea level of several tens of meters. The effects of such a rise would be catastrophic because a large portion of the world's population lives at or near sea level.

Glaciation also modified conditions in the ocean. The freezing of large quantities of water increased the salinity of the ocean (most of the salt remains in the water when sea water freezes). This freezing of sea water also lowered the temperature of the surface layers of the ocean. Deep-sea geochemical and micropaleontological (the study of microscopic fossils) work has detected some of these changes. The amount of various isotopes in the water and in the organisms living or that once lived in the water is a function of the water's temperature; therefore a study of these isotopes can reveal changes in oceanographic conditions. Some planktonic animals, such as Foraminifera, undergo changes in their shell characteristics, apparently in response to temperature changes. When the shells of these organisms are obtained in deep-sea cores it is possible to identify some temperature adaptations.

These well-documented changes show that geologically, oceanographic conditions of today are not completely representative of those of the geological past. The Pleistocene Epoch's effects on the chemical, biological, and physical properties of the sea are generally more subtle than the dramatic geological changes.

SUGGESTED FURTHER READING

Oparin, A. I. *The Origin of Life.* New York: Academic Press, 1957.

Rubey, W. W. "Development of the Hydrosphere and Atmosphere, with Special Reference to Probable Composition of the Early Atmosphere," *Geological Society of America.* Special Paper No. 62 (1955).

White, J. F., ed. *Study of the Earth: Readings in Geological Science.* Englewood Cliffs, New Jersey: Prentice-Hall, 1962.

Chapter 3

HISTORY OF

OCEANOGRAPHY

EARLY HISTORY

The study of the sea in man's early history was usually motivated by a practical rather than an abstract curiosity about the ocean. He simply wanted to go from one place to another in as short a time as possible. Therefore the beginning of oceanography is closely connected with man's early thoughts about geography and his development of trade. By 800 B.C., the Phoenicians and the Greeks knew the Mediterranean Sea reasonably well. By 600 B.C., voyages had been made around Africa. In 500 B.C., Parmenides stated that the earth was round. In 400 B.C., the rise and fall of tides had been related to the phases of the moon. The Greek mathematician Eratosthenes, in 250 B.C., determined the circumference of the earth with remarkable precision and made a fairly accurate chart of the world as it looked to man at that time (Figures 3-1 and 3-2).

There developed among ancient scholars two theories about the distribution of land and water. Eratosthenes and Strabo believed that

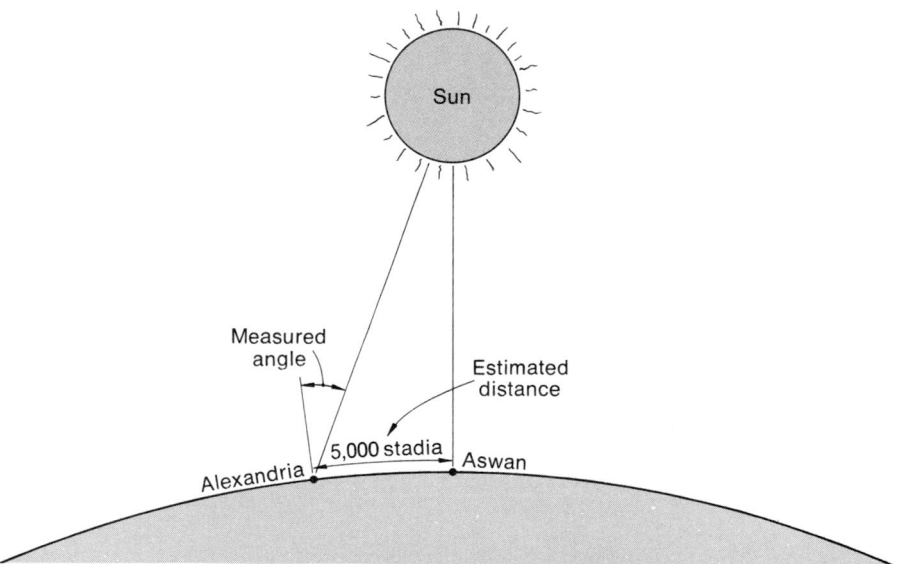

Figure 3-1 Eratosthenes determined the circumference of the earth by measuring the sun's angle with the vertical at Alexandria when he knew that the sun was directly overhead in Aswan, about 5,000 stadia away. The angle was 1/50 of a circle (7.2°), indicating that the circumference was 250,000 stadia. The best estimate of the length of a stadia used by Eratosthenes is 517 ft, which indicates a circumference of 24,500 miles. The accuracy of this measurement is remarkable: a recent determination of the earth circumference is 24,860 miles. (The dimensions in the figure are exaggerated.)

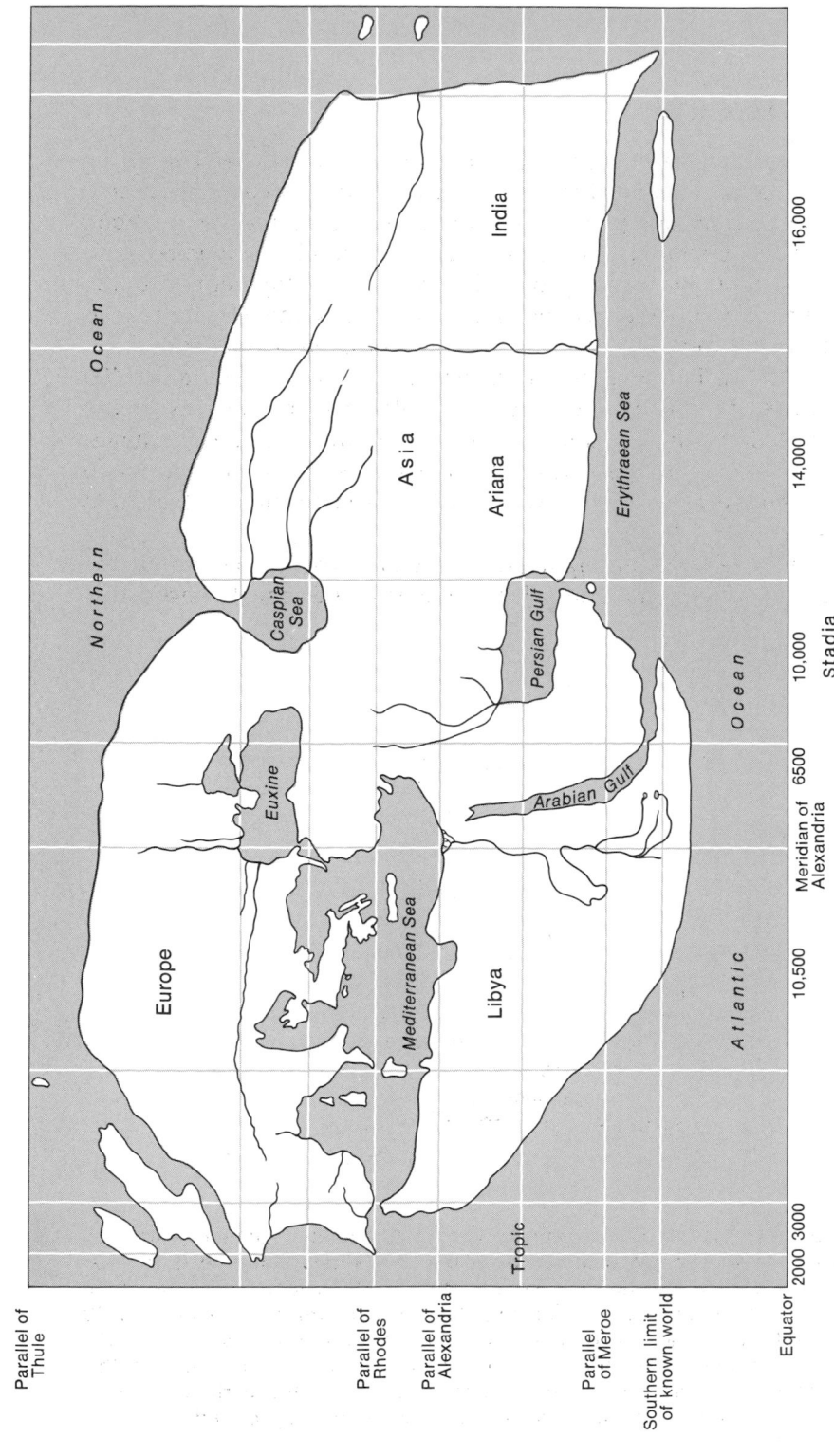

Figure 3-2 Eratosthenes' map of the world. (From M. R. Cohen and I. E. Drabkin, *A Source Book in Greek Science*, Cambridge, Mass.: Harvard University Press, 1948.)

the continents of the world formed a single island surrounded by the ocean. Ptolemy, who lived in the middle of the second century A.D., believed that the Atlantic and Indian Oceans were enclosed seas like the Mediterranean. He also held that the eastern and western points of the world approached each other very closely and that by sailing west one could reach the eastern extremity. It was this idea that led Columbus to sail west, where he discovered America instead of gaining his objective, India.

The Indian Ocean was the first ocean used for trade, but the last to be explored in detail. A condition exists in the Indian Ocean that makes it uniquely suitable for sailing vessels: during the summer monsoon season, the wind blows from the southwest, and during the winter monsoon season, it blows from the northeast. Thus vessels with the simplest square-rigged sails could travel across the entire ocean in one season and return in the next. (This scientifically important phenomenon has been the subject of recent intensive oceanographic study.) After the fall of the Roman Empire, trade decreased and during the Dark Ages most of the knowledge men had acquired about the sea was lost. It was not until the late 1400s that men again explored the sea. Some of the early explorers, Diaz, Vasco da Gama, and Columbus, are known to everybody.

AFTER THE DARK AGES

In the early 1500s, men had to accept the fact that the earth was round, not flat. Magellan's voyage around the world (1519–1522) proved this without a doubt. He also may have been the first to attempt a sounding in the deep sea. Magellan used a sounding line only 100 or 200 fathoms in length in the Pacific and did not reach bottom. He concluded that this was the deepest part of the ocean. Actually a more successful sounding attempt may have been made sixteen centuries before Magellan. Posidonius, who was born about 135 B.C., claimed that the sea near Sardinia had been sounded to a depth of about 1,000 fathoms. Unfortunately, there is little information about the methods he used.

After the last voyage of Captain Cook (1776–1779) the broad general outlines of the oceans were known but the character of the sea floor was still unexplored. Attempts at sounding the ocean deeps using a long line were made by Ellis in 1749, by Mulgrave in 1773, and by Soresby in 1817. The first real success was by Sir John Ross in 1818; he obtained a sounding and a mud sample from a depth of 1,050

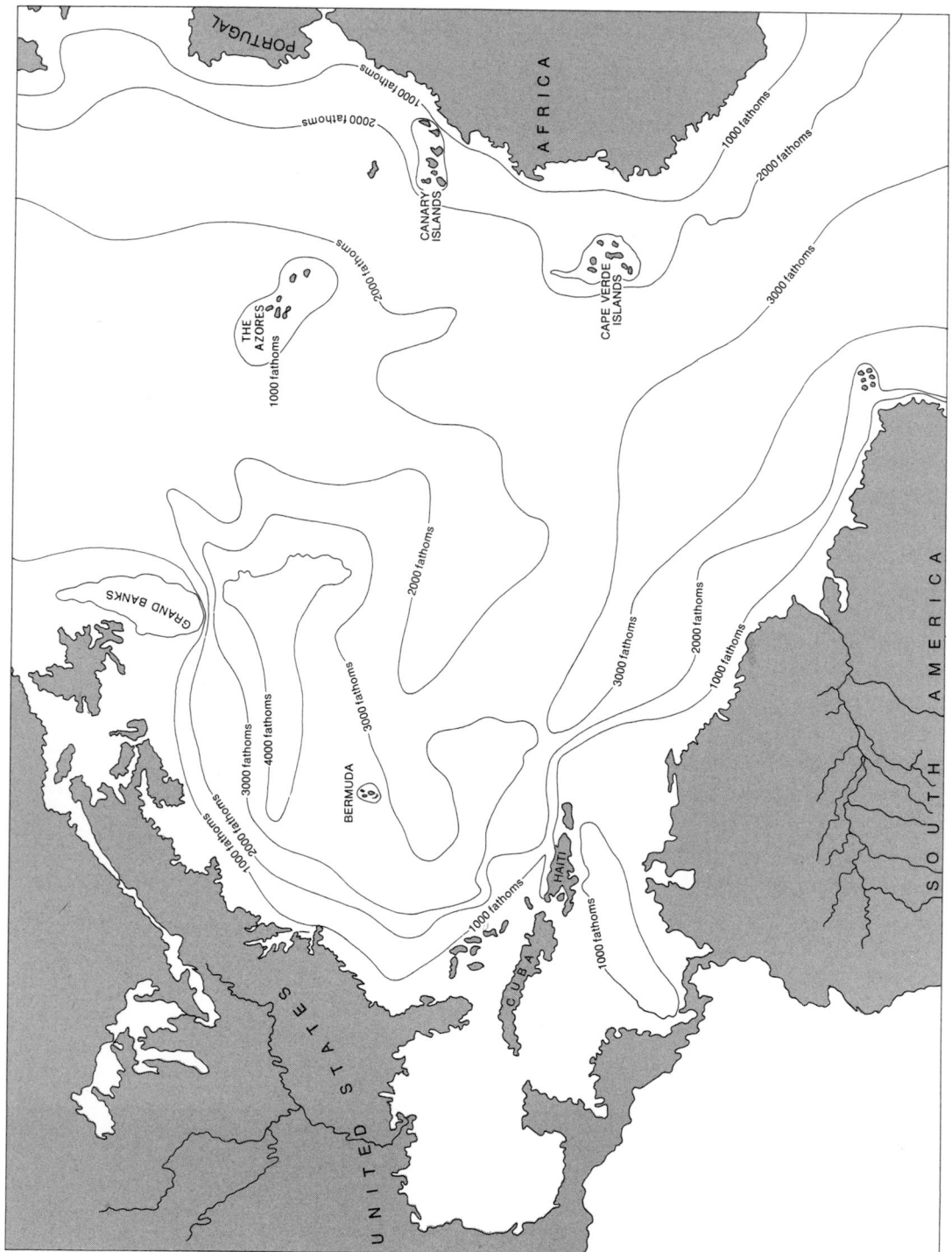

Figure 3-3 Maury's 1854 bathymetric map of the North Atlantic Ocean. (After Murray and Hjort, 1912.)

fathoms in Baffin Bay west of Greenland. Sir Clarke Ross, during an Antarctic expedition (1839–1843) obtained soundings of 2,425 fathoms in the South Atlantic and 2,677 fathoms off the Cape of Good Hope. On two occasions he could not reach the bottom using 4,000 fathoms of line. (In 1968, the research vessel DISCOVERER of the Environmental Science Services Administration returned to the same spot in the South Atlantic and found, using electronic equipment, a water depth of 2,100 fathoms. A water depth of 2,400 fathoms was found 3½ miles away.) The art of sounding was advanced by a device built by Midshipman Brooke of the U.S. Navy in 1854; to the end of the sounding line he attached a detachable weight which dropped off when the line hit the bottom. The dropping off of the weight made it easier to detect when the sounding line had reached the bottom. The introduction of steel cable in 1870 was another important advancement. But it was not until 1925, with the Meteor Expedition, that soundings were routinely and continuously made across the ocean. The METEOR measured depth electronically and did not have to stop for each measurement.

Oceanographic research in the United States probably started in 1770, when Benjamin Franklin published his map of the Gulf Stream. A significant contributor to American oceanography was Matthew Fontaine Maury of the U.S. Navy. Maury used data from the log books of ships that had crossed the Atlantic to establish the relationship between currents and oceanic weather. He published his findings in 1855, in a book called *The Physical Geography of the Sea*, one of the first books about oceanography written in English. Maury also accumulated records of deep-sea soundings, and in 1854 he published the first bathymetric map (a map that shows the bottom topography) of the North Atlantic Ocean (Figure 3-3). Another American, William Ferrel, intrigued by Maury's book, was the first to scientifically explain the motion of the surface waters of the ocean as being due to the winds.

An important, although not strictly oceanographic, expedition was the voyage of the BEAGLE from 1831 to 1836, with the young naturalist Charles Darwin aboard. Darwin's findings about evolution and other aspects of the natural world stimulated other scientists to further explore the ocean.

Numerous oceanographic expeditions took place between 1850 and 1870, but the beginning of deep-sea research is generally thought to have started with the Challenger Expedition (1872–1876). This expedition, under the direction of Sir C. Wyville Thomson, circumnavigated the world. The CHALLENGER, a 226-foot, 2,300-ton steam corvette (a fast vessel, somewhat smaller than a destroyer) made observations of many aspects of oceanography (Figure 3-4). She covered 68,890 nautical miles, made 492 deep soundings and 133 dredgings, and obtained data from 362 oceanographic stations. On these oceanographic

Figure 3-4 The research vessel CHALLENGER.

stations, data were collected on weather, currents, water temperature, water composition, marine organisms, and bottom sediments. More than 4,700 new species of marine life were discovered (an amazing average of about 5 new species for each day spent at sea). A deep-sea sounding of 4,475 fathoms (26,850 ft or 8,180 m), the deepest that had been made at that time, was made in the Marianas Trench. This area is now called the Challenger Deep.

The amount of data collected by the Challenger Expedition was immense. The reports of the expedition filled 29,500 pages in 50 volumes and took 23 years to complete. One of the great achievements of scientific exploration, the expedition also showed how little man knew about the sea.

After the Challenger Expedition, interest in oceanography increased. Many countries wanted to have world-wide expeditions, sometimes mainly for reasons of national pride. The German ship GAZELLE circumnavigated the world (1874–1876), as did the Russian steamer VITIAZ (1886–1889). During this period other smaller-scale expeditions were also making significant contributions to oceanography. Especially noteworthy were the Austrian ship POLA, which worked in the Red Sea and Mediterranean from 1890 to 1898; the United States ship BLAKE, under the direction of Alexander Agassiz, which worked the Caribbean region from 1877 to 1880; and the Norwegian expedition of the FRAM under the direction of Fridtjof Nansen from 1893 to 1896. The FRAM was a wooden ship so constructed that she could be frozen into the ice of the Arctic Ocean. One objective of this cruise was to drift across the North Pole. Although the attempt failed, it was established that the Arctic was not a shallow sea, as had been thought, but a deep ocean.

MODERN OCEANOGRAPHY

It was not until the early twentieth century that a good general picture of the oceans was obtained. Slowly the general topography of the ocean floor was mapped (Figure 3-5). A new era of oceanography started with the Meteor Expedition (1925–1927), which made one of the first detailed studies of a particular part of the ocean. Previously, most oceanographic expeditions had made only isolated, nonsystematic observations. The METEOR made 14 crossings of the South Atlantic in a 25-month interval. Collecting data day and night through all weather and seasons, the expedition was the first to use an electronic echo sounder to measure ocean depths, gathering more than 70,000 soundings of the ocean. The results of these soundings clearly revealed the ruggedness of the ocean floor.

After the Meteor Expedition, research became more thorough. Many important research laboratories were organized. In 1931, the ATLANTIS (Figure 3-6), one of the first United States vessels designed for oceanographic work, was built. Older research ships had been converted vessels originally designed for other purposes.

In 1942, H. U. Sverdrup, M. W. Johnson, and R. H. Fleming published an authoritative book on oceanography, *The Oceans: Their Physics, Chemistry, and General Biology.* It has become a standard reference book in the field.

During and after World War II interest in oceanography expanded rapidly. Advances in technology, the military use of the ocean, and a national disaster spurred research. The dive of the bathyscaphe TRIESTE to a depth greater than 10,850 m and the voyage of the nuclear submarine NAUTILUS under the North Pole showed that all parts of the ocean could be explored by man. However, the loss of the submarines THRESHER, in 1963, and SCORPION, in 1968, with their entire crews aboard, sadly showed that the ocean is still a formidable adversary.

Research is now sometimes done on an international scale, and scientists from many institutions and countries participate in joint programs, such as the International Geophysical Year studies of the Indian Ocean in the early 1960s. Large and expensive programs have been developed by oceanographers. Many of these programs have captured the imagination of the public with results reported almost daily in the newspapers. The first was Project MOHOLE, an attempt to drill through

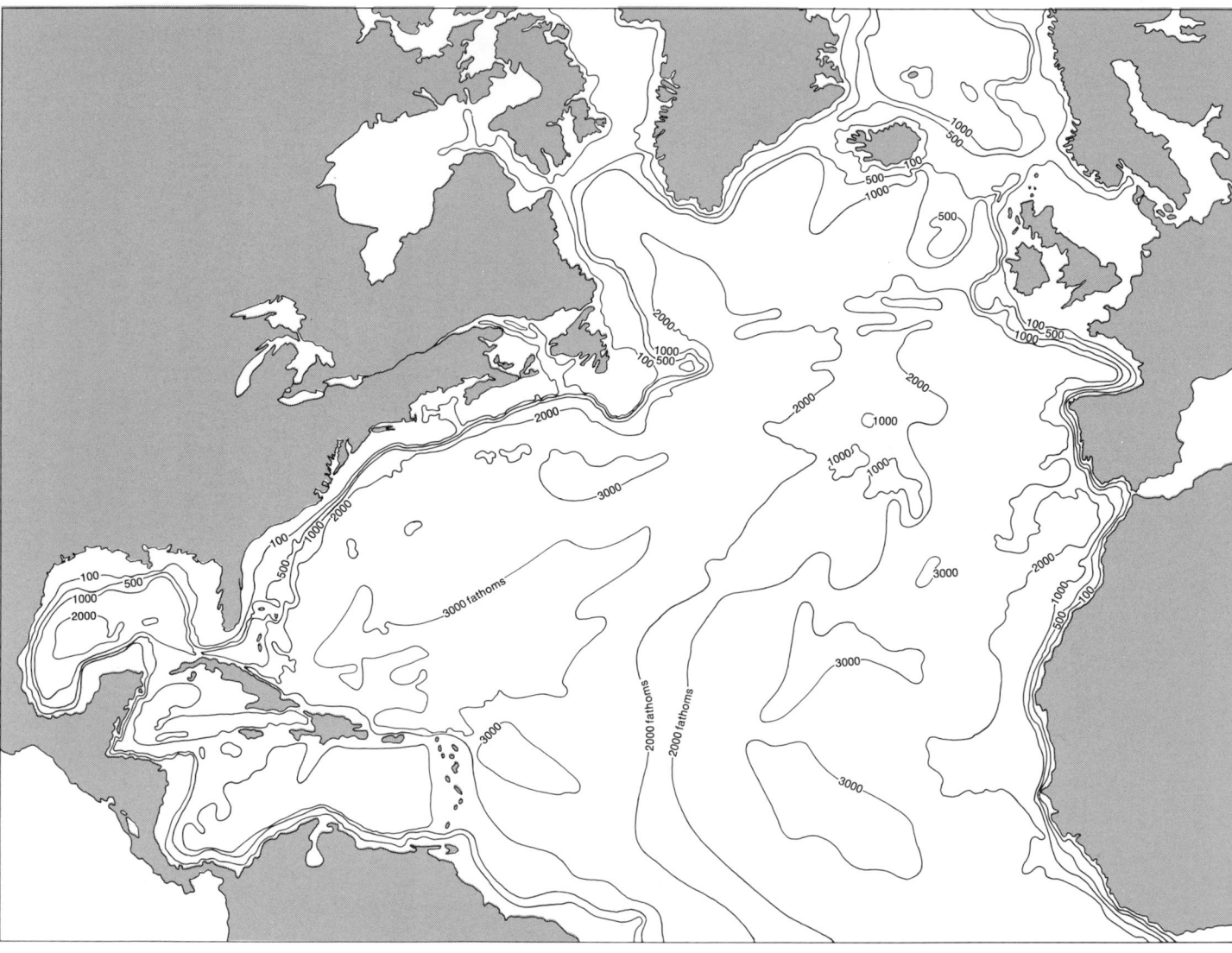

Figure 3-5 The bathymetry of the ocean as known in 1911. (After Murray and Hjort, 1912.)

Figure 3-6   The research vessel ATLANTIS. (Photograph courtesy of Woods Hole Oceanographic Institution.)

the earth's crust. Eventually abandoned, the project nevertheless gave impetus to the JOIDES (Joint Oceanographic Institutions Deep Earth Sampling) program. The objective of this project was to drill and sample just the upper layers of the earth's crust. An initial stage, off Florida in 1965, was successful and prompted a new program, the Deep-Sea Drilling Project, to drill many holes throughout the deep parts of the Atlantic, Pacific, and Indian Oceans. Started in 1968, this program has also been successful and undoubtedly will initiate more ambitious plans.

The possibility of man's living in the sea has always intrigued scientists. Jacques Yves Cousteau in France and members of the Sealab program of the United States Navy have been studying this possibility. Sealab I in 1964 had several divers stay at a depth of 193 ft for 11 days. Sealab II in 1965 had teams of divers stay at 205 ft for 10 days each. Sealab III, which has had some technical problems, plans to have five eight-man teams live 12 days each at 610 ft. Thus man may soon be able to spend extended periods of time on the deepest parts of the continental shelf. However deep 610 ft may sound, one should remember that the average depth of the ocean is greater than 12,000 ft, or nearly twenty times the depth of these proposed dives. Incredibly, man has already walked on the moon's surface before he has set foot on any part of the deep-sea floor. But the challenge is great and the prospects for the future are exciting.

SUGGESTED FURTHER READING

Cohen, M. R., and Drabkin, I. E. *A Source Book in Greek Science.* New York: McGraw-Hill, 1948.

Darwin, C. *The Voyage of the BEAGLE.* Edited by Millicent E. Selsam. New York: Harper and Row, 1959.

Deacon, G. E. R. *Seas, Maps, and Men: An Atlas-History of Man's Exploration of the Oceans.* Garden City, New York: Doubleday, 1962.

Murray, J., and Hjort, J. *The Depths of the Ocean.* London: Macmillan, 1912.

Sverdrup, H. U., Johnson, M. W., and Fleming, R. H. *The Oceans: Their Physics, Chemistry, and General Biology.* New York: Prentice-Hall, 1942.

Thomson, C. W. *The Voyage of the CHALLENGER.* New York: Harper, 1878.

Chapter 4

INSTRUMENTS

AND TECHNIQUES

Before proceeding with the detailed aspects of oceanography, we should consider the different techniques and instruments that an oceanographer uses to study his environment. J. D. Isaacs and C. O. D. Iselin, two oceanographers who have designed many instruments, said in 1952, "the ship is the arm of the oceanographer, the cable his sinew, and the instruments his fingers groping into the unknown." Instruments and techniques are constantly being changed and improved due to the curiosity of the oceanographer about his underwater world, which in most instances he cannot touch, see, hear, feel, or smell.

Some instruments are lowered into the ocean at the end of a long cable; they then either transmit their information directly to a ship on the surface or record it in place, the data being obtained when the instrument is returned to the surface. Instruments of this type have to be very sensitive to whatever they are measuring, and very strong to withstand the pressures of the sea. Other instruments are used to take samples of the water, the organisms living in the water, or the sediment or rock on the ocean floor.

Instruments and techniques can be divided into two groups: those common to all fields of oceanography and those used in individual specialties. The following discussion of instruments is mainly restricted to major and proved ones. Even as this text is being written, new devices are being developed and techniques are being formulated by oceanographers who want to consider special problems concerning the sea.

GENERAL INSTRUMENTS AND TECHNIQUES

Research Ships

The most important oceanographic instrument is the research vessel —without a ship the oceanographer would have no platform on which to carry and use his other instruments at sea. Most oceanographic vessels were converted from other uses into research vessels (Figures 4-1 and 4-2). These vessels have performed admirably even though they had certain limitations imposed by their original nonresearch design. Modern oceanographic research requires vessels that can perform numerous different tasks, that can accommodate many kinds of equipment, and that are seaworthy. The following are some of the important considerations in the acquisition of a research ship:

1. Cost—initial and daily operating and maintenance thereafter
2. Agility—the ability to maneuver at low speeds, or when stopped
3. Seaworthiness—relative stability in rough seas

Figure 4-1 Research vessel CHAIN operated by the Woods Hole Oceanographic Institution. This 214-ft, 2,100-ton displacement vessel is a former Navy salvage tug, converted for oceanographic research in 1958. She is equipped with several laboratories, a winch capable of lowering instruments to the deepest parts of the ocean, and many pieces of scientific gear and equipment. With a cruising speed of 12 knots and a range of 9,000 miles, she carries a crew of 33 and can accommodate a scientific party of 25. (Photograph courtesy of Woods Hole Oceanographic Institution.)

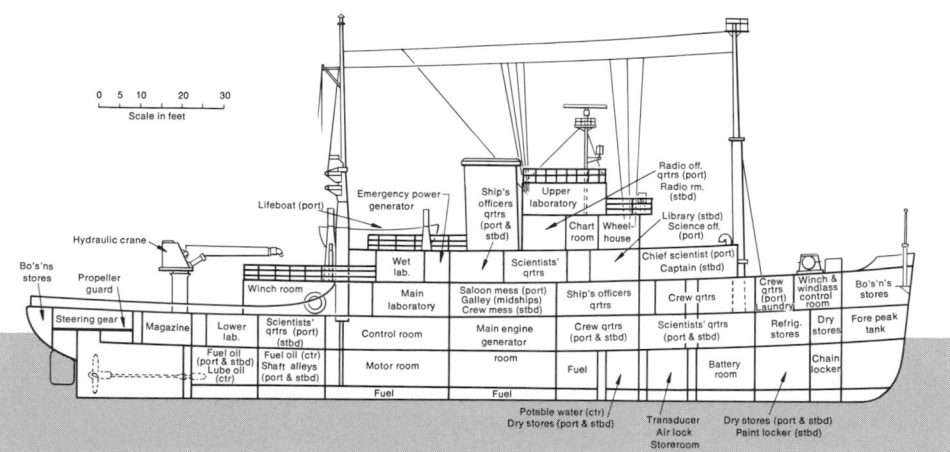

Figure 4-2   Inboard profile of CHAIN. Port and Starboard (stbd) refer to the left and right sides of the vessel. Note the small percentage of the ship that is available for laboratory space.

4. Laboratory facilities
5. Quietness of electronic equipment used in operating the ship —no interference with electronic equipment used in collecting oceanographic data (Figure 4-3)
6. Winch capabilities—ability to lower instruments to the bottom of the deep sea
7. Endurance—ability to stay at sea for at least a month
8. Recreation and living facilities sufficient for officers, crew, and scientists.

Research vessels being designed today incorporate the above requirements, and also have facilities for new and unique instrumentation and techniques. Some new ships are able to handle deep submergence vehicles, drilling rigs, and large oceanic buoys (Figure 4-4).

A recent addition to research vessels is the use of shipboard computer systems. These systems (Figure 4-5) can, among other things, be used for calculating and evaluating data on the earth's gravity and magnetic field, computing the ship's position, and determining the correct ocean depth. Among numerous advantages in having a computer at sea, one stands out: by presenting data in a form that is immediately usable and understandable, the computer allows the formation and testing of hypotheses while the scientist is still at sea. Computers on a research vessel must withstand a wide range of conditions, especially those of high humidity and the rapid up and down movements of the ship.

Figure 4-3　Typical collection of electronic equipment on a research vessel. From left to right: instrumentation for a proton magnetometer, a very low frequency navigation device, a multi-channeled tape recorder, and some temperature-measuring equipment. (Photograph courtesy of Woods Hole Oceanographic Institution.)

Figure 4-4　Model of a new design of the class of ships designated as AGORs by the U.S. Navy. This vessel has cranes and winches strong enough to handle large objects such as submersibles. They can also be modified to drill in several thousands of feet of water. The ship is equipped with cycloidal propellers (one fore and one aft are visible on the model) which provide excellent maneuverability. (Photograph courtesy of Woods Hole Oceanographic Institution.)

Figure 4-5　Photograph of a computer system (IBM 1710) that has been used on CHAIN. (Photograph courtesy of Woods Hole Oceanographic Institution.)

Figure 4-4

Figure 4-5

Deep Submergence Research Vessels

Deep submergence research vessels have recently become an important research tool for oceanographers. Prior to 1961, no research submersibles had been built in the United States. The THRESHER disaster in 1963 and the U.S. Navy's interest in deep submergence programs have stimulated the development of numerous research submersibles. Submersibles come in a variety of shapes, sizes, and capabilities (Table 4-1), and these vessels can perform different and sometimes very specialized tasks.

TABLE 4-1   CHARACTERISTICS OF SOME RESEARCH SUBMERSIBLES

Name (Built)	Operating Depth-feet/ Speed-knots*	Operating Endurance	Length in feet	Crew/ Passen-gers	Owner/ Operator
ALUMINAUT (1965)	15,000/3.5	32 hours at 2.5 knots	51	3/4	Reynolds Metals Company
ALVIN (1965)	6,000/2.5	8 hours at 1.6 knots	22	1/2	Office of Naval Research/ Woods Hole Oceanographic Institution
ASHERAH (1964)	600/3	10 hours at 1 knot	17	1/1	University of Pennsylvania
DEEP STAR 4000 (1966)	4,000/3	10 hours at 1 knot	18	1/2	Westinghouse Electric Corp.
DEEP QUEST (1967)	8,000/4.5	24 hours at 2 knots	40	2/2	Lockheed Aircraft Corp
BEN FRANKLIN (1968)	2,000/5	6 weeks (drifting)	49	2/4 (maximum of 12)	Grumman Aircraft

* A knot is a speed of one nautical mile (6,000 feet) an hour.

Figure 4-6   Some underwater photographs taken from ALVIN. (a) Taking a sample of the bottom using a small coring tube (upper left). Depth 1,600 m. (b) Examining and measuring ripple marks on a rock terrace. Markings on the mechanical arm are 1 inch apart. The orientation of the ripples is measured relative to a compass (lower right). Depth 1,594 m. (c) Examining a steep slope (about 40°) that is covered with sediment. Depth 1,580 m. (From D. A. Ross, *Nature* **218** [1968].)

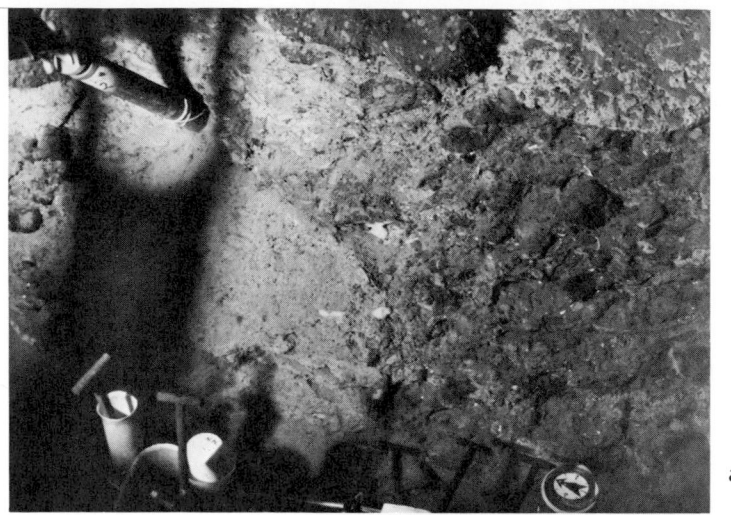

a

b

c

Figure 4-6

A submersible possesses numerous advantages over a surface vessel. The most important is direct observation, permitting a scientist to see and photograph what he is trying to measure or sample. An example of the value of direct observation is shown in Figure 4-6. Other advantages of submersibles are their ability to operate independently of the sea surface and to avoid in particular such disadvantages as movement of instruments due to wave motion. A submersible is also able to explore small features that may not even be detected from a surface vessel. By using a submersible, measurements can be made in the same place for several hours whereas an unanchored ship would drift away from a given area. Another advantage is that a submersible can return to the same area of the bottom after a period of time, while a surface vessel is limited by navigational problems in finding any given area (see the section on navigation).

A disadvantage of submersibles is their dependence on surface ships to tow or carry them to their dive site. Difficulties in launching and retrieving usually limit the use of a submersible to mild sea con-

Figure 4-7 The ALUMINAUT, an aluminum submersible built and operated by the Reynolds Metals Company. The vessel is 51 ft long and has dived to more than 6,000 ft. Besides the usual complement of scientific equipment, the submersible has a manipulation device consisting of two 9-ft arms that are capable of collecting samples weighing up to 600 lbs. (Photograph courtesy of Reynolds Metals Company.)

ditions. Because submersibles are generally very small, observers must remain in an uncomfortable position. The small size is the result of their having to be strong enough to withstand the pressure of the overlying water, and the need to reserve much of the inside space for equipment and life-support systems. Another disadvantage is that the cost of each dive usually is very high. But despite these disadvantages, submersibles are one of the most important research tools of the oceanographer.

Some of the adventures of the submersibles are quite amazing. The bathyscaphe TRIESTE, on January 23, 1960, made a dive into the Challenger Deep to a depth of 10,910 m. The ALUMINAUT (Figures 4-7 and 4-8) and ALVIN (Figures 4-9 and 4-10) in 1966 participated in

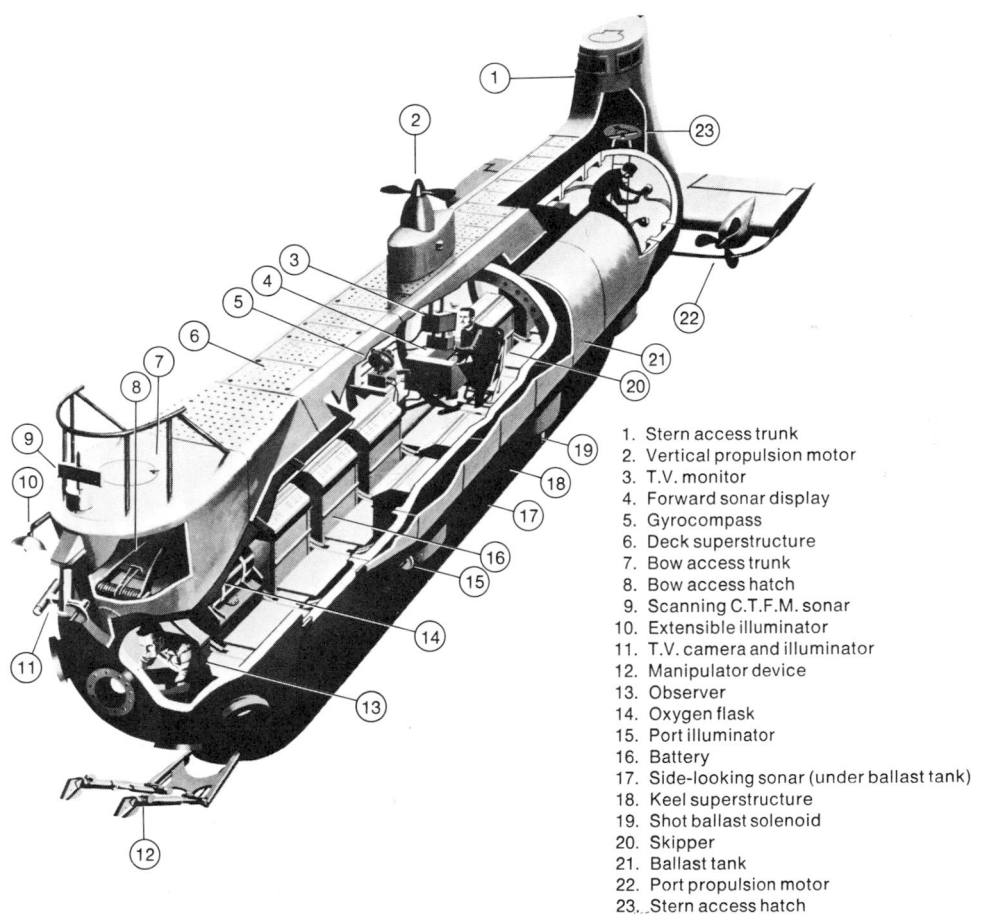

1. Stern access trunk
2. Vertical propulsion motor
3. T.V. monitor
4. Forward sonar display
5. Gyrocompass
6. Deck superstructure
7. Bow access trunk
8. Bow access hatch
9. Scanning C.T.F.M. sonar
10. Extensible illuminator
11. T.V. camera and illuminator
12. Manipulator device
13. Observer
14. Oxygen flask
15. Port illuminator
16. Battery
17. Side-looking sonar (under ballast tank)
18. Keel superstructure
19. Shot ballast solenoid
20. Skipper
21. Ballast tank
22. Port propulsion motor
23. Stern access hatch

Figure 4-8   A cut-away view of the ALUMINAUT. (Photograph courtesy of Reynolds Metals Company.)

WOODS HOLE
OCEANOGRAPHIC
INSTITUTION
ALVIN
OFFICE OF
NAVAL RESEARCH
MS 1512 M
7
6
TOW
PAD

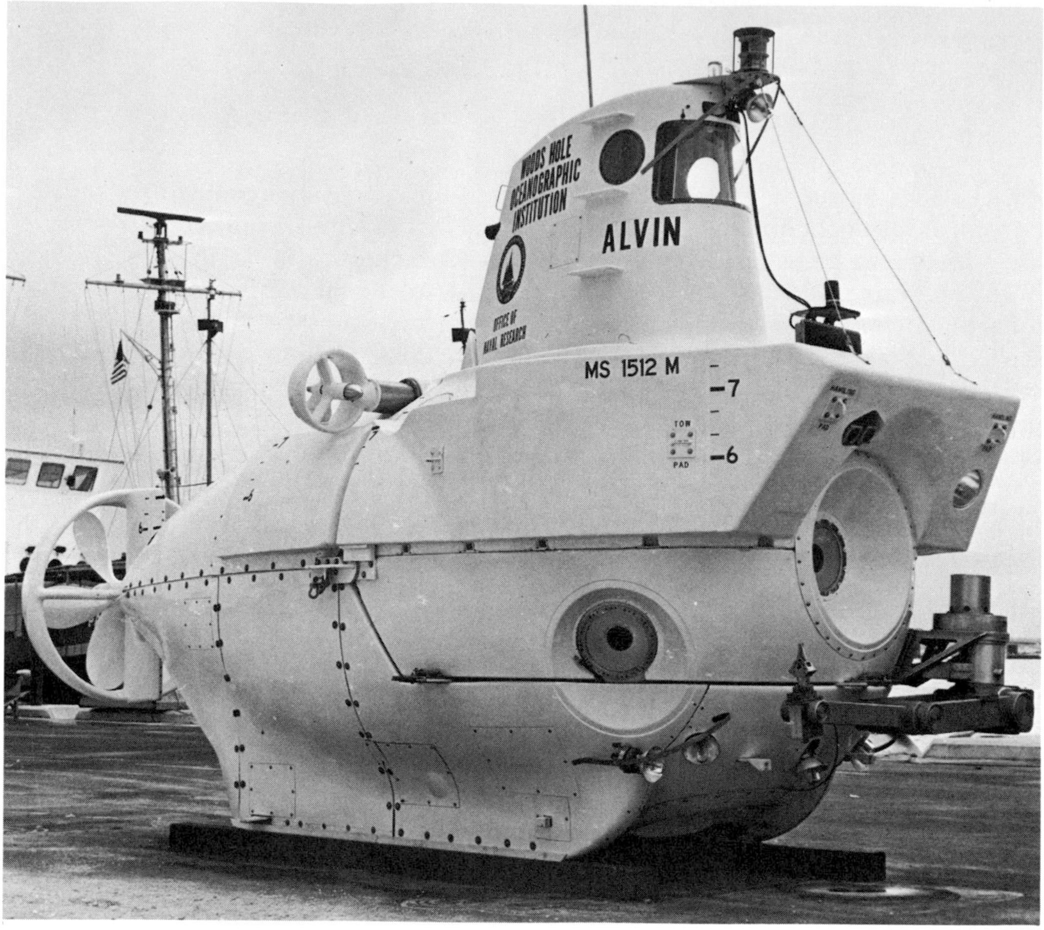

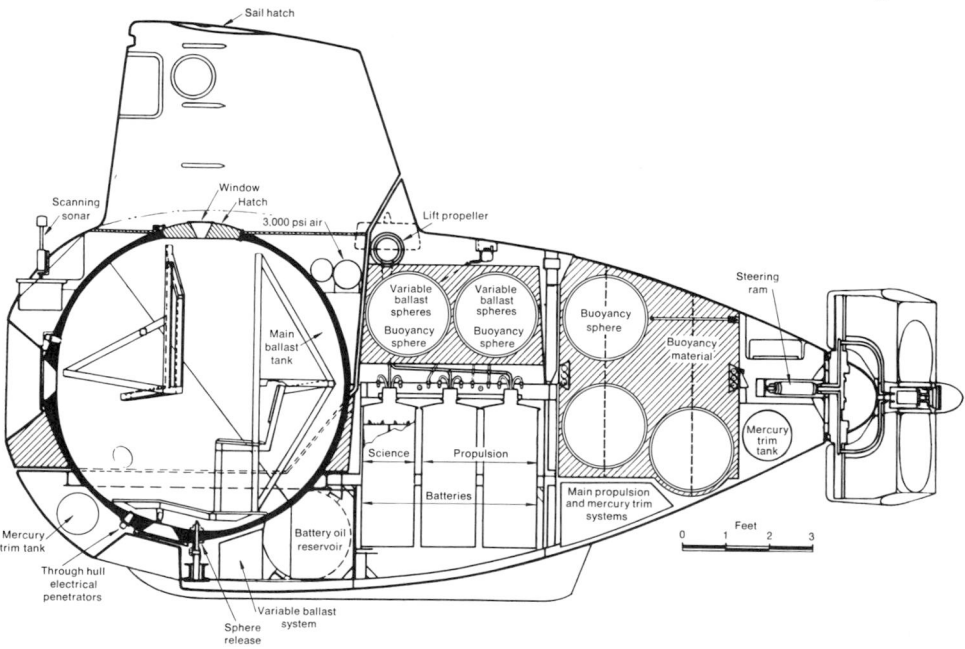

Figure 4-9

Sail hatch
Window
Hatch
Scanning sonar
3,000 psi air
Lift propeller
Variable ballast spheres
Buoyancy sphere
Variable ballast spheres
Buoyancy sphere
Main ballast tank
Buoyancy sphere
Buoyancy material
Steering ram
Mercury trim tank
Science
Propulsion
Batteries
Main propulsion and mercury trim systems
Feet
0
1
2
3
Battery oil reservoir
Mercury trim tank
Through hull electrical penetrators
Variable ballast system
Sphere release

Figure 4-10

Figure 4-9   Submersible ALVIN, owned by the U.S. Navy (Office of Naval Research) and operated by Woods Hole Oceanographic Institution. Visible to the right is a mechanical arm, which was lost and subsequently recovered from the sea floor (see Figure 4-12). The device on the upper part of the conning tower is a current meter. (Photograph courtesy of Woods Hole Oceanographic Institution.)

Figure 4-10   Cut-away view of ALVIN. The submersible uses a variable ballast system, consisting of inter-connected pressure-proof aluminum spheres and collapsible rubber bags partially filled with oil. As oil is pumped from the spheres into the bags, the amount of sea water displaced by the vehicle is increased (thus increasing the buoyancy and making the submersible lighter) while the weight of the vehicle remains the same. (Photograph courtesy of Woods Hole Oceanographic Institution.)

Figure 4-11   Photograph of swordfish that attacked ALVIN and got stuck in the external hull of the submersible. The fish was about 8 ft long and weighed about 200 lbs (Zarudski, 1967). A good meal was had by the crew of ALVIN. (Photograph courtesy of Woods Hole Oceanographic Institution.)

the successful search and recovery of an H-bomb lost off the Spanish Coast. ALVIN, while on a dive on the Blake Plateau off Florida, was attacked by an apparently nearsighted swordfish (Figure 4-11). ALVIN had another interesting experience: while finishing a dive 160 km off Martha's Vineyard in New England, it collided with its support ship and lost its mechanical arm and sample basket in an area where the water was about 1,300 m deep. Three weeks later the submersible returned to the area and, after three dives, found and recovered the arm and basket (Figure 4-12). On October 16, 1968, ALVIN itself was lost at sea, fortunately without the loss of any life. About a year later, in September of 1969, ALVIN was recovered from the ocean bottom. The recovery was accomplished using ALUMINAUT and MIZAR (a surface vessel); ironically, these three ships were previously teamed in the H-bomb recovery. In 1969, the BEN FRANKLIN drifted submerged in the Gulf Stream for 30 days, covering a distance of 1,650 miles.

Figure 4-12   Photograph of ALVIN's mechanical arm lying on the sea floor at a depth of about 1,300 m approximately 160 km south of Martha's Vineyard, Massachusetts. The arm and sample had been lost 3 weeks earlier and were found and recovered when this picture was taken. The small channel in the foreground was made in an attempt to lift the arm before the picture was taken. (From K. O. Emery and D. A. Ross, *Deep Sea Research* **15** [1968].)

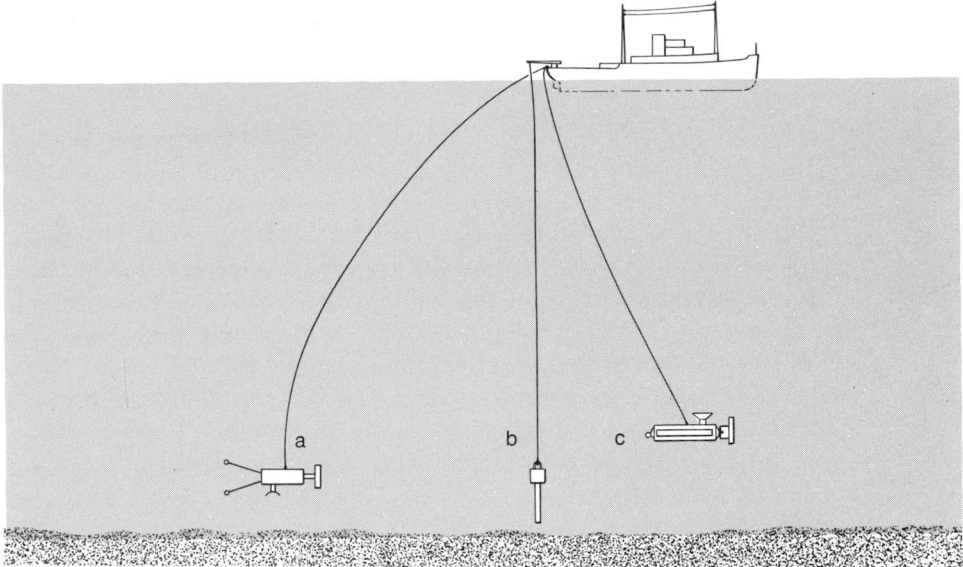

Figure 4-13 Different types of tethered instruments: a=towed type, b=suspended type, c=self-powered type. Only one type of instrument is lowered from the ship at a time.

Figure 4-14 A deep-towed device built in cooperation with the Office of Naval Research and Scripps Institution of Oceanography. This instrument has been used to make detailed bathymetric and magnetic charts of portions of the sea floor. (Photograph courtesy of J. D. Mudie, Marine Physical Laboratory, Scripps Institution of Oceanography.)

Instruments attached to wires and controlled from surface ships may also be thought of as a type of submersible even though they are unmanned. These attached or tethered instruments can be of three types (Figure 4-13): (1) towed over the bottom, the surface ship supplying the movement; (2) suspended from the ship; and (3) self-powered.

Instruments suspended by wire from surface ships are the most common type of oceanographic instrumentation; numerous examples will be given in the following sections. Towed instruments (Figure 4-14) have been used to make detailed charts of different features of the sea floor. Self-powered instruments have not been developed to any extent, but have the potential of being important instruments in the near future.

Drilling Ships

Drilling ships have recently become very useful vessels for oceanographic research, mainly because of their ability to obtain deeper samples of the earth's crust. The use of drilling vessels in the deep sea was first successfully demonstrated during the beginning stages of Project MOHOLE. Samples from about 180 m below the sea-floor surface were obtained in a water depth of 3,500 m. Drilling ships and platforms used by oil companies can routinely drill in water depths of about 300 m, but this was the first example of deep-sea drilling. In 1965, the JOIDES drilling program drilled six holes on the continental shelf and slope off eastern Florida. From 1968 to 1972, the more extensive Deep-Sea Drilling Project drilled numerous deep holes on major geological features in the Atlantic, Pacific, and Indian Oceans.

Floating and Fixed Platforms

Important contributions to oceanography have been made by the MAUD and FRAM, vessels which were frozen into the polar ice and allowed to drift with it for several years. These expeditions showed

Figure 4-15 (a) FLIP, a 355-ft long Floating Instrument Platform, was developed by the Marine Physical Laboratory of the University of California, San Diego's Scripps Institution of Oceanography. She is shown here in the horizontal position. In this position she is towed to the research site where ballast tanks are flooded to "flip" her into the vertical position for research work. (b) FLIP is photographed here in the process of "flipping" from the horizontal position to the vertical position where she will afford scientists an extremely stable platform from which to conduct scientific studies. (c) FLIP when in the vertical position as shown here displays only 55 ft of her 355-ft length. The extended cranes are for lowering instruments into the water. (Photographs courtesy of Scripps Institution of Oceanography.)

a

b

c

Figure 4-15

the value of permanent or semipermanent observational stations on the ocean.

A drifting ice station was first established by the Soviet Union in 1937 in the Arctic Ocean. The United States started its first scientific camp in 1952 on Fletcher's Ice Island, more commonly known as T-3. The drift track of this ice island was observed, either by airplane or by its temporary occupants, from 1947 to 1964.

One advantage of floating islands, besides permitting normal oceanographic observations in the polar region, is the large geographic coverage they afford. Many unique Arctic phenomena, such as auroras, magnetic conditions, and ice drift, can be conveniently studied from these floating oceanographic platforms.

A new type of oceanographic instrument is FLIP (FLoating Instrument Platform). FLIP, when she is in her "flipped" position (Figure 4-15), is very stable and her up and down motion is only a small fraction of the waves around her. Because of her great stability she has been used successfully in studies of, among other things, wave movements and sound transmission in the ocean.

Another type of platform used in oceanography is the anchored buoy system (Figure 4-16). Buoys, or buoy systems, may be placed at the ocean's surface or on the bottom. Usually one or more buoys are placed at the surface as markers and store information obtained from underwater sensors attached to the buoy line. These surface buoys can also record weather conditions, surface currents, and waves. Subsurface buoys permit accurate measurements of currents by keeping the mooring line taut and reducing horizontal and vertical motion of the system. The subsurface buoy may contain a power supply and recorders for other sensing devices. The mooring line often ends at a release mechanism near the bottom that may be triggered at command, allowing recovery of the buoy system.

Information obtained by buoys may be collected and recorded within the system until retrieved by a surface vessel. Newer buoy systems transmit data to an onshore station or relay it to a passing satellite.

Permanently fixed platforms, attached to the sea floor, have been used for the measurement of numerous oceanographic parameters. These platforms include radar and navigational towers, piers, and weather and lighthouse ships. Two advantages of fixed platforms are relatively small cost in comparison with ships and stability for long-term, uninterrupted measurements.

One platform designed especially for oceanographic research is the U.S. Navy Undersea Center's tower located a mile off Mission Beach, California (Figure 4-17). This 90-ft structure, which is attached to the sea floor by steel pins driven 63 ft into the bottom, is in a water depth of 60 ft.

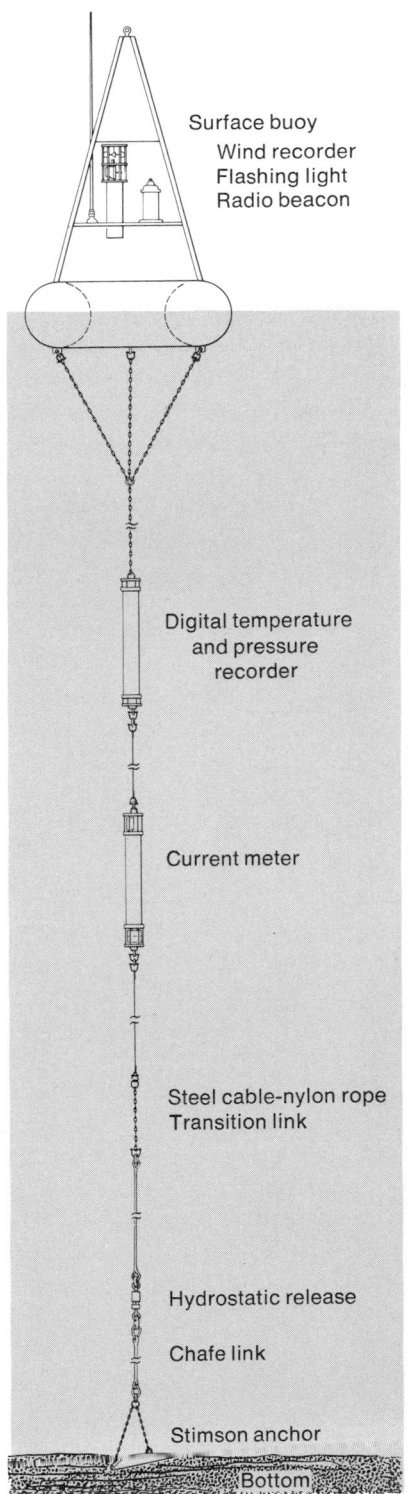

Surface buoy
  Wind recorder
  Flashing light
  Radio beacon

Digital temperature
and pressure
recorder

Current meter

Steel cable-nylon rope
Transition link

Hydrostatic release

Chafe link

Stimson anchor

Bottom

Figure 4-16 A single buoy system similar to the type used at Woods Hole Oceanographic Institution.

Figure 4-17 U.S. Naval Undersea Center's oceanographic tower. The three 50 ft booms support temperature-sensitive elements that record the depth of specific water temperature layers. (Photograph courtesy of E. C. LaFond, U.S. Naval Undersea Center.)

Other Instruments

Man, himself, can function as a submersible with the use of SCUBA. Exploration of the sea bottom to depths of 50 fathoms (300 ft) has been routinely performed by experienced divers (Figure 4-18). Newer techniques, using a mixture of gases and portable decompression chambers, will allow man to work for extended periods of time in even greater depths.

Another potentially valuable research instrument is the airplane. Airplanes have been used routinely in meteorological and geophysical studies. In oceanography, airplanes can measure sea surface temperature with an airborne infrared radiation thermometer, and observe wave patterns. A new device, an expendable bathythermograph, al-

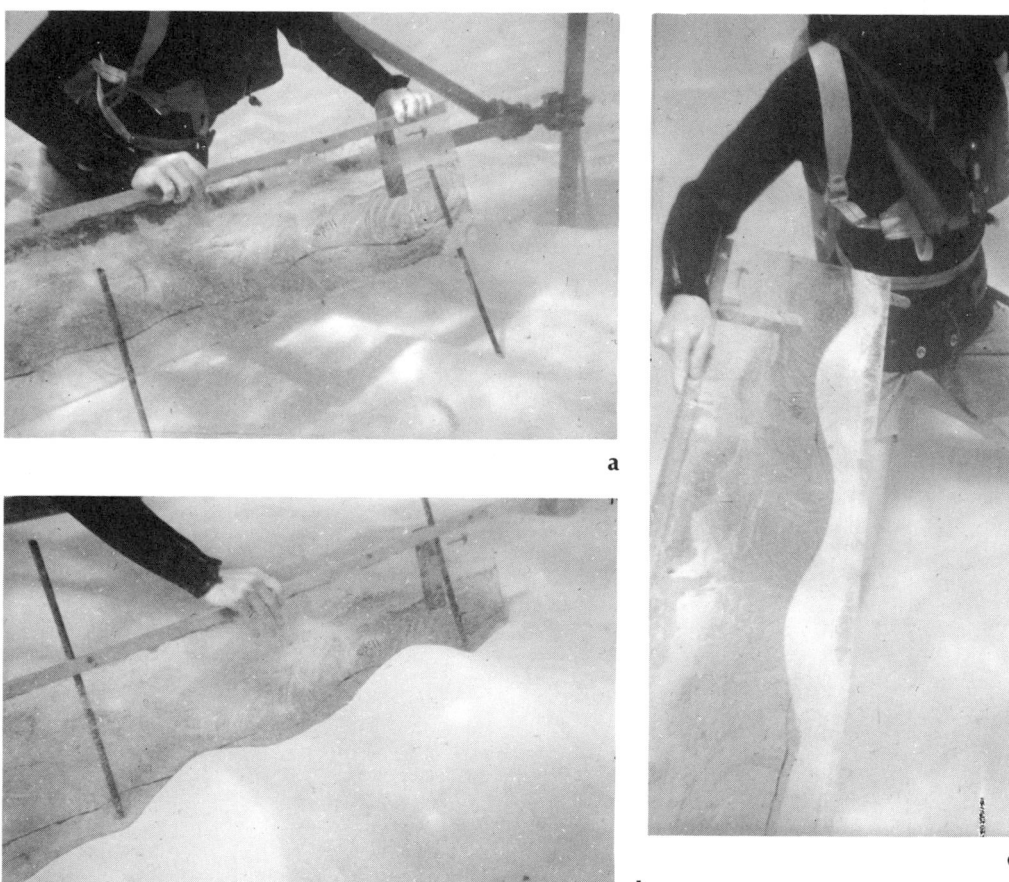

a

b

c

Figure 4-18 Sequence of photographs showing a diver measuring and obtaining a graphic record (on a grease covered board) of ripple marks. (Photograph courtesy of D. O. Owen, Woods Hole Oceanographic Institution.)

lows an airplane to measure the ocean's temperature down to a depth of 1,000 ft. The device is dropped into the water and temperature changes measured during its descent through the water are transmitted to the airplane. The airplane can also be used for biological observations, such as tracking and observing schools of fish. In physical oceanography, different surface currents are measured by noting temperature variations and observing the growth of waves under different meteorological conditions.

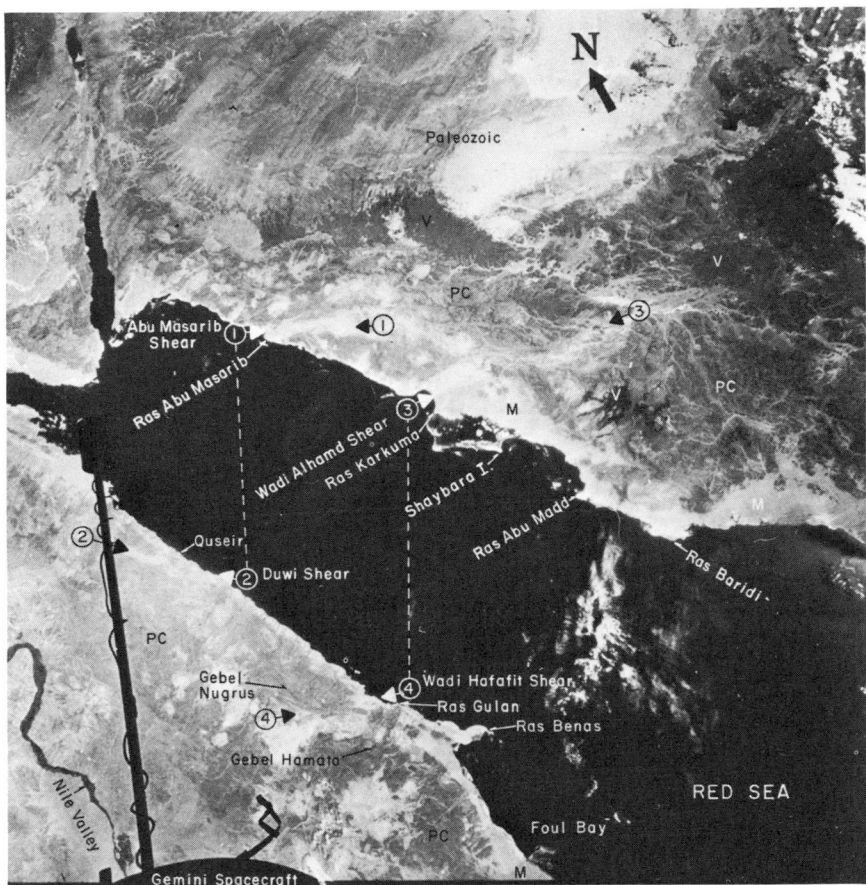

Figure 4-19   A Gemini XI satellite photograph, looking north along the Red Sea. The Gulf of Aqaba and Dead Sea are seen in the upper left part of the picture. Dr. Abdel-Gawad has used these photographs to detect areas of Arabia (background) and Africa (foreground) that apparently were originally connected, for example 1-1 (the Abu Masarib Shear) and 2-2 (the Duwi Shear), but have become separated by large-scale earth movements. (From Abdel-Gawad, 1969 and NASA. Abdel-Gawad, M.: "Geological structures of the Red Sea area inferred from satellite pictures." Fig. 3 In *Hot Brines and Recent Heavy Metal Deposits in the Red Sea*, edited by E. T. Degens and D. A. Ross. New York. Springer-Verlag, 1969.)

Satellite observations also hold potential for oceanography. They are already employed as navigational aids, to locate icebergs, to survey for marine organisms, for weather observations, and to obtain large-scale pictures of the earth's surface. These pictures (Figure 4-19) can be used to study currents and geological structures, and to locate areas of high biological productivity.

Navigation

Navigation, or knowing the position and directing the course of one's ship at sea, is of primary importance to oceanographic work. Most navigational techniques, however, do not determine positions very accurately.

One of the simplest methods of navigation is that of dead reckoning. The initial position of the vessel is determined either by star sighting or by reference to an object on land, then a course is plotted that will lead the ship to its intended objective. By knowing the speed of the vessel, one can estimate its position during any part of the voyage (Figure 4-20a). The accuracy of the technique is poor, because of the effect on the vessel of currents, winds, and waves. Departures from the predicted position and arrival time can, however, provide information concerning currents and surface winds.

Within visual or radar sight of land (usually less than 50 miles) several techniques can be used. With a sextant, the horizontal angle between three well-located objects on land can be used to locate the observer's position (Figure 4-20b). Radar sights taken on known objects on land will produce a range (distance) and bearing (angle). These can be used, like sextant sights, to obtain a position (Figure 4-

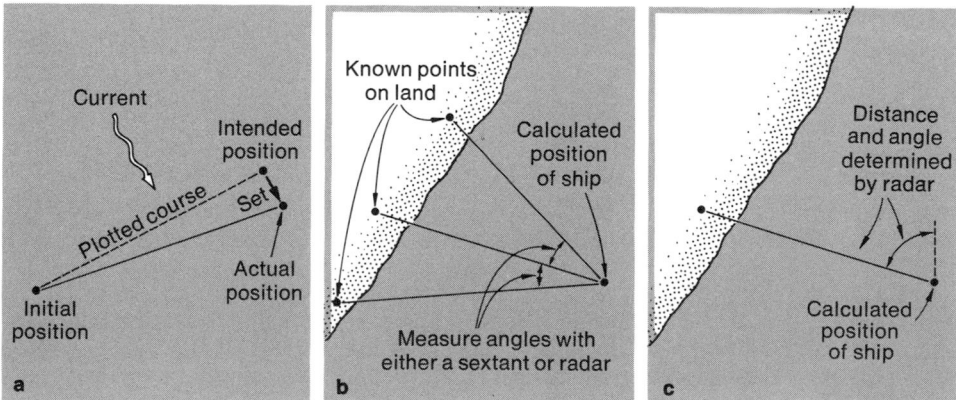

Figure 4-20 Some different methods of navigation: (a) dead reckoning; (b) using bearings; (c) using range and bearing.

20c). Positions having an accuracy of several hundred meters are possible with a good radar system, although in practical experience the error generally is larger. A good survey of an area may be made by putting radar reflecting buoys in the survey area. All positions are then made relative to these buoys. This type of survey can be very accurate (±50 m), but the position of the entire survey area relative to the rest of the ocean may be inaccurate by as much as 2 km.

If the bottom topography of an area is well known, and a good chart of it exists, it can be used as a navigational aid. For example, a ship's position can be determined from the chart when the ship passes over a known feature of the sea floor. This technique requires the use of echo-sounding equipment (see the following section).

Several electronic systems can be used to obtain a position when a ship is as far as 1,000 miles from land. The most widely used system is the Loran navigational system. Loran utilizes land stations which produce an electronic signal, and compares the arrival time of two of these signals. The difference in arrival time between these signals is a measure of the distance the ship is from the stations. Using two or more sets of these stations, a very accurate estimate (±50 m) of the ship's position can be made. The main shortcoming of this and other electronic techniques is that they are not available in many parts of the world.

A recently developed satellite navigation system is being used by some of the newer oceanographic vessels. This technique requires sophisticated electronic equipment and is not routinely used by most ships.

When a ship is out of sight of land or range of electronic devices, celestial navigation is the main method of obtaining a position. Determining a ship's position by star sighting is a technique that has been used for many centuries. The accuracy of the method depends upon the skill of the observer, and at best is usually about ±2 km.

Sounding Methods

Before the development of electronic techniques, sounding, or determining the depth of the ocean, was done by lowering a heavy line of known length and noting how much of the line had been paid out when it hit the ocean bottom. This tedious technique did not always result in correct depth values. One reason is that a wire, when lowered to the sea floor, does not necessarily go straight down but can be deflected either by surface currents or by movements of the surface vessel. Another disadvantage is that this technique gives only one depth with each lowering rather than a continuous picture of the bottom. The development of sounding techniques using electronically controlled sound impulses (called echo sounding) solved these problems, but introduced a few smaller difficulties.

Echo sounding is a technique whereby an outgoing signal or pulse from a ship travels through the water to the ocean bottom, is reflected off the bottom, and travels back to the ship (Figure 4-21). The time that it takes the signal to make this trip is accurately measured. After necessary corrections, with knowledge of the speed of sound in water, the depth can be calculated. Or in other words, the water depth equals one-half the travel time (half going down, half coming up) multiplied by the speed of sound in the water.

A modern echo-sounding device (Figure 4-22) will produce a permanent graphic record of the returning sound (Figure 4-23a). These records give the oceanographer a better feeling for the character of the ocean floor. Echo-sounding records from the ocean have shown that

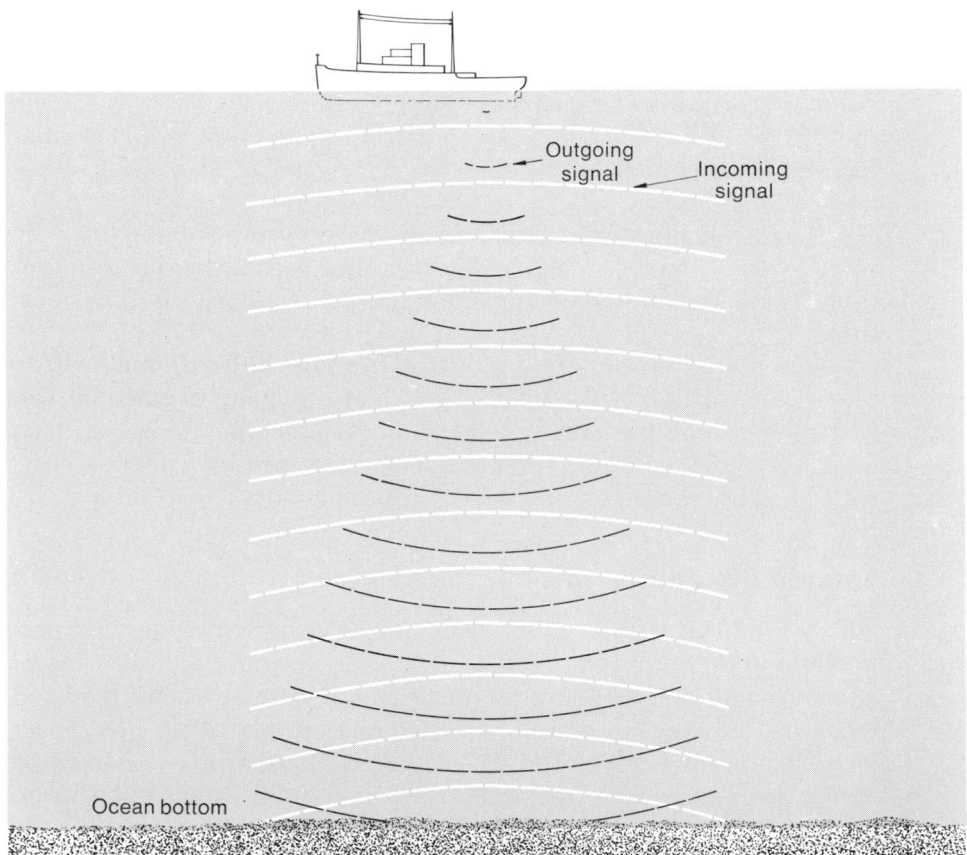

Figure 4-21   Echo-sounding technique. Sound from the ship travels to the ocean bottom and is reflected back to the ship. The time the sound takes to make the trip can be used to determine the water depth.

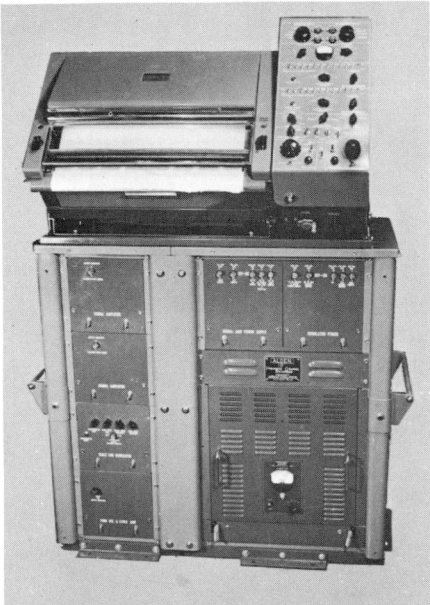

Figure 4-22   A Precision Graphic Recorder, an instrument used in echo-sounding operations. This device accurately measures how long the sound takes to travel to the bottom and return and it also produces a visual record of the returning signals (see Figure 4-23). (Photograph courtesy of Woods Hole Oceanographic Institution.)

its floor has many large mountains, valleys, and flat areas. The gross topography of the sea floor is at least as irregular as that of the land.

There are some problems in the interpretation of the echo-sounder record. One is the exaggeration in scale. The surface vessel is traveling at a speed of about 10 or 12 knots. This represents the horizontal scale of the record. The vertical scale of the record shows the depth, commonly measured in hundreds of fathoms, and is usually smaller and exaggerated relative to the horizontal scale. In other words, one scale is in hundreds of feet, the other in thousands of feet. If, however, both scales were made with the same dimensions (Figure 4-23b), it would be very difficult to observe any details of the bottom features.

Another problem is the shape of the outgoing sound beam; it is a wide cone and will cover a relatively large circular area when it hits the ocean bottom. The first returning echo, therefore, will come from the point closest to the ship, which—in the case of underwater canyons or mountains—does not have to be directly below the vessel, and the following echoes will be masked or obscured by the first one. The effect makes it difficult to accurately define small features on the sea floor and to be sure that the feature is directly below the ship.

A third echo-sounding problem is determining the actual speed of sound in water. Sound velocity increases with increasing temperature, salinity, and depth (this is discussed in more detail in Chapter 7). Therefore, these parameters have to be known and corrected for if a very accurate survey is desired.

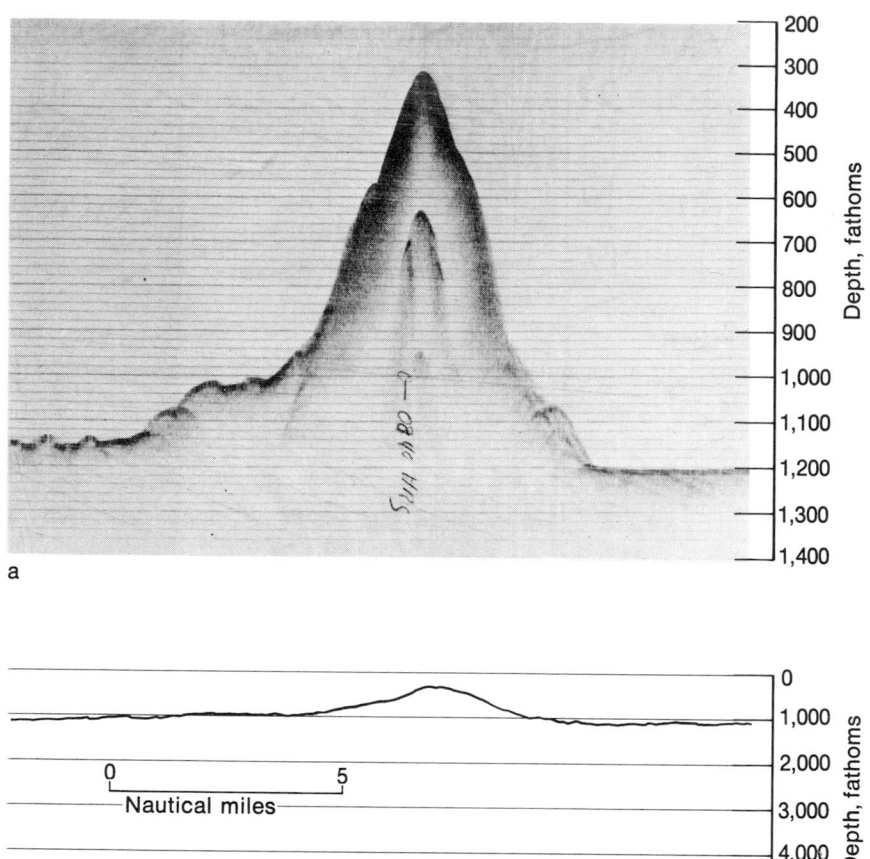

Figure 4-23 (a) Echo-sounding record made over a large hill, which is probably a submerged volcano. The vertical exaggeration of this record is 12 times. (Photograph courtesy of Woods Hole Oceanographic Institution.) (b) The same data shown with no vertical exaggeration.

Oceanographic vessels routinely use their echo-sounding equipment at sea. Many crossings over an area can be used to produce a model (Figure 4-24) or bathymetric chart (Figure 4-25) of the ocean floor.

Under certain conditions echo sounding can provide information about the sedimentary layers under the ocean floor. In this instance some sound energy is reflected from layers beneath the ocean floor and the resulting echo-sounding record shows a cross section of the upper several meters of the ocean floor (Figure 4-26). Similar marine geophysical techniques, using considerably more sound energy, can obtain reflections from layers two or more kilometers below the ocean floor (see Figures 8-34 and 8-39).

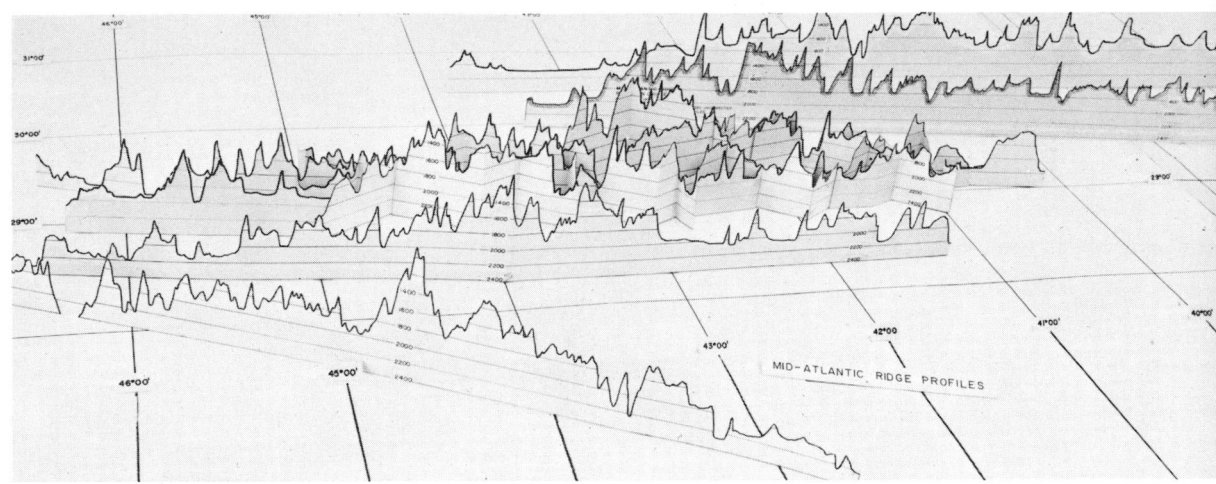

Figure 4-24   Model of a small portion of the Mid-Atlantic Ridge. Numerous echo-sounding records were used to construct this model. (Model constructed by R. M. Pratt.)

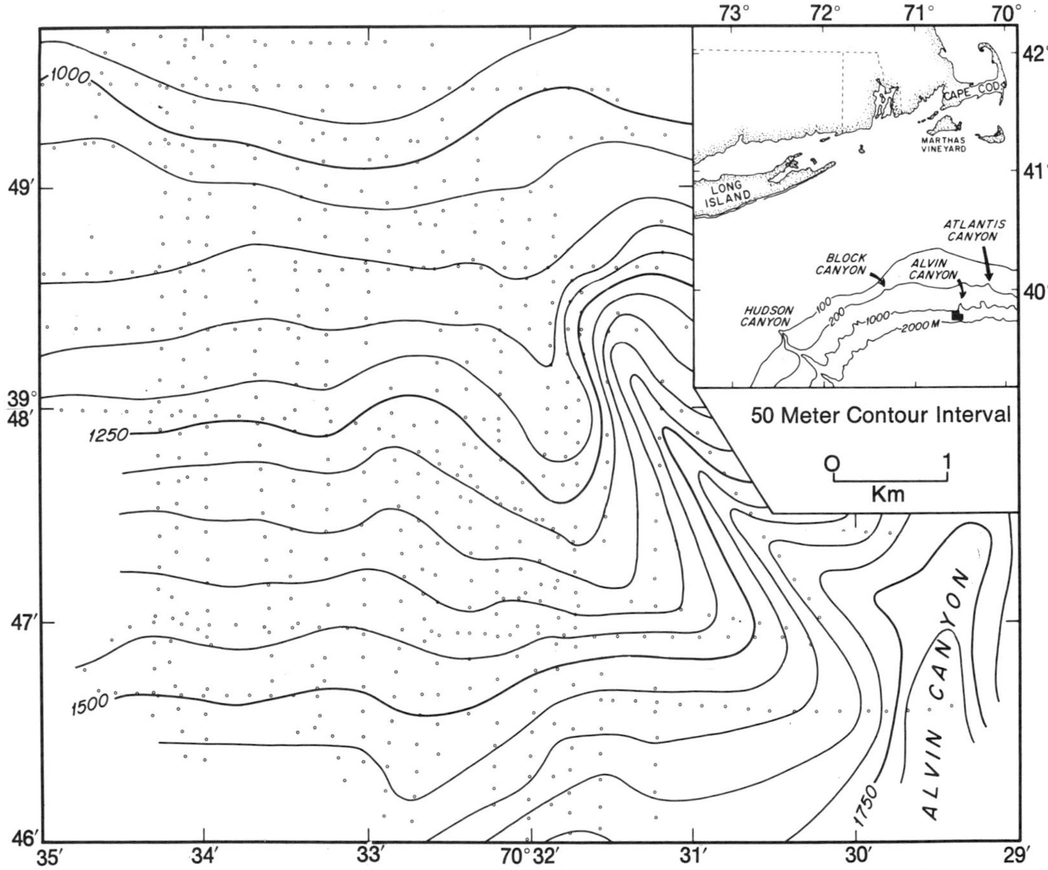

Figure 4-25   Bathymetric chart of part of the continental slope off the east coast of the United States. The small dots are the individual depth readings used to construct the chart. The insert chart shows the area surveyed. (From K. O. Emery and D. A. Ross, *Deep Sea Research* **15** [1968].)

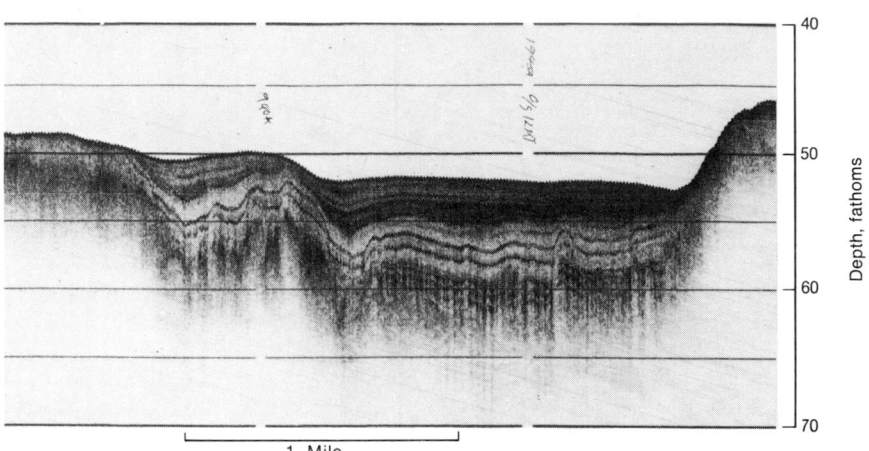

Figure 4-26

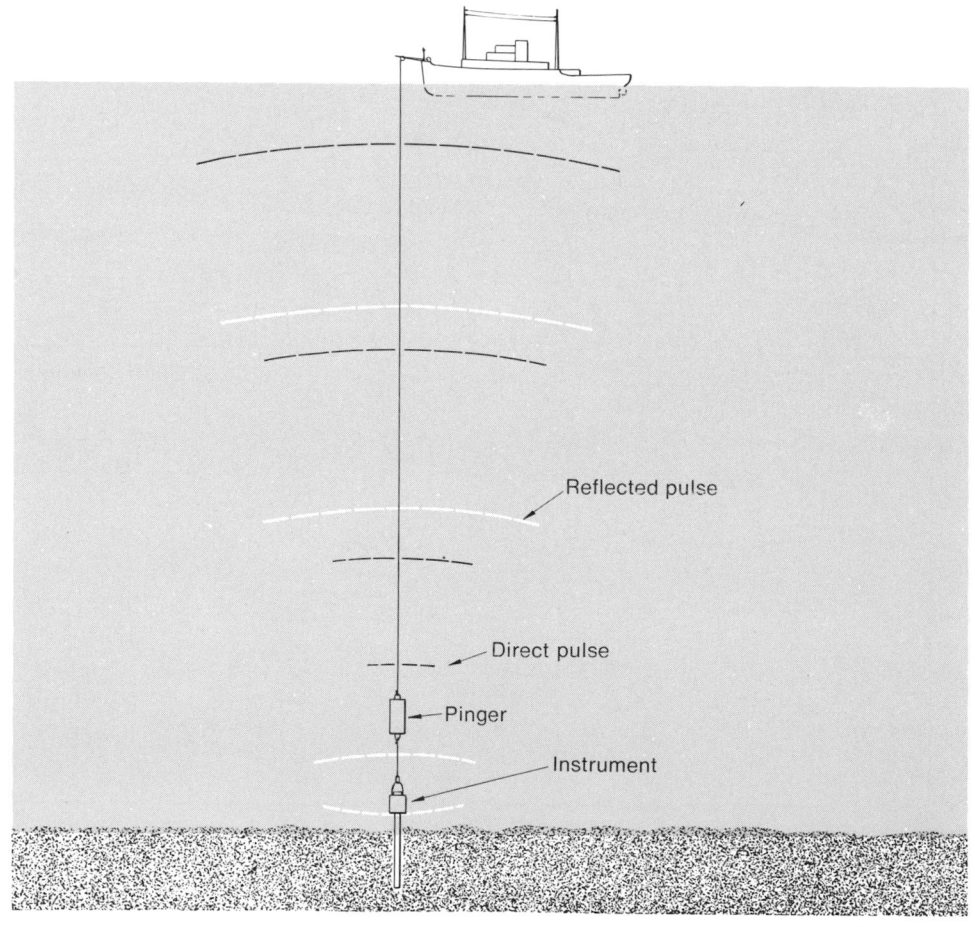

Figure 4-27

Figure 4-26 Echo-sounding record showing some subsurface layers below the surface sediments. These layers probably are due to differences in sediment type, that is, a change from a clayish to a sandy sediment. Vertical exaggeration is about 50 times. This record is from a Woods Hole Oceanographic Institution cruise to the Baltic Sea. (Record courtesy of Woods Hole Oceanographic Institution.)

Figure 4-27 The use of a pinger to determine relative height above the bottom. The difference in arrival time of the direct pulse and the reflected pulse indicates the height of the pinger above the bottom. If the pinger was on the bottom, both pulses would arrive at the same time.

Pingers

Pingers are devices used to position instruments, suspended on wires, relative to the sea floor. These devices are attached to the wires, usually near the instruments. The pinger will emit sound pulses at precise intervals, usually exactly one second apart. The ship's echo sounder receives the outgoing (or direct) pulse and the reflected signal from the sea floor. The difference in arrival times between the direct and reflected signals indicates the height of the pinger above the bottom (Figure 4-27). Some more sophisticated pingers, called telemetering pingers, have been devised to measure temperature or other variables and transmit the information to the ship's echo sounder.

Other Devices

Other devices that have application to all fields of oceanography are underwater cameras, underwater television, and side-looking sonar.

The old axiom that one picture is worth a thousand words is certainly true in oceanography. Underwater photography has become a very important part of oceanographic research. Ocean-bottom photographs can be used to study the sediments and rocks on the sea floor, examine biological activity, and observe indirect evidence of currents, such as ripple and scour marks. Camera systems (Figure 4-28) protected against pressure have been lowered by wire into the deepest parts of the ocean. Because most of the light in the ocean is absorbed within the top one hundred meters, these camera systems must include powerful light sources. They must also have a pinger so the camera can be accurately positioned above the sea floor. Pictures (Figures 4-29 and 4-30) are usually taken with the camera only a few feet above the bottom. Most camera systems will take several hundred pictures with each lowering. When the instrument is near the bottom a surface operator, guided by the pinger returns displayed on the ship's echo

Figure 4-28   A multi-camera system. The light source is to the right, the cameras are to the left, and in the center is the power and sound source for determining height above the bottom. (Photograph courtesy of Woods Hole Oceanographic Institution.)

Figure 4-29   A photograph taken in the Puerto Rico Trench (19° 59′ N, 66° 30′ W) by the research vessel CHAIN using a camera system similar to that shown in Figure 4-28. (Photograph courtesy of Woods Hole Oceanographic Institution.)

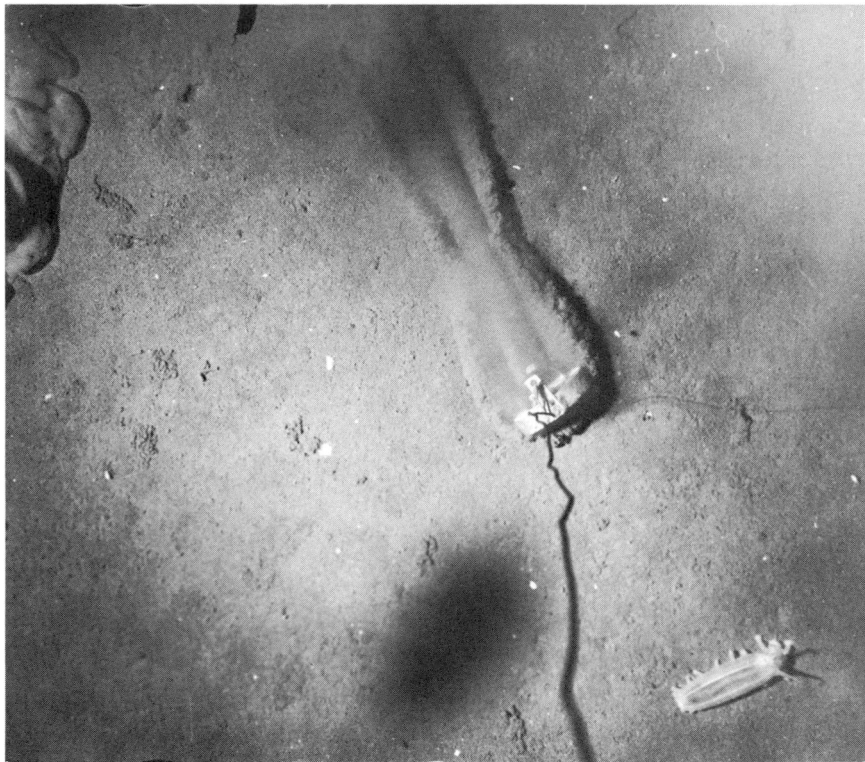

Figure 4-30 Underwater picture taken by the research vessel CHAIN at a depth of about 4,000 m in the Romanche Trench (on the Mid-Atlantic Ridge near the equator). The object being dragged along the bottom is an underwater compass. Unfortunately it is being dragged toward a holothurian, or sea cucumber; the next picture did not show the animal's fate. (Photograph courtesy of Woods Hole Oceanographic Institution.)

sounder, will try to keep the camera a few feet above the ocean floor. This is done to keep the distance above the bottom within the camera's optical depth of field so that the pictures will be in focus. In some instances two cameras are used to obtain stereoscopic pictures, which can be used to measure the dimensions of small features on the sea floor.

Underwater television cameras, although not used as often as still cameras, have unique advantages, chiefly continuous observation of a particular part of the sea floor or the overlying water. The Institute of Marine Sciences at the University of Miami has operated an underwater television system in the Bahamas at a depth of 20 m since 1963. This system has provided important information on the behavior of marine organisms. A common problem with underwater television systems is that they present an environment attractive to many fish. In

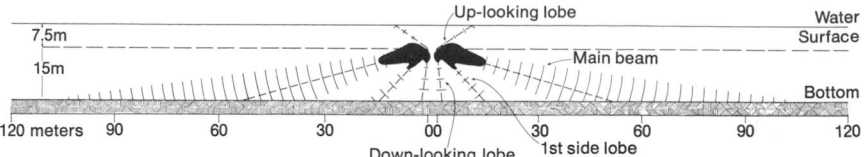

Figure 4-31   Configuration of side-scanning sonar. (From Sanders and others, 1969.)

some instances, the fish will completely block the view of the camera; in other instances, encrusting organisms will attach themselves to the lens of the camera. These problems can be partially overcome by coating the lens with material toxic to the encrusting organisms.

Usually underwater television works in conjunction with current meters, temperature and light sensing instruments, and other equipment. The data from such a combined system can be used to understand the ecology of marine organisms.

A relatively new and exciting instrument is the side-scan sonar. This device, which is similar to conventional sonar, or echo-sounding equipment, transmits sound at an angle from the ship, rather than just straight down as in the case of echo sounding (Figure 4-31). The difference in intensity of the returning sound signals from the bottom can sometimes be used to distinguish between types of sediment (such as sand from gravel) or observe other features on the sea floor such as sunken ships. Such intensity differences occur because the sound energy is reflected best from rocky or irregular sandy parts of the bot-

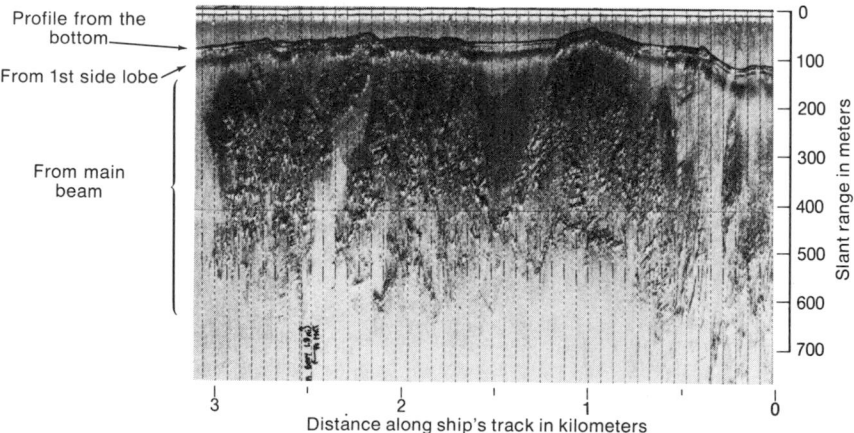

Figure 4-32   One side of a side-scanning sonar record made over a shallow ledge in the Gulf of Maine. See Figure 4-31 for an explanation of the different returns. The shallow irregular areas indicate rock, the flat areas sand waves and gravel (dark) and smooth sand (light). (From Sanders and others, 1969.)

tom that slope toward the instrument; areas covered with smooth sand or finer-sized sediment do not reflect as well (Figure 4-32). The ability of this device to detect sunken vessels could be very useful in submarine archaeological investigations and in the search for, and recovery of, vessels lost at sea. It could also serve to help evaluate mineral resources on the continental shelf.

SPECIFIC INSTRUMENTS AND TECHNIQUES

This section will describe some of the instruments used in the different fields of oceanography. Actually the distinction between instruments of different fields is artificial, as one instrument is rarely in the exclusive domain of an individual discipline. To best discuss these instruments, I have simplified the individual oceanographic fields and consider only the more common tools and techniques.

Chemical Oceanography

The chemical oceanographer is mainly interested in the distribution of the various components of sea water and the causes of this distribution. He needs a sample of sea water and a technique for detecting the elements or compounds. The sampling device must have certain important characteristics:

1. It must obtain a sufficient volume of water for analysis.
2. It must be easily and accurately located as to depth or any other property.
3. It must not allow or introduce contamination.

The volume of water needed depends, of course, on the type of analysis. Salinity determinations use less than a pint of water. Carbon-14 analysis, however, can require as much as 50 gallons of water (Figure 4-33) and introduces a shipboard storage problem, so that in many instances chemical analyses must be done on ship or a method of concentration must be developed.

To obtain samples from a particular water depth a device that can be opened or closed from the ship is usually required. An excellent instrument for collecting water samples from individual depths is the Nansen bottle (Figure 4-34). This old and trusted instrument comes equipped with thermometers that measure the temperature at the time of collection and can indicate at what depth the sample was collected (see p. 82).

To obtain uncontaminated samples the chemical oceanographer may use stainless steel or teflon-coated samplers. In some studies

Figure 4-33

Figure 4-33 Large volume water sampler being brought aboard ship. (Photograph courtesy of Woods Hole Oceanographic Institution.)

Figure 4-34 Nansen bottle in three positions—before tripping, during tripping, and after tripping. When the messenger hits the bottle it overturns, trapping the water inside, and if desired can release another messenger to trip a lower bottle. (From U.S. Naval Hydrographic Office Publication No. 607.)

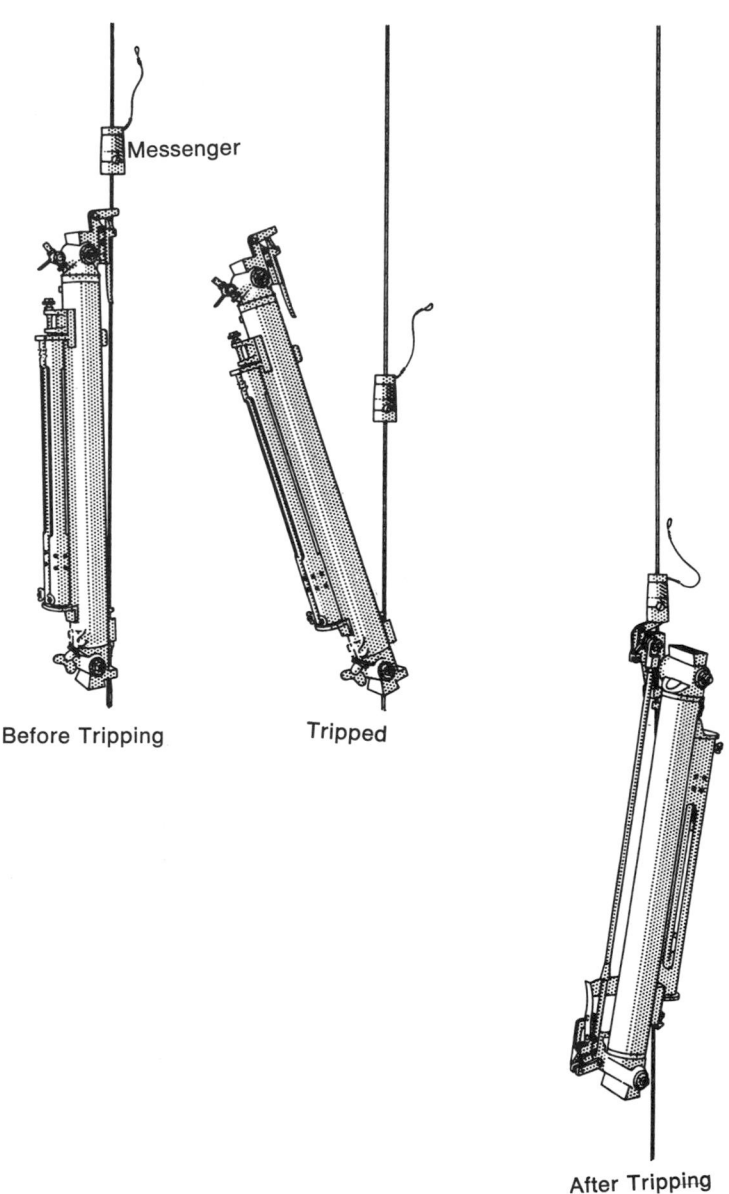

Messenger

Before Tripping   Tripped

After Tripping

particular care has to be taken to avoid chemical alteration after collection; refrigeration may be necessary.

After a sample is collected there are numerous chemical techniques that may be applied in the determination of its different elements. Most of these techniques are not unique to marine operations and are therefore not described here. Shipboard analyses are common for salinity or chlorinity, oxygen-content, and sometimes for determination of one or more of the nutrients. In the past most of these analyses were done by chemical titration, a slow and tedious operation at sea. Salinity is now determined by the faster and more accurate technique of measuring the electrical conductivity of the water. New instrumentation has been developed that can make *in situ,* or in place, measurements; the instrument is lowered into the ocean and makes its measurement in place within the environment. An *in situ* measurement can avoid many sources of error, particularly pressure effects on gas content.

It is possible that, in the near future, electrode systems can be used to measure almost any element in the ocean. These instruments could be lowered or towed through the ocean and the results could be telemetered to the ship's echo sounder producing an instantaneous chemical profile of the ocean.

Many chemical oceanographers and geochemists are concerned with the sediments of the ocean floor. Their sediment sampling techniques are similar to those employed by geological oceanographers (see Chapter 8).

Biological Oceanography

The biological oceanographer is primarily concerned with the distribution and relationships of animals and plants in the ocean. Therefore, he needs a way of sampling the population of the sea. A common method is to pull some device, usually a net, through the water. A typical device is the plankton net (Figure 4-35) which can be towed through the water. One question raised by this type of sample is, does it really represent the environment? Obviously, large and fast fish will avoid the net, while slower moving organisms will be more easily caught. In addition, certain species tend for some (usually unknown) reason to be caught more easily than others. Thus it is very probable

Figure 4-35   (a) Plankton net being towed along the surface of the ocean. The same net could also be used to sample at any depth below the surface. (b) The plankton net has been retrieved from its tow and is being washed down so that all the plankton will collect in the glass container at the end of the net. See Figure 6-9 for some typical animals caught in a plankton net. (Photographs courtesy of Woods Hole Oceanographic Institution.)

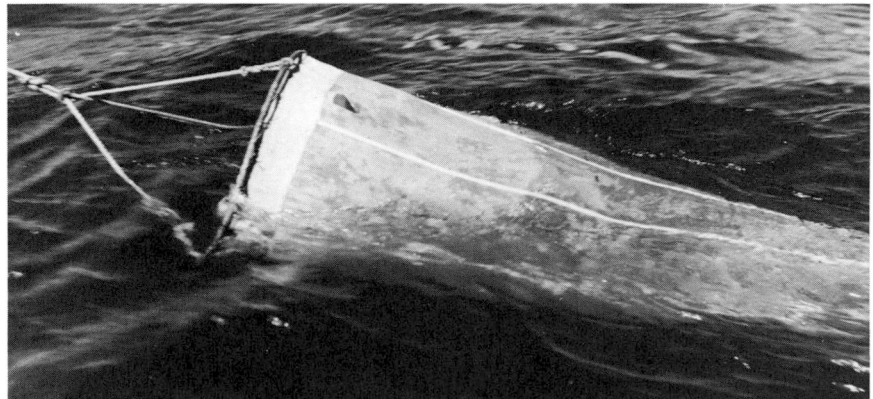

a

b

Figure 4-35

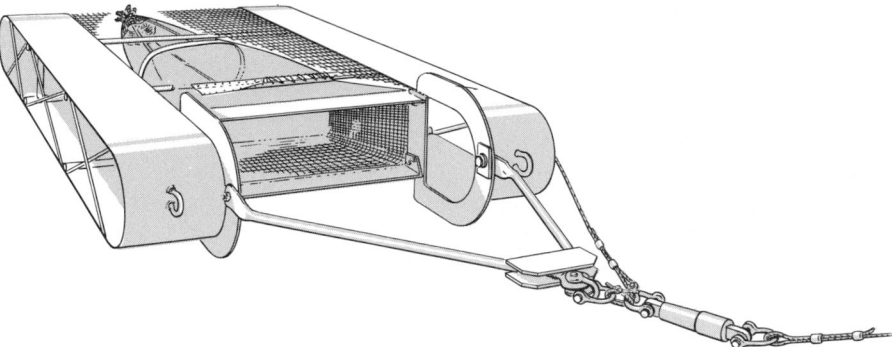

Figure 4-36 A biological dredge. This device is dragged along the ocean bottom, collecting bottom-living (benthic) organisms and sediment in the net held between the two runners; most of the sediment will pass through the net, but the larger animals will be caught. (Photograph courtesy of Woods Hole Oceanographic Institution.)

that this type of sampling device can discriminate against certain organisms and present an unrealistic picture of the biological population.

The bottom-living fauna can be sampled by devices pulled and dragged along the bottom (Figure 4-36). Additional sources of information concerning bottom fauna are bottom photographs (see Figure 4-30), and rocks and submarine cables when they are brought up to the surface. The latter two can be very informative because of the many creatures that attach themselves to these objects.

Other methods of observing the organisms in the ocean include direct observations by diving, either in a submersible or by using SCUBA. Certain electronic devices, such as echo-sounding equipment, can detect large individuals or groups of animals in the water. The sound made by, or the echo pattern from, different organisms can sometimes be used by oceanographers to determine what the species is (see Figures 6-40 and 6-41). Many modern fishermen use sonic devices to locate schools of fish. Fishermen and fish-tagging programs have supplied considerable information about the migratory patterns of fish (Figure 4-37).

The biological oceanographer needs more sophisticated instrumentation to study the ecology and environmental changes of the different organisms in the ocean. Automated instruments that can measure temperature, salinity, light, and other characteristics of the environment are now used with observing devices such as television and photography. The data obtained from such systems will allow scientists to evaluate the effect of the environment on the marine life. Laboratory facilities that can simulate marine conditions will eventually be among the more important instruments of the biological oceanographer.

Figure 4-37   A tag being inserted into a white marlin. After tagging the fish is released. If it is later caught by a fisherman, information can be obtained about the migratory patterns of the fish (see Figure 6-38). (Photograph courtesy of R. K. Brigham.)

Physical Oceanography

The physical oceanographer is concerned with measuring the various physical properties of sea water, such as its temperature, salinity, density, and opacity. These measurements can then be used to deduce the evaporation, heat exchange, and other physical processes occurring in the ocean.

There are three common ways of measuring the temperature of ocean water. The most frequently employed is a very accurate recording thermometer. This thermometer is usually attached to a Nansen bottle (see Figure 4-34) and lowered into the ocean. When the Nansen bottle is at the desired depth, a weight (called a messenger) is sent down the wire; when the messenger hits the bottle, the bottle overturns releasing another messenger to perform the same task on other bottles further down the line. When the bottle overturns it obtains a sample of sea water that will be used for salinity determinations. The overturning of the bottle also breaks the mercury column inside the thermometer, preserving the temperature measurement made at that time. If this did not happen, the temperature would rise as the thermometer is lifted back to the ship and passes through the warmer surface waters. Usually two of these thermometers are used. One is exposed to the pressure of the overlying sea water, the other is protected from this pressure. The difference in the temperature will then be a measure of the pressure or depth, since pressure is closely related to depth. A high degree of accuracy is necessary for these temperature measurements; values should be accurate to less than 0.05° C. Accuracy is necessary because temperature has a very important effect on density and other physical properties. It is also necessary because temperatures in the deep sea are relatively constant and have such extremely small variations that only a very accurate thermometer could record them. The lowering of several Nansen bottles creates what is called a hydrographic station; in Chapter 7 I describe how data obtained from a station can be used to determine oceanic currents. The two disadvantages of such measurements are that they are time-consuming and limited to a particular point.

To overcome these disadvantages two other types of temperature measuring instruments have been devised. One is the BT or bathythermograph (Figure 4-38) which can be quickly lowered from a vessel even while it is in motion. Pressure- and temperature-sensitive elements produce a continuous plot of temperature versus depth on a coated glass slide. The BT, which is simple to use, is not as accurate as a good thermometer, but has the advantage of producing a continuous picture. Expendable BTs have recently been developed. These transmit their data directly to the surface vessel, and can be used by helicopters and airplanes, as well as fast moving ships.

Other new instruments combine the accuracy of thermometers with the speed and continuous measurement capabilities of the BT by using thermistors or other types of temperature sensors and by either transmitting the data by telemetry or storing it until the instruments are retrieved. Because they can also measure other variables and are very accurate and sensitive, they can be used to examine the small-scale structure of the various physical properties of the ocean.

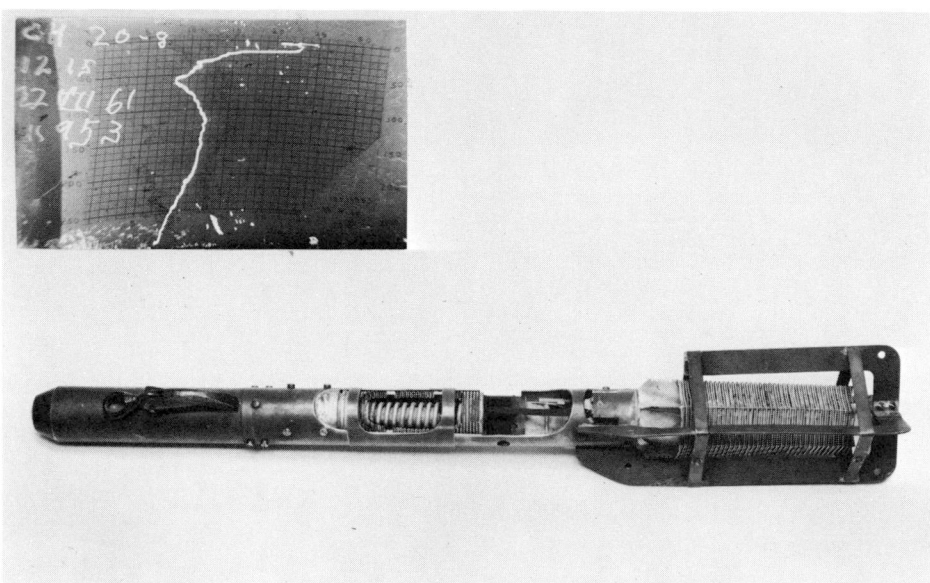

Figure 4-38   A bathythermograph, or BT. This device is lowered from a ship and will produce the record shown in the upper left. The horizontal scale is temperature, the vertical is depth. The notation indicates the cruise and time of measurement. Note the rapid decrease in temperature (called the thermocline) within the upper part of the ocean. (Photograph courtesy of Woods Hole Oceanographic Institution.)

Speed and direction of currents in the ocean are measured by both direct and indirect methods. A direct method uses ship drift; the difference between the anticipated and the actual arrival point of a ship is usually assumed to be due to currents (Figure 4-39a). Another method of measuring currents is to put objects into the water and either note their movements or let them drift freely unobserved (Figure 4-39b and c). Drift bottles usually have a card inside them offering a small reward if the finder returns the card and tells where and when he found it. Drift bottles have certain disadvantages. Their exact route to the place they are found is not known, nor is the degree to which they were influenced by the wind. Nevertheless, by plotting the launchings and recoveries of many of these bottles, a general notion of large-scale surface oceanic circulation can be gained.

Drogues can be used to measure currents slightly below the surface, away from the direct effects of the wind (Figure 4-39c). A sophisticated type of drogue is the Swallow float, a sealed aluminum tube that is dropped into the ocean. The instrument is heavier but less compressible than salt water; and at a certain depth its density will equal that of sea water. (In other words, water has a relatively greater increase in density with depth than the Swallow float.) If a sound device is attached to the float, its movement at a given depth can be

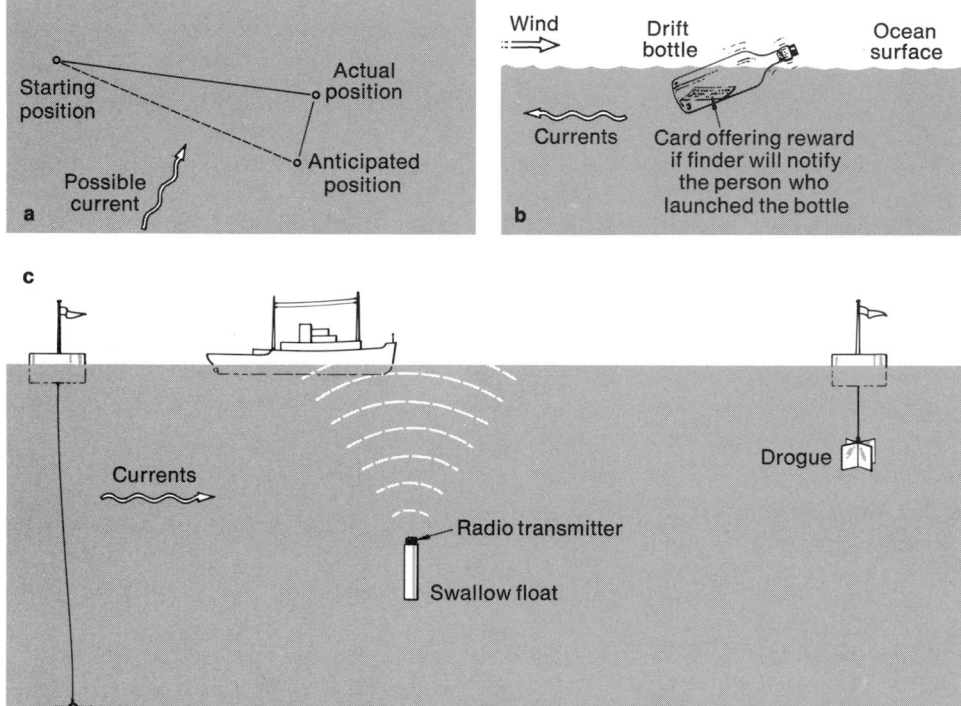

Figure 4-39   **Some direct** methods of measuring currents: (a) ship drift; (b) drift bottles; (c) drogue and Swallow float. In the last method, the ship maintains its position relative to a buoy and observes the movement of the drogue (visually) or Swallow float (electronically).

followed. The surface ship must, however, have some method of positioning itself, as it will drift with the surface currents. A buoy is often used so that the movements of the ship and of the Swallow float or drogue are determined relative to the buoy. Measurements obtained from the Swallow float show that the deep ocean, which had been thought to be relatively stagnant, can have currents moving at a speed of almost 50 cm per second.

Other types of current-measuring devices are telemetering surface buoys (see Figure 7-1) and current meters (see Figures 4-9 and 4-40). Some current-measuring devices are suspended from fixed objects such as buoys and lightships and thus can monitor currents for long periods of time. More sophisticated devices transmit the data to shore-based laboratories or computers. Some current-measuring devices record average current velocity rather than an instantaneous value. A current measured thus as flowing to the north at 50 cm per second may have been moving part of the time at other speeds or even in another direction. There are current meters in use which will make continuous

Figure 4-40   A current-measuring device. Water moving by the rotor on the bottom of the instrument causes it to turn; the number of turns (recorded inside the instrument) per unit time is a measure of the current. Instruments like this are commonly used in buoy systems (see Figure 4-16). (Photograph courtesy of Woods Hole Oceanographic Institution.)

instantaneous measurements of the water velocity. They are employed in measurements of oceanic turbulence.

Indirect methods of measuring currents include the measurement of temperature, salinity, oxygen, or other properties of sea water. Because many of these properties are strongly influenced by surface phenomena, their change with depth or distance is a measure of oceanic mixing and currents. Carbon-14 distribution through the ocean is an example. Carbon-14 enters the ocean from the atmosphere. It is absorbed in the ocean by plants and eventually, after the plants die and decay, becomes part of the deep ocean water. All during this process the Carbon-14, which is radioactive, is itself decaying at a known rate. A sample from this deep ocean water will contain both radioactive Carbon-14 and regular carbon, the ratio of the two indicating how long this water has been away from the atmosphere. Using other techniques, one can determine the source of the water or the area where the water was in contact with the atmosphere. By knowing the area of origin of the water and the length of time it has been away from that area, one can make an indirect evaluation of ocean circulation.

The distribution of certain organisms can also indicate current systems. The occurrence of nonswimming, floating organisms in an area far removed from their usual habitat suggests that they were transported there by currents.

Physical oceanographers, like other oceanographers, are using modern electronic techniques of instrumentation as well as the more conventional equipment described above. Satellites, airplanes, and large electronically-laden buoys provide data about various oceanic parameters. Analysis of these data is commonly done by high-speed computers, in many cases directly on the ship (see Figure 4-5).

Geological Oceanography

The geological oceanographer is primarily interested in obtaining a sample of, or information about, the sediment or rock on the sea floor. To obtain samples, generally one of three types of instruments is used: (1) snappers or grab-type samplers; (2) coring devices; or (3) dredges.

Snappers or grab samplers (Figure 4-41) will only obtain a surface sample, which may be disturbed by the instrument. This device, because of its relatively light weight, is generally used in shallow water such as on the continental shelf. If a rock or some other large object gets caught in the jaws of the sampler it will not close properly and the sample may be lost.

Coring devices are used to obtain a long vertical section (or core) of the sediment. This is achieved by forcing a long pipe, sometimes with an inner plastic liner, vertically into the sediment. The simplest type of coring device is the gravity corer, which is a pipe with a heavy weight at one end that is forced into the bottom by its own weight (Figure 4-42). This instrument will only obtain short 2- or 3-m cores. To obtain longer cores, B. Kullenberg developed the piston corer (Figures 4-43 and 4-44). This device has a piston inside the core tube

Figure 4-41 An orange-peel sampler in the open and lowering position (right) and the closed position (after sampling) with its canvas cover removed (left). The jaws of the sampler close after the device strikes the bottom and penetrates the sediment. Once the jaws close the sampler is lifted to the surface; the canvas cover prevents the loss and washing of the sediment on the trip to the surface. (Photograph courtesy of Woods Hole Oceanographic Institution.)

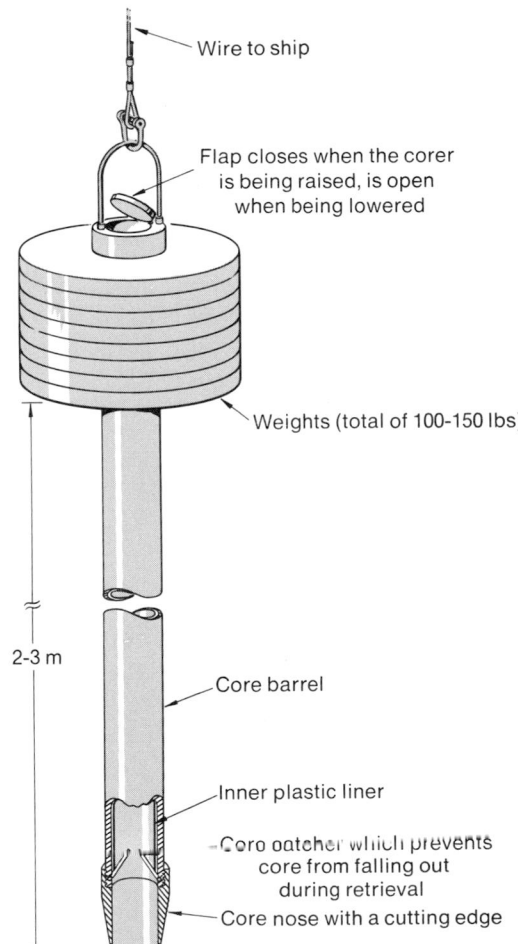

Wire to ship

Flap closes when the corer is being raised, is open when being lowered

Weights (total of 100-150 lbs)

2-3 m

Core barrel

Inner plastic liner

Core catcher which prevents core from falling out during retrieval

Core nose with a cutting edge

Figure 4-42 Typical type of gravity corer.

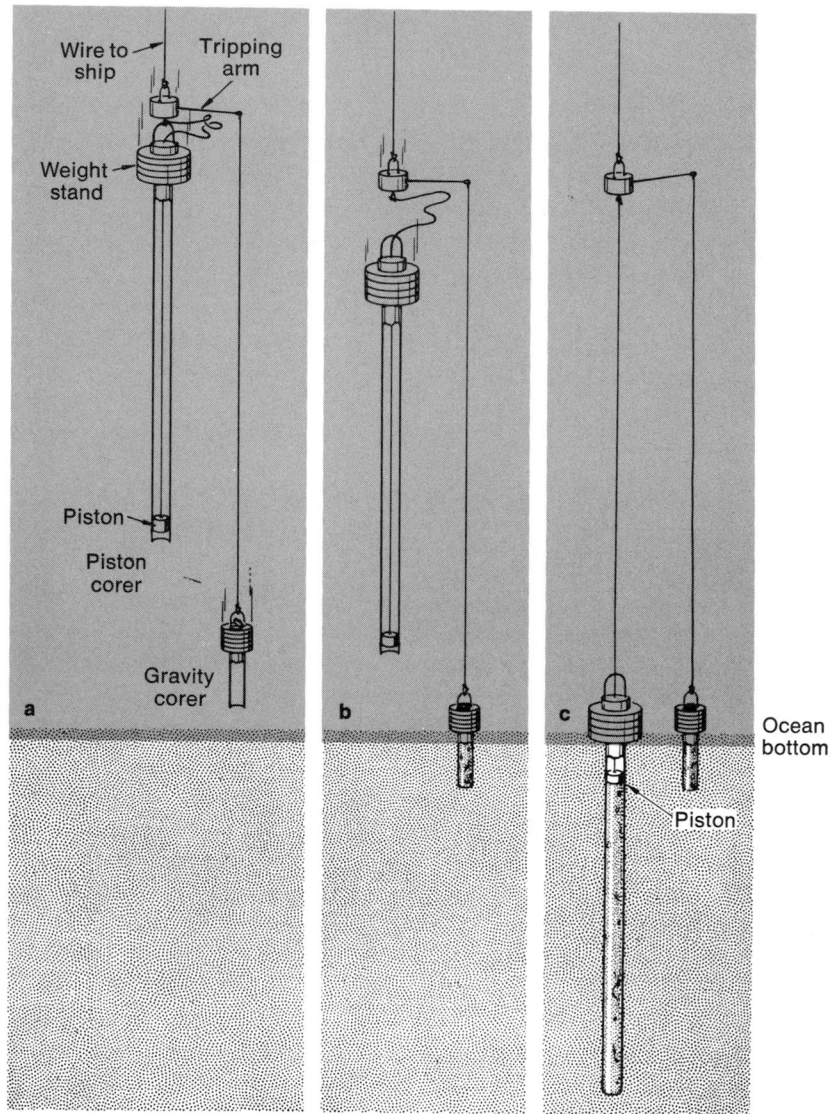

Figure 4-43 Operation of a piston corer that is tripped with a gravity corer. (a) Lowering position (see Figure 4-44). (b) When the gravity corer hits the bottom the piston corer is released and free-falls to the bottom. At moment of impact the line to the piston is tightened and the core barrel moves past it; this reduces friction within the core barrel. (c) Completion of the coring operation prior to retrieval.

Figure 4-44 Lowering of a piston corer. The line on the tripping arm is attached to a gravity corer. The line hanging loose is attached to the piston in the core barrel. (Photograph courtesy of Woods Hole Oceanographic Institution.)

that reduces friction and utilizes hydrostatic pressure during the coring operation, and therefore takes up to 30-m long cores. The use of stronger cable and pipe and heavier weights would undoubtedly result in even longer cores. The piston corer is usually triggered by a gravity corer. These sampling devices are positioned above the bottom with the use of a pinger.

Recently the weight stand portion of some piston cores has been used to hold other instruments, such as cameras. Photographs taken by these cameras during the coring operation can be used to measure bottom currents and to evaluate the coring operation (Figure 4-45).

A new and ingenious coring device is the free-fall corer. This instrument is not attached to the ship's wire, but is dropped free from the side of the ship. When the device hits the bottom, buoyant glass spheres are released which pull the plastic liner containing the sediment core out of the core barrel, and both float to the surface where

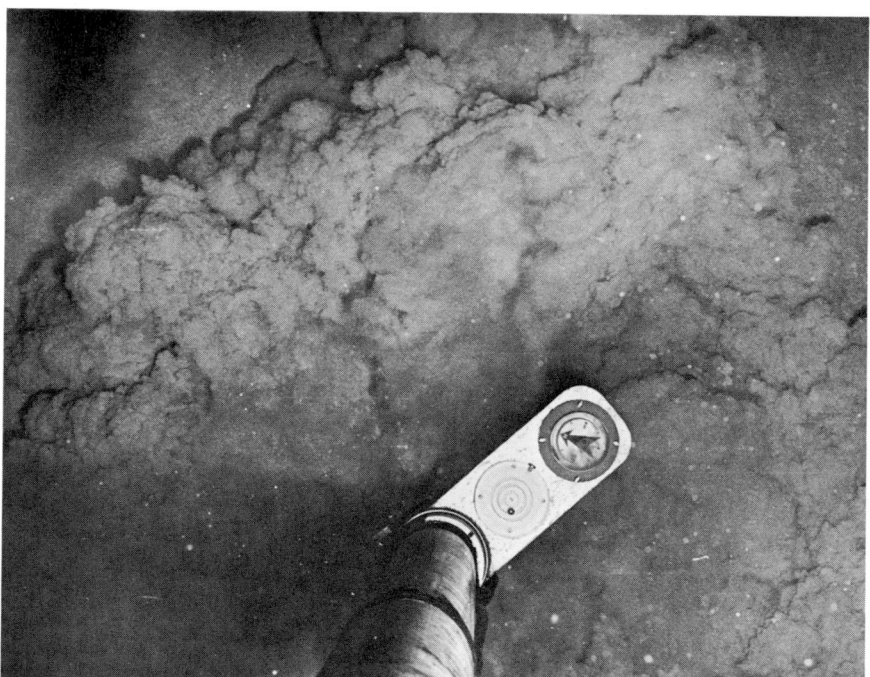

Figure 4-45 Bottom photograph taken by a camera mounted in the weight stand of a piston corer. The large sediment cloud has been produced during penetration of the corer into the bottom. Note the compass and inclinometer mounted on the core barrel to record the attitude of the piston corer in the bottom, which this moment has penetrated about 25 ft into the bottom sediment. Movement of the sediment cloud, as observed in subsequent pictures, provides information about bottom currents. (Photograph courtesy of F. McCoy.)

they are retrieved (Figure 4-46). There are two advantages to these free-fall devices:

1. Many samples can be taken within a short period of time.
2. The corer can be accurately positioned with respect to certain features on the sea floor.

For example, if one wanted to take a core with a piston or gravity corer in a submarine canyon, first the ship would have to be stopped,

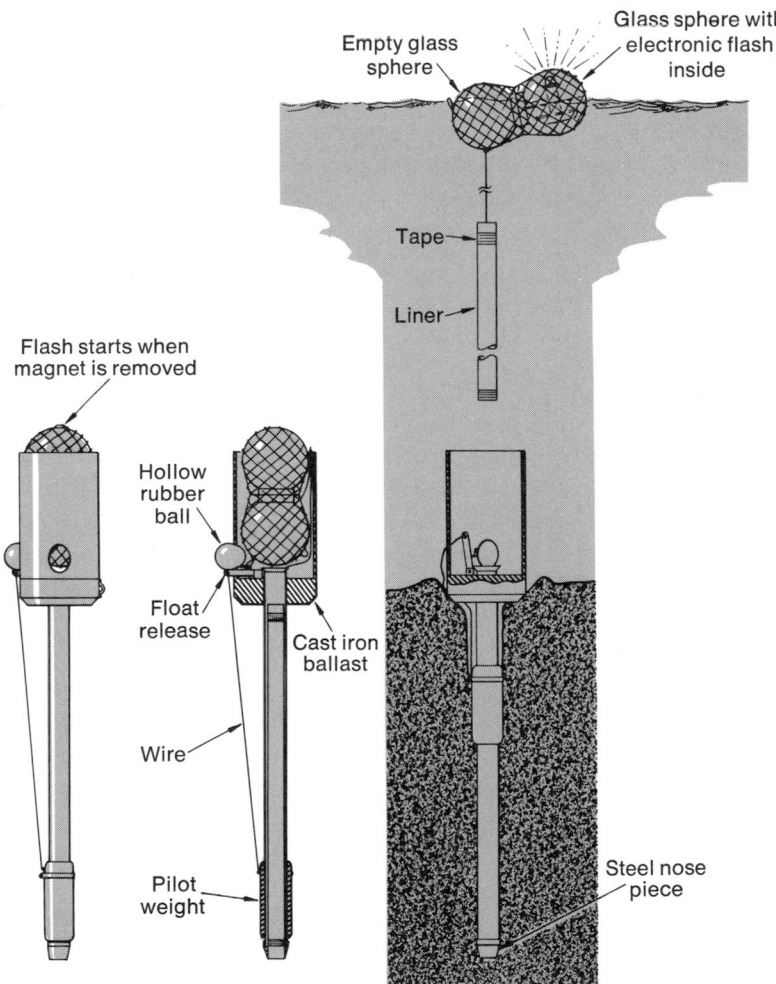

Figure 4-46   Free-fall corer. The corer is freely dropped from the vessel, without being attached to a wire. When the corer penetrates the bottom the pilot weight is pushed up, releasing the hollow glass spheres which, due to their buoyancy, pull out the plastic liner containing the core. Both then float to the surface where they can be retrieved by the surface vessel. (After Sachs and Raymond, 1965.)

then the corer would have to be lowered from the ship to the bottom. This operation, even in water of a few hundred fathoms' depth, could take as long as a half hour during which time the vessel would probably drift, due to surface currents and winds, away from the canyon. The corer itself, when it is being lowered, could be affected by subsurface currents and deflected from its target. The free-fall corer could, however, be immediately dropped from the moving ship when it is over the selected sample area. The device falls rapidly enough to avoid the effect of subsurface currents.

The third type of geological sampler is the dredge, which usually is or resembles a large-diameter pipe that is partially closed at one end. Dredges are rock-sampling devices dragged at slow speed along the ocean floor. If the open end of the pipe encounters a rock, the pulling power of the ship on the rock will sometimes break the rock so that part of it will be caught in the dredge (a biological dredge is shown in Figure 4-36).

Marine Geophysics

The marine geophysicist is interested primarily in the internal structure of the earth. His instruments are designed to measure the earth's gravity and magnetic field, to examine the subsurface layers and their structure beneath the ocean, and to determine the amount of heat being lost from the earth's surface to the ocean and atmosphere. In some instances the same instruments that are used on land can be used at sea. Usually, however, the ocean environment necessitates a new instrument system. An example of this is the measurement of gravity. The force of gravity, which varies from place to place, is measured by noting either the period of a pendulum or the pull of gravity against a delicately calibrated spring. On land these measurements can be easily and quickly made. Due to waves at sea, however, a ship will experience up and down accelerations that will produce errors in the gravity measurements thousands of times greater than the anticipated variations in gravity. F. A. Vening Meinesz partially solved this problem by devising a pendulum system that could be used on a submarine. In recent years gravity-measuring instruments or gravimeters have been successfully used at sea when they are mounted in devices that keep them in one position regardless of the movements of the ship.

Gravity differences are usually interpreted as being due to changes in geological structure. Because of the many possible causes of variations in gravity, the gravity data alone cannot provide a unique explanation for the subsurface structure and must be used in combination with other geophysical data, such as magnetic and seismic refraction data.

Measurement of the earth's magnetic field at sea is a relatively simple operation. A magnetometer can be towed through the ocean by ship or over the ocean by airplane. Magnetic measurements can reveal information about the composition of the upper parts of the earth's crust. Igneous rock bodies, such as volcanoes, can be identified by their magnetic properties. The magnetic properties of a rock body depend mainly on how much magnetite (a magnetic mineral) it contains, the thickness of the rock body, and its depth below the surface. The magnetization of a rock is also a function of the direction and strength of the earth's magnetic field when the rock cooled. The cooled rock will have a magnetization similar in direction and proportional in magnitude to the earth's magnetic field. This fact is very important because the earth's magnetic field changed often in geological times (that is, the magnetic poles wandered, and even reversed). Thus the rocks on the sea floor will have magnetic patterns that are characteristic of different geological times; the geophysical significance of this is discussed in more detail in Chapter 8.

The amount of heat coming through the crust from the interior of the earth can be measured by heat probes attached to piston coring devices. The heat flow is the product of the vertical temperature gradient in the sediment multiplied by the thermal conductivity of the sediment; usually the heat flow is very small, about one microcalorie (a millionth of a calorie) per cm² per second. A calorie is the amount of heat necessary to raise the temperature of one gram of water at atmospheric pressure one degree centigrade. Areas where the heat flow is several times higher than the average value may be areas of crustal instability.

The study of the layering and structure of the ocean bottom is mainly done by seismic reflection and refraction techniques. Both these techniques are based on essentially the same principle (Figure 4-47). Sound waves generated by an explosion will travel to the ocean bottom and its subsurface layers and then be reflected back to the surface ship (reflection). Some energy will also travel along the various subsurface layers of the crust and could be received by a second ship (refraction). The receiving devices are called hydrophones. In the reflection technique only one ship is necessary. The returning signals are, after amplifying and filtering, printed by the ship's echo sounder (Figure 4-48).

Seismic refraction requires two ships (or one ship and a receiving buoy); the receiving ship lays to, while the other vessel, which is moving, fires explosive charges at prearranged times. As the two ships get further apart, returns from deeper layers are received first, because the speed of sound is proportional to the density of the rocks through which it passes and the density and velocity increase with depth. A

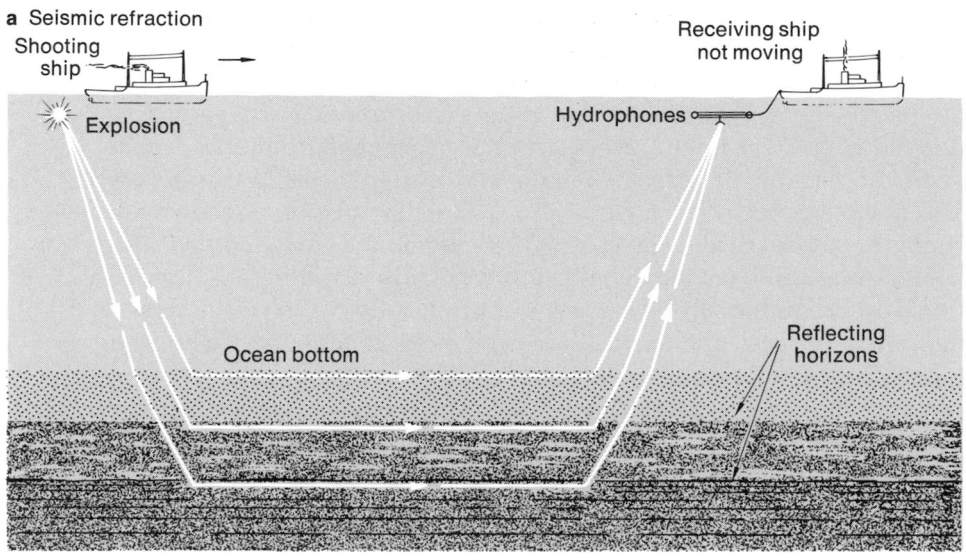

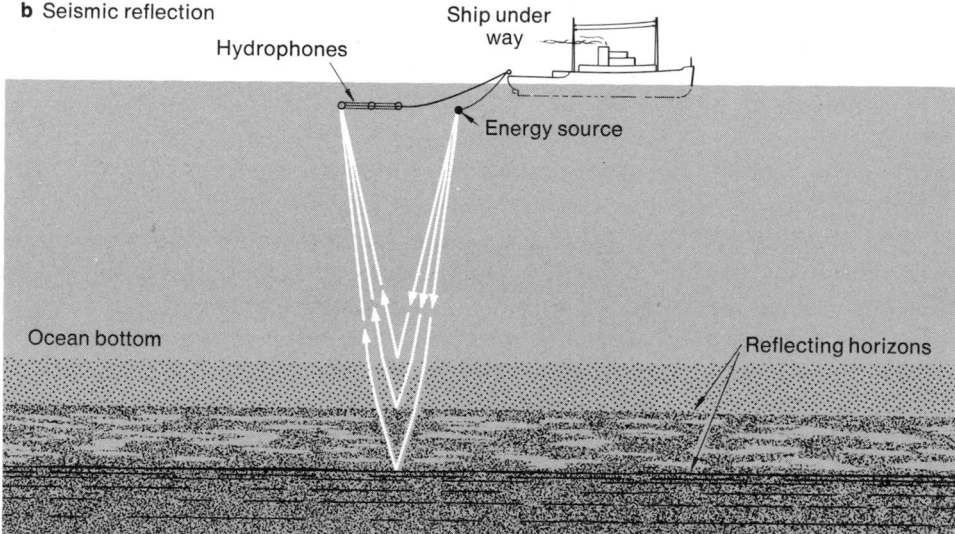

Figure 4-47 (a) Procedure for seismic refraction. (b) Procedure for seismic reflection.

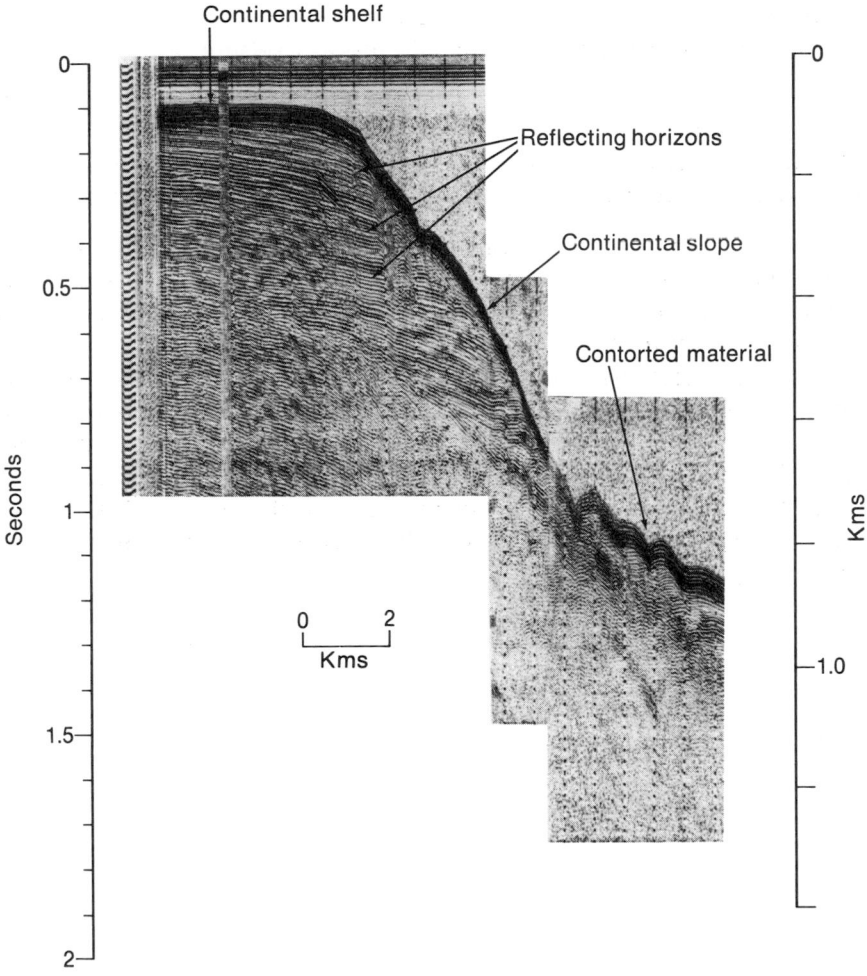

Figure 4-48 A continuous seismic reflection profile made across the outer continental shelf and slope off the west coast of Mexico. The time scale is the time the sound takes to travel through the water to a reflecting horizon (see Figure 4-47b) and back to the ship. Note the abrupt termination of the continental shelf and the contorted reflections on the slope which may be material that had slumped down from above. (From D. A. Ross and G. G. Shor, *Journal of Geophysical Research* **70** [1965].)

plot of the distance between the ships and the time of the first arrival of refracted sound energy can be used to determine the depth and velocity of sound in the different layers.

Three important assumptions are used in seismic work:

1. Sound velocity in the sediments and rocks increases with depth.
2. All interfaces between the different layers are planes.
3. Sound velocity does not vary in the horizontal direction.

In practice some of these assumptions are not absolutely valid, but data obtained using seismic techniques have provided oceanographers with valuable information about the near-surface structure of the earth (see Chapter 8).

Geophysical instrumentation is constantly being modified, primarily to increase instrumental sensitivities. Another objective is to devise instruments that can be routinely used while the ship is traveling from one station to another. Part of this objective has been met; gravity and magnetic measurements can be made while the vessel is moving at full speed, and acoustical reflection work can now be routinely done at speeds of about 9 knots.

Chapter 5

CHEMICAL

OCEANOGRAPHY

INTRODUCTION

The chemical oceanographer is primarily concerned with two questions about the ocean:

1. What is the composition and distribution of the materials in the water?
2. What are the processes that influence and control the composition of the ocean?

The use of radioactive materials, either natural or artificially introduced into sea water, has recently allowed the chemical oceanographer to evaluate the effects of changes in the ocean over great periods of time.

Before considering the chemistry of the sea, let us examine the history of this field of oceanography and how its emphasis has changed with time.

HISTORY OF CHEMICAL OCEANOGRAPHY

The sea and its saltiness have puzzled man since prehistoric times. Early in his intellectual development, however, man learned to obtain salt from sea water by solar evaporation, a technique that is still used in many parts of the world. Greek and Roman philosophers speculated, usually incorrectly, on the origin of the salt in the water.

The first scientific study of the chemistry of sea water is usually attributed to Robert Boyle, who published a book in 1670 describing his work. He had observed a white precipitate when he mixed sea water and silver nitrate, but relatively little precipitate when fresh water was substituted for the sea water. Boyle found that salt was being leached from land, carried by rivers into the sea, and concentrated there.

Near the end of the eighteenth century, Lavoisier discovered that water is a mixture of oxygen and hydrogen. He also devised techniques for analyzing some of the dissolved materials in sea water. Lavoisier and another chemist, Bergman, made the first chemical determinations of sea water at about the same time. Bergman collected and analyzed water obtained from a depth of about 100 m. Both men evaporated sea water and then tried to extract different compounds from the residue. The results varied with the techniques and none were very accurate.

By 1819, only chloride, sulfate, calcium, potassium, magnesium, and sodium had been detected in sea water. Boron, iodine, strontium, silver, lithium, arsenic, and fluorine were discovered during the following 50 years.

A major advance in the understanding of the chemistry of sea water was made in 1865 by Forchhammer, who noted that there may be marked differences in total salt content among samples of sea water taken from any area, but that the ratio of major dissolved components is essentially constant. This concept is known as Forchhammer's Principle. Forchhammer also observed that silica and calcium were abundant in river water, but nearly depleted in sea water; he concluded that this depletion in sea water was due to the action of marine organisms which were absorbing these elements into their shells. Thus he recognized the fact that biological activity plays an important part in the chemistry of the oceans.

The Challenger Expedition (1872–1876) further advanced the chemical study of the ocean. Dittmar, an excellent chemist, analyzed many of the CHALLENGER's water samples and made determinations of dissolved gases (Figure 5-1). Dittmar's work, which compares favorably with recent work, confirmed many of Forchhammer's ideas. Dittmar suggested that given Forchhammer's Principle, the determination of a single major component could be used to determine the salinity of sea water (approximately the weight in grams of dry salts in 1,000 g of sea water). Dittmar also noted a general decrease in oxygen content with depth (about 1,500 m was the deepest sample) and an increase in carbon dioxide in the surface waters. The importance of these

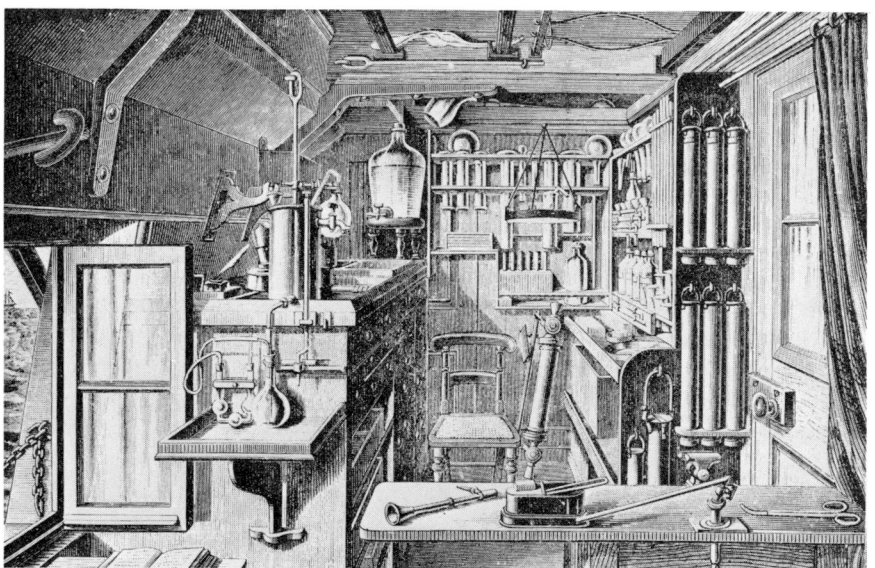

Figure 5-1 Chemical laboratory aboard the CHALLENGER.

differences, which are due to the processes of photosynthesis and respiration, was not realized at the time.

In the late nineteenth and early twentieth centuries chemists studied the relationship of salinity, density, and chloride content and established in 1902 that salinity = 1.8050 chlorinity[1] + 0.03. In 1967 the relationship was redefined as salinity = 1.8066 chlorinity. Average values (expressed in parts per thousand) are $35^o/_{oo}$ for salinity and $19^o/_{oo}$ for chlorinity. A standard sea water of known chlorinity is available from the Hydrographic Laboratory in Copenhagen, so that methods and results of chlorinity determinations of different laboratories can be compared. Within recent years the determination of salinity by chemical precipitation has been replaced by new methods, such as electrical conductivity, which are faster and usually more precise.

Early in the twentieth century chemical oceanographers started to associate the variations of oxygen in the upper parts of the ocean with the biological activity of plants. Other elements were also believed to be involved in the biological processes and this led to the study of nutrients such as nitrate, phosphate, silica, iron, and manganese. Scientists studying nutrient content in sea water noted vertical and seasonal changes. Nutrients are still being studied, but emphasis has shifted to studies of vitamins, trace elements (elements present in very small quantities), and organic compounds and their influence on biological growth and development.

Improved analytical techniques have yielded considerable knowledge of the elements that occur in trace concentrations in the sea. Measurements, sometimes accurate to values as small as one part per billion, have shown that more than 60 different elements are present in sea water in measurable quantities. Many of these elements were found in marine organisms before they were found in sea water. It is probable that as our techniques for measurements improve still further, traces of every naturally occurring element, as well as some of the artificially produced radioactive isotopes, will be found in the sea.

Present Objectives

In recent years a considerable interest has developed in stable and unstable radioactive isotopes. Through use of radioactive materials, the effects of time on the chemical and physical processes of the ocean can be evaluated. This is especially useful in studying marine

---

[1] Chlorinity (Cl $^o/_{oo}$) is defined as the total weight of chlorine, bromine, and iodine in grams in a kilogram (1,000 g) of sea water, assuming that the bromine and iodine are converted to their equivalent weight of chloride. This definition was changed, because of its dependence on the value of the atomic weight of silver, to the weight of silver (Ag) precipitated by 1 kg of sea water, that is, the chlorinity, Cl $^o/_{oo}$ = 0.3285234 Ag.

a Unetched

b Etched

0   2   4cm

Figure 5-2 Cross section of a manganese nodule. Deposits of these nodules cover vast areas of the sea floor. The lower nodule (b) has been etched with acid and shows its growth rings. The white material is calcium carbonate which is deposited within small cracks. (Photograph courtesy of F. T. Manheim.)

Top

End

Bottom

0   8   16cm

Figure 5-3   Piece of phosphorite that forms a thin pavement-like deposit on the Blake Plateau, off eastern Florida. Some parts of this sample have been replaced by manganese. (Photograph courtesy of F. T. Manheim and R. M Pratt.)

sediments and the age and mixing processes of sea water. Stable isotopes have been used to study the evaporation processes of the ocean.

Of equal interest is the chemical balance of the ocean, involving processes whereby the products of rock weathering on land are carried to the sea by rivers and then are removed from the sea by chemical and biological reactions.

The determination of chemical-biological reactions in sea water and their influence on the biological composition of the ocean will soon become one of the more important objectives of chemical oceanography, especially if the oceans are to help feed the increasing population of the world.

Still another field of active research is that of exploiting the mineral wealth of the ocean. Large quantities of valuable elements are present both in the water and on the ocean floor. Salt, bromine, manganese, and other elements are presently being extracted directly from sea water. Many important economic materials. such as manganese, nickel, lead, cobalt, copper, and zinc are concentrated in manganese deposits found on some parts of the sea floor (Figures 5-2 and 8-44). Deposits containing large quantities of phosphorite can be mined and used as fertilizer (Figure 5-3).

PROPERTIES OF WATER

Perhaps the one thing that makes the earth unique among the planets is its vast quantities of liquid water, without which life as we know it would be impossible. There are over 326 million cubic miles of water on the surface of the earth's crust, an amount that would make a layer 90 miles thick over the United States. Almost all, 97.2 percent to be exact, of this water is contained in the oceans (Table 5-1); 99.35 percent is contained in the oceans, glaciers, and ice caps. The water actually circulates between the oceans, the atmosphere, and the land. This **hydrological cycle** is discussed in Chapter 7 (see Figure 7-7).

Pure water is one of the simplest compounds found on earth, yet its properties and behavior are remarkably complex. Its chemical composition is simply H_2O, two parts hydrogen to one part oxygen. But it has certain unique properties. Its great solvent power and its high surface tension exceed that of any other liquid. Water also has an exceptionally large capacity for absorbing heat. It heats and cools more slowly than other liquids, and so has a modifying effect on the earth's temperature. Pure water boils at 100° C and freezes at 0° C.

The water molecule is a very strong one. At one time, water was believed to be a separate and indivisible element rather than a chemical compound consisting of two elements. Considerable energy must

TABLE 5-1   THE WORLD'S WATER SUPPLY (DATA FROM LEOPOLD AND DAVIS, 1966)

Area		Water Volume (cubic miles)	Percentage of Total
Surface water			
	Fresh-water lakes	30,000	0.009
	Saline lakes and		
	inland seas	25,000	0.008
	Rivers and streams	300	0.0001
	Total	55,300	0.017
Subsurface water			
	Soil moisture	16,000	0.005
	Ground water	2,000,000	0.62
	Total	2,016,000	0.625
Ice caps and glaciers		7,000,000	2.15
Atmosphere		3,100	0.001
Oceans		317,000,000	97.2
	Totals (approx.)	326,000,000	100

be applied to break the bond of the one oxygen atom with the two hydrogen atoms. The bonding between oxygen and hydrogen atoms is called a **covalent bond** (Figure 5-4). Hydrogen has one electron in its outer shell, and space for one more; the outer shell of oxygen has six electrons with space for two more. These electron shells are not completely stable when they are unfilled, but become very stable when filled, such as by the formation of a water molecule.

This covalent bonding explains some of the unique properties of water. When oxygen and hydrogen atoms are united, they produce a somewhat lopsided molecule (Figure 5-4); the oxygen and hydrogen are at an angle of 105° to each other. This causes an unequal distribution of electrical charges; the hydrogen side of the molecule is slightly positively charged, the oxygen side negatively charged. A molecule of this type is called a dipole molecule, and its action is similar to that of a magnet. In other words, its positive side will be attracted to (or will attract) particles having a negative charge, and likewise, its negative side will be attracted to positively charged particles. This action becomes important when water comes in contact with the numerous compounds whose elements are held together not by covalent bonds, but by electrical charges. If the water molecule comes between two atoms held together by electrical charges, it will, because water is a dipole, cancel some of the electrical attraction

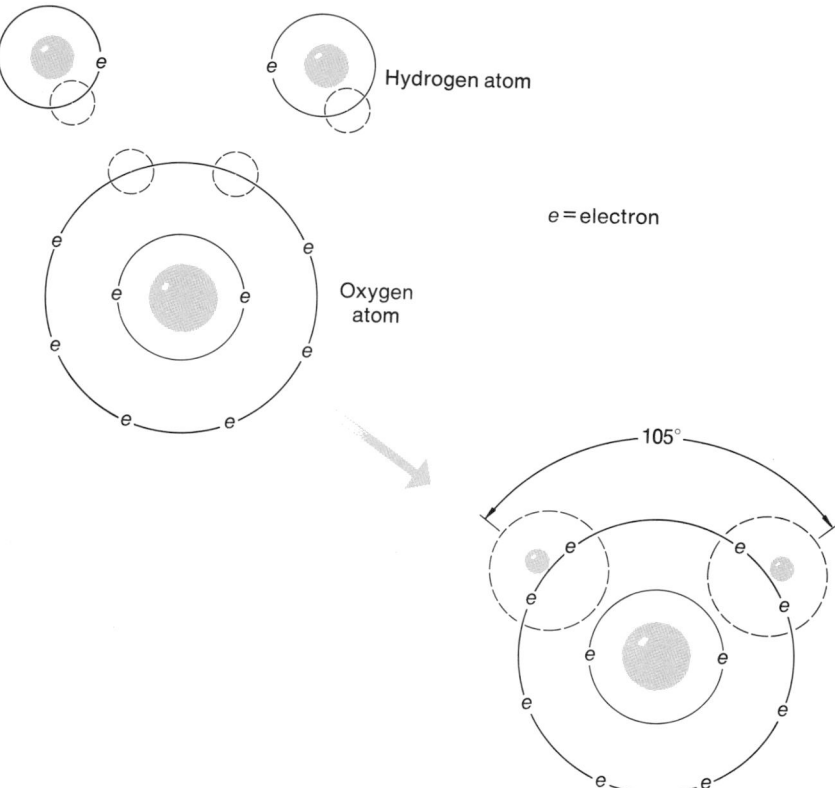

Figure 5-4   An approximation of the water molecule structure, formed from the joining of an oxygen atom and two hydrogen atoms.

between the two atoms. As some of this attraction is cancelled, the two atoms will move further apart and more water molecules will come between the atoms, until finally the initial attraction between the atoms is eliminated and the atoms are separated. The compound, some of whose atoms are now surrounded by water, has thus been partly or wholly dissolved by the water. The dipole characteristic explains why water is an excellent solvent, capable of dissolving most other compounds.

Water occurs naturally in three phases: solid (ice), liquid, and gas (water vapor). The liquid state of water is due to its surprisingly high boiling point; other similar hydrogen compounds such as hydrogen sulfide have boiling points considerably lower. The high boiling point is also due to the dipole structure of the water molecule. Because of their polarity, individual water molecules can cluster together in aggregates of two to eight molecules. These molecules are held together by hydrogen bonds. The strength and nature of these bonds determine some of the physical characteristics of water. For water to boil, the hydrogen bonds have to be broken, which requires considerable energy and results in the high boiling point. If water consisted of single unclustered molecules, it would boil at $-80°$ C and would be a gas under normal conditions.

In ice crystals, the water molecules, although tightly bound to each other, have a relatively large separation between the molecules. In liquid form, the water molecules are less tightly bound to each other, but the molecules are closer together. Thus ice is bulkier and less dense than water and will therefore float on water. When sea water freezes, the ice contains relatively fresh water (the salts are left behind) and it also floats. This is an important point because if the ice sank the deeper waters of the ocean, where the temperature is below the freezing point of fresh water, would be composed of ice.

The density of fresh water is at a maximum at $4°$ C (Figure 5-5). Above this temperature the density decreases with rising temperature; below $4°$ C, water expands (its density decreases); and at $0°$ C the volume of a block of ice is 10 percent greater than the same amount of water at $4°$ C. This phenomenon is important in the weathering and erosion of rock, because water, by freezing and expanding in the cracks of rocks, will cause them to fracture. Another important effect occurs in fresh water lakes. When the surface water is cooled to $4°$ C it sinks and is replaced by lighter and warmer bottom water. If the bottom waters were not well oxygenated, the foul odor of hydrogen sulfide might prevail over the area. The hydrogen sulfide would kill most of the organisms living in the surface waters.

Effect of Adding Salt to Water

The addition of salt to water, in effect, reduces the normal properties of the water. Before the addition of salt, water molecules can react easily with each other and go from the gaseous to the liquid state in a continuous process (Figure 5-6). **Ions,** such as sodium and chloride,

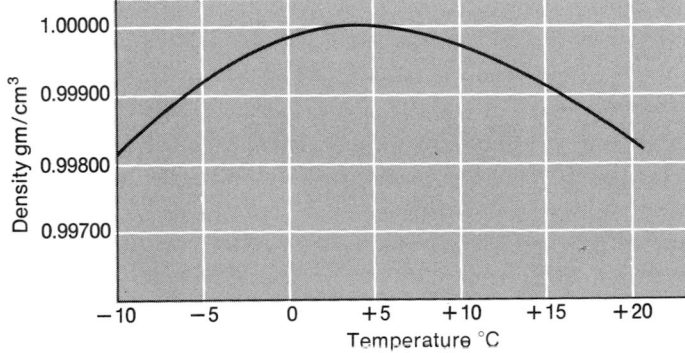

Figure 5-5 Density-temperature relationship of fresh water. Note that the maximum density occurs at $4°$ C.

when added to water will absorb water molecules and become hydrated.

The bond between the salt and the water molecules has to be overcome for salt water to freeze or boil. This results in an increase in the boiling point and a decrease in the freezing point of sea water, as compared to fresh water. When sea water boils or freezes, most of the salts remain in the liquid phase, increasing the salinity.

Some of the important changes in the properties of water that occur with the addition of salt are:

1. The specific heat [amount of heat necessary to raise the temperature of 1 g of water (at constant pressure) 1° C] decreases with increasing salinity. However, the specific heat also increases with increasing temperature in waters of normal salinity. In other words, as the temperature of the water increases, it becomes harder to remove the last few water molecules from the hydrated salt. Thus the boiling point of sea water is increased with increasing salinity.

2. The density increases approximately linearly with increasing salinity. Pure water has a maximum density at 4° C. The addition of salt lowers the temperature of maximum density and at salinities greater than $20^0/_{00}$ the maximum density occurs at a temperature below the normal (0° C) freezing point (Figure 5-7).

3. The freezing point is lowered with the addition of salt (Figure 5-7). This characteristic combined with the temperature and salinity effect on density (the density of sea water increases as the temperature decreases) means that the highest density water in the ocean is the coldest, most saline water. Sea water of normal salinity can exist as a liquid when its temperature is as low as about −2° C. The light or low density water is that with high temperature and low salinity.

4. The vapor pressure (which is a measure of how easily the water molecules escape from the liquid phase into the gaseous phase) is lowered with increasing salinity, because the salts tend to make the water molecules less available for evaporation. Fresh water will evaporate more quickly than sea water.

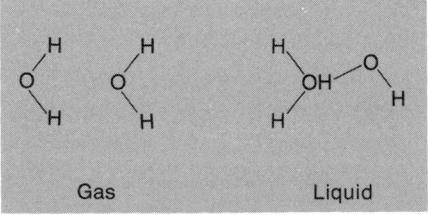
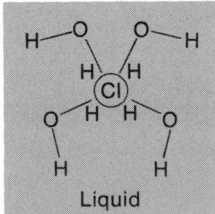

Fresh water   Salt water

Figure 5-6 Diagrammatic illustration of the various states of water and the effect of adding an ion to the water.

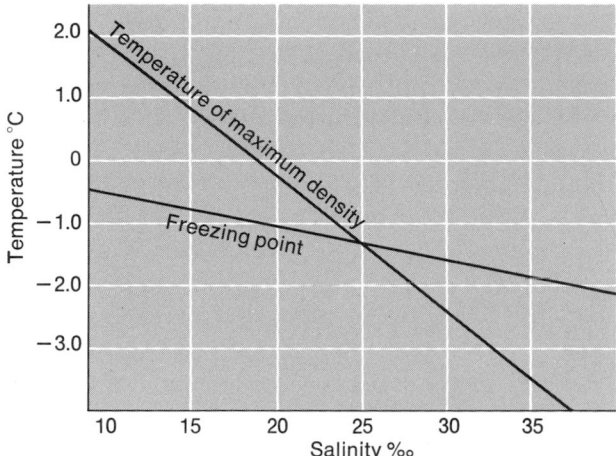

Figure 5-7   Relationship of temperature of maximum density and of freezing point to salinity. (After Sverdrup, Johnson, and Fleming, 1942.)

5. The osmotic pressure of water is increased with increasing salinity. Osmotic pressure relates to the flow of solutions (not elements dissolved in solution) through semipermeable membranes. The amount of flow increases with increasing salinity. This characteristic is very important to organisms since their cell membranes act as semipermeable membranes through which fluids can flow. The direction of flow depends on whether the osmotic pressure of the internal medium (the organism) is higher or lower than the external medium (the ocean). The flow will be toward the more concentrated medium.

Some of the above properties are called **colligative properties,** namely the boiling-point elevation, freezing-point depression, vapor-pressure lowering, and osmotic pressure. The colligative properties depend on the number of chemical species in solution and not on their composition. If the magnitude of one of the properties is known, under a given set of conditions, the others may be calculated.

An important consequence of the relationships among salinity, temperature of maximum density, and freezing point is that, in waters having a salinity greater than 24.7⁰/₀₀, the temperature of maximum density is lower than the freezing point. Thus as ocean water continues to cool, it will continue to grow denser (see Figure 5-7). Since the cooling is from the surface, the surface water will become heavier than the underlying water and will sink. The underlying warmer and less dense water will rise to replace the cooled water and will, in turn, itself be cooled and sink. In this manner a deep circulation will be initiated, and freezing will not occur until the entire body of water is cooled to the freezing point. This generally will not occur in a large body of water.

If, however, the salinity of the water is less than 24.7°/₀₀, the temperature of maximum density is reached before the freezing point is reached. As the surface water is cooled, it reaches its maximum density and will then decrease in density. This means that the water will remain near the surface and be cooled further; eventually the freezing point is reached and a layer of ice forms on the surface. Thus the relationships of salinity, temperature of maximum density, and freezing point prevent the ocean from freezing over.

COMPOSITION OF SEA WATER

The normal salinity of the oceans, away from rivers or melting ice, usually ranges from 33°/₀₀ to 37°/₀₀.

Six major elements (chlorine, sodium, magnesium, sulfur, calcium, and potassium) constitute more than 90% of the total salts in solution. These elements, and the minor elements strontium, bromine, and boron, have a constant ratio to each other (Forchhammer's Principle) and are the "conservative" constituents of sea water. By knowing the concentration of one of these elements the others can be calculated. Most of the remaining constituents of sea water including other elements, dissolved gases, organic compounds, and particulate matter, occur in differing proportions. These differences are in part due to biological reactions.

Actually the composition of sea water is not very accurately known. One reason is that many areas of the ocean have not been sampled and analyzed. Furthermore, the elements involved in biochemical processes may vary in concentration by a factor of 1,000 or more. Another difficulty of accurately assaying sea water is that the chemical reactions in the sea generally take place at the boundaries of the ocean, namely the water-atmosphere boundary, the water-biosphere boundary, and the water-sediment boundary, precisely where the chemical processes are least understood.

I will consider the chemical composition of the ocean in four sections: (1) dissolved inorganic matter; (2) dissolved gases; (3) dissolved organic matter; and (4) particulate matter. A separate section will be devoted to the biological effects on the chemical composition of the ocean.

Dissolved Inorganic Matter

Most sea water is relatively pure water (Figure 5-8), the dissolved inorganic components constituting only about 3.5% (= 35°/₀₀) of it by weight. The major inorganic elements (those present in quantities greater than 100 parts per million [ppm], or 100 mg per liter) are:

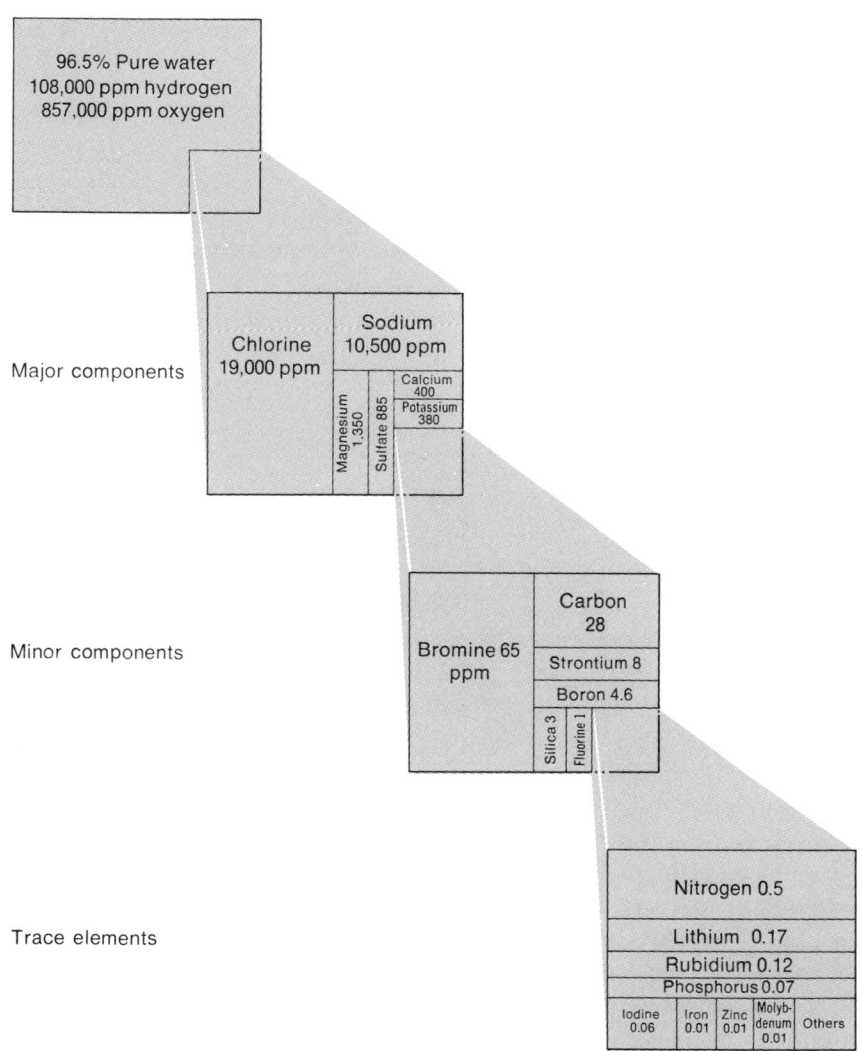

Figure 5-8   Dissolved inorganic compounds in sea water. (All values in ppm.)

chlorine, sodium, magnesium, sulfur (usually expressed as sulfate), calcium, and potassium. Minor elements (more than 1 ppm and less than 100 ppm) are bromine, carbon, strontium, boron, silicon, and fluorine. Common trace elements (concentrations less than 1 ppm) are nitrogen, lithium, rubidium, phosphorus, iodine, iron, zinc, and molybdenum. At least 50 other elements (Table 5-2), and possibly all the known naturally occurring elements, are present in quantities of less than 10 parts per billion (ppb). It should be emphasized that the concentrations of many of these elements can vary considerably with location, time, or season, and with biological activity. An example is copper, which was shown by W. R. G. Atkins in 1953 to have a season-

TABLE 5-2   TRACE ELEMENTS IN SEA WATER (DATA FROM GOLDBERG, 1963; HOOD, 1963 AND 1966)

Element	Concentration (ppb)	Element	Concentration (ppb)
Carbon	200–3000	Cobalt	0.2–0.7
Lithium	170	Mercury	0.15–0.27
Rubidium	120	Silver	0.145
Barium	10–63	Chromium	0.13–0.25
Molybdenum	4.0–12.0	Tungsten	0.12
Selenium	4.0–6.0	Cadmium	0.11
Arsenic	3.0	Manganese	0.1–8.0
Uranium	3.0	Neon	0.1
Vanadium	2.0	Xenon	0.1
Nickel	2.0	Germanium	0.07
Iron	1.7–150	Thorium	0.05
Zinc	1.5–10	Scandium	0.04
Aluminum	1.0–10	Bismuth	0.02
Lead	0.6–1.5	Titanium	0.02
Copper	0.5–3.5	Gold	0.015–0.4
Antimony	0.5	Niobium	0.01–0.02
Cesium	0.5	Gallium	0.007–0.03
Cerium	0.4	Helium	0.005
Krypton	0.3	Beryllium	0.0005
Yttrium	0.3	Protactinium	2×10^{-6}
Tin	0.3	Radium	1×10^{-7}
Lanthanum	0.3	Radon	0.6×10^{-12}

al variation in the English Channel from about 25 ppb in winter to 1.5 ppb in autumn.

If ocean water is diluted by river water from land drainage the relative percentages of the conservative salts can be altered, since river waters generally contain more sulfate than chloride and more calcium than magnesium.

Elements in sea water are virtually always present as component parts of chemical compounds. Some compounds, such as those containing sodium and potassium, are very stable; others, such as those containing silicon and manganese, are relatively unstable. The relative stability of these chemical compounds is important in controlling the composition of the ocean. Apparently some elements are being concentrated in the ocean while others are quickly passing through the ocean system. In other words the residence time of the elements in the ocean can be quite variable. (This interesting concept of residence time is further discussed on p. 119.)

Dissolved Gases

The major gases in sea water are nitrogen, oxygen, and carbon dioxide; occurring in lesser quantities are helium and the inert gases neon, argon, krypton, and xenon. Gases present in the ocean generally enter it from the atmosphere; however, some very rare gases come from radioactive decay processes within the sediments on the ocean bottom.

The solubility of a gas, or its ability to go into solution, depends on three factors: (1) temperature of the gas and solution; (2) atmospheric partial pressure of the gas; and (3) salt content of the solution. The quantity of most gases in sea water, with the notable exceptions of oxygen and carbon dioxide, is mainly determined by these three factors. The gases whose concentrations can be predicted are relatively unreactive in the marine environment. If the quantity of gas is higher or lower than indicated by these three factors, it would suggest that something in the marine environment is causing the variation. Oxygen and carbon dioxide are gases whose concentration can vary independently of the previously mentioned factors. These two gases thus are reactive in the marine environment.

The oxygen concentration in sea water is variable (Figures 5-9 and 5-11). In the surface waters, oxygen concentration is related to temperature: the higher the temperature the lower the solubility of a gas. However, a few hundred meters below the surface an oxygen-minimum zone or oxygen-poor layer is usually found. This layer is due to a biological phenomenon.

Sea water has two sources of oxygen, the atmosphere and the plants that live in the ocean. Surface waters, because of their contact with the atmosphere, generally contain their expected amount of oxygen. In some instances a supersaturation, or extremely large amount, of oxygen is observed. This is usually due to **photosynthesis,** the process whereby plants utilizing carbon dioxide, water, and solar energy produce organic material and oxygen. This photosynthetic reaction, because it is dependent on sunlight, takes place only in the upper layers of the ocean, usually above 200 m and thus can result in an increase in the oxygen content in the surface waters. Organic material and oxygen are utilized, mostly below the surface layers, by organisms including bacteria. These related processes, called **respiration** and **oxidation,** result in oxygen being consumed and removed as a gas from the water. The two reactions can be expressed as follows:

Photosynthesis (plants)

$$CO_2 + H_2O + \text{nutrients} + \text{solar energy} \rightarrow \text{organic matter } (CH_2O) + O_2$$

Respiration (plants and animals)

$$\text{Organic matter } (CH_2O) + O_2 \rightarrow CO_2 + H_2O$$

The oxygen-minimum zone then is mainly due to the respiration of animals and plants, and to the bacterial oxidation of organic debris.

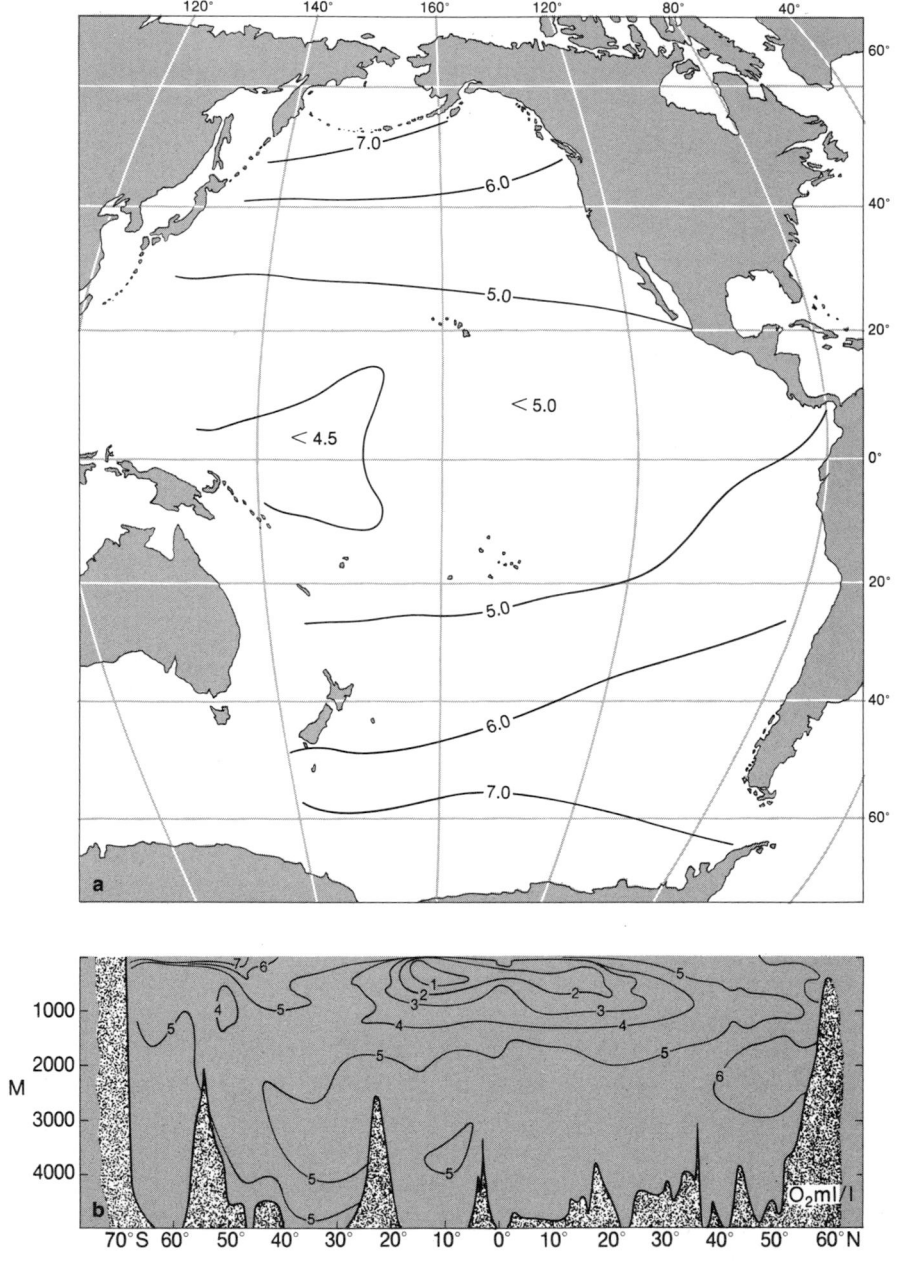

Figure 5-9   (a) Distribution of oxygen in the surface waters of the Pacific. Oxygen concentration in milliliters/liter. (b) Vertical section of oxygen distribution in the Atlantic Ocean. Section runs east of and essentially parallel to the Mid-Atlantic Ridge. (After Wattenburg, 1933.)

The presence or absence of the oxygen-minimum zone depends on whether the depletion of oxygen by respiration exceeds the renewal of oxygen by mixing of surface and deeper waters. The increase of oxygen in depths below the oxygen-minimum zone is believed to be due to the influx of oxygen-rich waters from the polar regions into the deeper parts of the ocean (see Figure 7-14).

Most or all of the oxygen at depth in the ocean is used up, when the oxidation of organic matter utilizes all the available oxygen or when an area is isolated from the potential oxygen source of the deeper polar waters. One such isolated area is the Black Sea. Waters devoid of oxygen are called anaerobic; organic material in these waters is decomposed by sulfate-reducing bacteria. The sulfide formed can combine with hydrogen to form hydrogen sulfide which is odorous and lethal to many organisms. If the deep waters of an anaerobic area are brought to the surface by some form of water movement, mass mortality of the animal life in the surface waters usually occurs.

Carbon dioxide is present in sea water at considerably higher concentrations than in the atmosphere. One reason for this is that water, volume for volume, can absorb a larger quantity of carbon dioxide than can air. A more important reason is that sea water is slightly alkaline and contains certain cations such as magnesium and calcium in excess of equivalent anions. This allows carbon dioxide to combine with sea water to form carbonates and bicarbonates.

$$CO_2 + H_2O \leftrightharpoons H_2CO_3$$
$$\uparrow \downarrow$$
$$2H^+ + CO_3^= \leftrightharpoons HCO_3^- + H^+$$

If carbon dioxide is removed from sea water, for example by growing plants, the bicarbonates (HCO_3^- and H_2CO_3) and carbonates ($CO_3^=$) will give off carbon dioxide. This mechanism will provide a large reservoir of carbon dioxide for photosynthetic reactions. At night when carbon dioxide is being produced by respiration, it will again be chemically combined and stored.

Carbon dioxide in sea water has a complex relationship with pH,[2] temperature, and salinity. Keeping pH constant, the total carbon dioxide content increases with rising salinity and decreasing temperature. However, pH depends in part on the amount of carbon dioxide and also is influenced by the water temperature and pressure. The understanding of the complex dynamic relationship of carbon dioxide in the air, sea, and sediments has been the most difficult problem in chemical oceanography.

[2] The unit pH is the negative logarithm of the hydrogen ion activity (or essentially the hydrogen ion concentration). A pH of less than 7 indicates an acidic solution, higher than 7 a basic solution.

Dissolved Organic Matter

Dissolved organic matter is present in sea water in moderately small and usually variable amounts (between 0 and 6 mg per liter). The source of this material is excreta and dead organisms. Included as dissolved organic material are the nitrogen and phosphorus which are chemically combined in organic compounds and will eventually be oxidized, in some instances by bacteria, to nitrate and phosphate.

Other dissolved organic compounds in sea water are organic carbon, carbohydrates, proteins, amino acids, organic acids, and vitamins. Aside from the nutrients, nitrogen and phosphorus, very little is known about the vertical and horizontal distribution of dissolved organic material. The chemistry and distribution of the nutrients are discussed in a following section.

Particulate Matter

Particulate matter, excluding living organisms, in sea water includes organic detritus, some complexes of organic and nonorganic material, and fine-grained minerals. The complexes of organic and nonorganic material may account for local variations in concentration of some elements; the high iron abundance in nearshore waters may be due to the formation of ferric-organic complexes. Fresh-water diatoms and minerals were extracted from the surface waters of the ocean more than 3,800 km from their probable source, by D. W. Folger and B. C. Heezen in 1967. They suggest that the material was transported by winds. Particulate matter in the ocean, thus, is highly variable in concentration. It may be seen to respond to local geography, biological production, atmospheric conditions, and other unknown conditions.

In summary we have seen that many factors control or influence the chemical composition of the sea:

1. Exchange with the atmosphere
2. Solubility of different compounds
3. Reduction by anaerobic bacteria
4. Precipitation and exchange with the ocean bottom
5. Inflow of fresh water
6. Freezing and melting of sea ice
7. Chemical reactions that control or influence the concentrations of different elements
8. Biological processes, including life processes and decomposition of organic matter.

Because of their importance I will treat chemical reactions and biological processes in detail in the next section.

REACTIONS THAT INFLUENCE THE OCEAN'S CHEMICAL COMPOSITION

Chemical Reactions

Different elements in sea water have different abilities to react with the marine environment. The difference in these reactivities can be shown by constructing a simple model of the input of elements supplied to the ocean (Figure 5-10). This concept, introduced by T. F. W. Barth in 1952, assumes that the amount of an element introduced into the ocean per unit time equals the amount deposited as sediment, in other words, a steady condition. Another assumption is that the elements are uniformly and quickly mixed in the ocean. Using these assumptions, the **residence time** of an element in the ocean is defined as the total amount of the element in the ocean, divided by its rate of introduction (or rate of precipitation to the sediments). When Barth examined residence times he considered estimates of the amount of the elements introduced by rivers. E. D. Goldberg and G. O. Arrhenius in 1958 examined the same problem but they considered the amount of the elements in the sediments. Unquestionably, the model is an oversimplified picture of the ocean. Yet it appears to be significant that the results of two different investigations are so similar (Table 5-3); the only major difference is the result for calcium. What is more important to the understanding of the ocean's composition is the wide relative range in residence time of various elements; some elements, such as aluminum and iron, remain in sea water only hundreds of years while others, such as sodium and magnesium, remain for millions of years.

The significance of these calculations is that the elements with

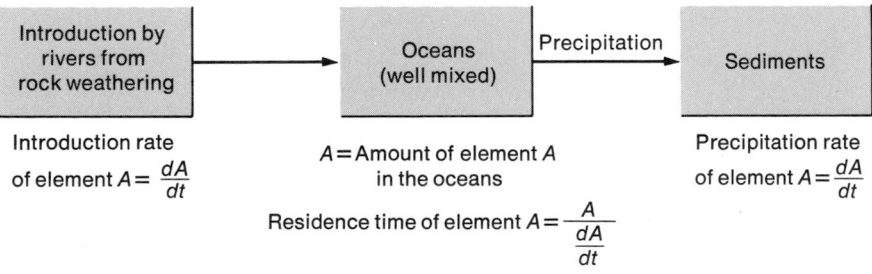

Figure 5-10   Simple residence time model.

TABLE 5-3   RESIDENCE TIMES OF SOME ELEMENTS IN SEA WATER

| | | Residence Time in Years | |
		Based on river input[a]	Based on sediment deposition[b]
Element	Amount in ocean		
Na	147×10^{20}	2.1×10^8	2.6×10^8
Mg	18×10^{20}	2.2×10^7	4.5×10^7
K	5.3×10^{20}	1.0×10^7	1.1×10^7
Ca	5.6×10^{20}	1.0×10^6	8.0×10^6
Si	5.2×10^{18}	3.5×10^4	1.0×10^4
Mn	1.4×10^{15}		7.0×10^3
Fe	1.4×10^{16}		1.4×10^2
Al	1.4×10^{16}		1.0×10^2

[a] Data from Barth, 1952.
[b] Data from Goldberg and Arrhenius, 1958.

long residence times are also the elements that have very low reactivities, and therefore remain in the ocean for considerable amounts of time. The low residence times of silicon, manganese, iron, and aluminum are to a degree related to biological activity; and important to an even greater degree for silicon, iron, and aluminum is the fact that significant quantities enter the ocean in the particulate phase. These particulate phases are usually minerals such as quartz or feldspar, or material from volcanic activity, which will quickly settle to the ocean bottom. The high chemical reactivities of manganese, iron, and aluminum are also due to their oxidation and tendency to form mineral deposits on the sea floor, such as manganese minerals, glauconite, and zeolites. These mineral deposits can cover considerable portions of the ocean floor.

Another method of examining the relative reactivities of elements in sea water is to consider the degree of saturation of the different compounds that an element forms. K. B. Krauskopf in 1956 calculated the theoretical maximum concentrations of some metal ions in sea water based on the least soluble compound formed by the ion. The argument was that if the calculated value of saturation was similar to the observed value, the solution was saturated and therefore nonreactive; if the observed value was considerably less than the calculated value, it was undersaturated and reactive. Elements such as lead, nickel, copper, and zinc were found to be reactive, while calcium and strontium were relatively unreactive. The concentration of these highly reactive or undersaturated elements in sea water is therefore not controlled simply by the solubility of their different compounds in sea water but by some other reaction. One of these possible reactions, taking place at the water-sediment interface, is the formation of mineral deposits on the sea floor.

Biochemical Reactions

The influence of the animals and plants of the ocean on the composition of sea water is considerable. The effects of photosynthesis and respiration (the biochemical cycle) on oxygen and carbon dioxide content in the surface waters have been described. During photosynthesis, carbon dioxide is utilized and oxygen is released; at depth, during respiration or oxidation, this process is reversed. Thus surface waters can be supersaturated with oxygen while waters of intermediate depth are depleted of it. Other elements are involved in the biochemical cycle; the most important of these are nitrogen, carbon, phosphorus, and trace elements such as silicon and iron. These elements are withdrawn from sea water by the formation of organic material during the growth phases of marine plants, and are returned to sea water as waste products and as decomposition products of the organic material.

Generally there is little accumulation of organic matter on the sea floor, because the organic material usually has decayed or been consumed while falling through the water, or, once on the bottom, it is digested by bottom-dwelling organisms. There are certain areas, such as the Black Sea, where the accumulation of organic material is considerable, and the available oxygen has been consumed and organic matter is oxidized by anaerobic bacteria.

The average ratio of the major nutrients in plankton was first determined by A. C. Redfield in 1934 and later by R. H. Fleming in 1940 (Table 5-4). To oxidize organic material having this composition, 276 atoms of oxygen are necessary, 2 atoms of oxygen for each carbon atom, 4 atoms of oxygen for each nitrogen. None are necessary for the phosphorus. This helps explain the relative absence of oxygen at intermediate depths of the ocean (see Figure 5-11). The oxidation phases, unlike photosynthesis, are independent of light and may take place at any depth.

TABLE 5-4   ATOMIC RATIOS OF THE MAJOR NUTRIENTS IN PLANKTON

	Carbon	Nitrogen	Phosphorus
Phytoplankton	108	15.5	1
Zooplankton	103	16.5	1
Average	106	16	1

The vertical distribution of the nutrients in the water can be characterized by four layers (see Figure 5-11 for phosphorus):

1. A surface layer, usually about 100 or 200 m thick, where the concentration is low (utilization during photosynthesis)

2. A layer, several hundred meters thick, where the concentration increases very rapidly
3. A layer of maximum concentration usually between 500 and 1,000 m (nitrogen usually occurs deeper than phosphorus) in depth
4. A layer, usually extending to the bottom, where the concentration is uniform.

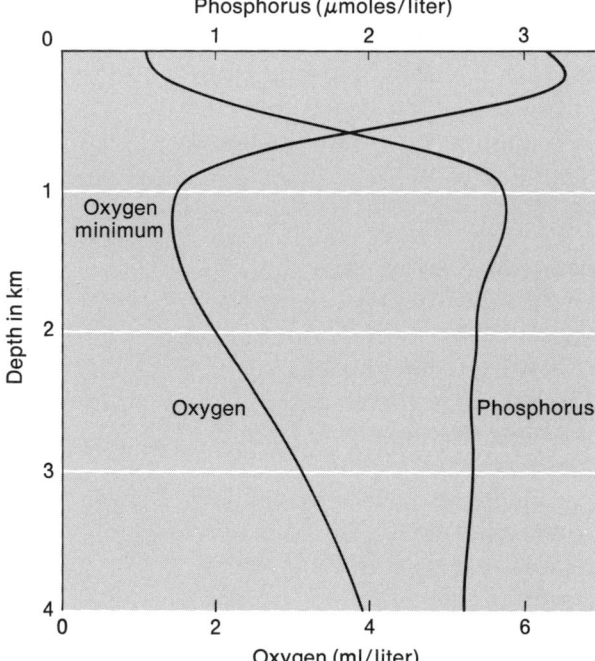

Figure 5-11 Vertical distribution of oxygen and phosphorus in the ocean.

In some instances the maximum concentration of the nutrients does not coincide with that of the minimum concentration of oxygen. This can be due to the presence of preformed (from a previous cycle) nutrients or differences in initial oxygen content.

The oxidation and subsequent return of the nutrients to the water results in a large reservoir of nutrient-rich water below the photosynthetic zone. These nutrients can only return to the photosynthetic zone (where they will become reincorporated into the biochemical cycle) by the physical circulation of the water. This movement takes place in several ways; by the worldwide circulation of the oceans, by **upwelling** (a type of vertical mixing, see p. 124) in coastal and equatorial regions, and by annual vertical mixing in temperate and high latitude areas. How these movements occur is described in Chapter 7. The result is a downward movement of nutrient elements, due to biochemical reactions, compensated by an upward movement of these same elements as a result of water circulation. Some material that is deposited in sediments is removed from the system, but this is balanced by material being added from rivers and other sources.

In addition to vertical differences in nutrient concentration, there are also ocean-wide differences and smaller seasonal variations superimposed upon these. The deeper waters of the Pacific and Indian Oceans contain significantly more phosphorus and less oxygen than the Atlantic and Arctic Oceans. This fact is related to the source of the waters, their composition at that time, and subsequent modification by biological and physical factors.

Seasonal changes in nutrient content are most evident in temperate areas, where phytoplankton have two growth periods each year— the spring and early autumn. In 1950, H. W. Harvey observed the composition both of the animals living in the water and of the water itself, to determine the seasonal patterns and changes in phases of phosphorus (Figure 5-12). The result notably shows two animal plankton growth periods, each accompanied by an increase in dissolved organic phosphorus.

The preceding discussion has centered on the biochemical reaction affecting the nutrients. However, many other elements are concentrated by organisms and eventually liberated after death or as

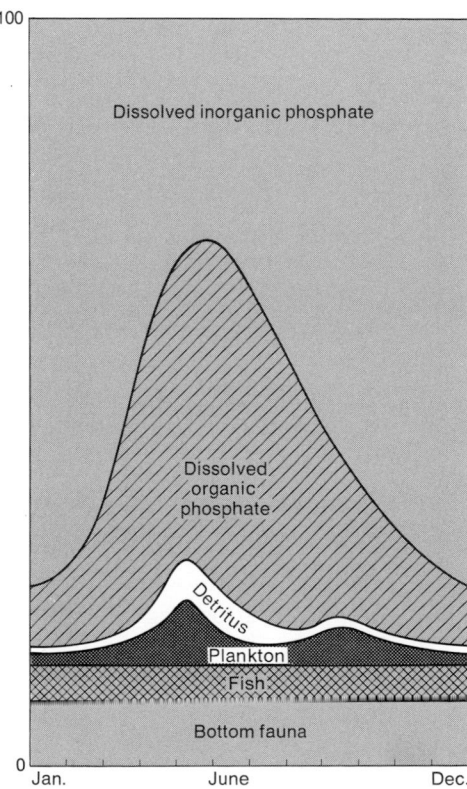

Figure 5-12 Seasonal variation of phosphate in water of the English Channel. (After Harvey, 1950, 1960.)

waste. Calcium and silicon are used by some organisms in forming their shells. Extensive deposits of these materials are found on the sea floor. Several crustacean species concentrate copper; and other organisms such as tunicates concentrate large quantities of vanadium. In many marine organisms, trace elements occur in greater concentrations than in the sea water.

When one considers the distribution of the reactive elements in sea water, he must remember that the dynamics of the water must also be evaluated. For example, if the movement or flow of water is sufficiently large, it can obscure differences in composition caused by biological effects, evaporation, heating, or other phenomena.

Physical Processes

Changes in the salt content of the ocean are mainly caused by differences in evaporation and precipitation. Surface waters of lower salinity are found in polar areas where precipitation is relatively high, and those of higher salinity occur in subtropical areas where evaporation is relatively high.

Currents, waves, and other forms of turbulence usually keep the upper layers of water moderately well mixed. Near land the warm surface water may be blown away by strong offshore winds and replaced by cooler subsurface water. This process, called upwelling, permits nutrient-rich water to be brought into the surface layers where it can be utilized during photosynthesis.

ISOTOPE CHEMICAL OCEANOGRAPHY

The last aspect of chemical oceanography that I consider is isotope chemistry, a field of considerable interest and importance.

After World War II, significant advances in analytical techniques made possible the study of stable and radioactive isotopes in the ocean. The natural fractionation or separation of stable isotopes has been useful in interpreting some chemical and physical processes of the ocean, such as evaporation and changes in temperature. The distribution of radioactive isotopes, both those naturally occurring and those man-made by atomic bomb explosions, can be used to study the past history of the oceans and the presently active dynamic processes such as circulation and mixing of the water in the ocean. Radioactive isotopes are also useful in the measurement of the rates of accumulation of ocean sediments and, by absolute dating of the sediments, in comparing past events that occurred in the ocean with past events on the continents.

Stable Isotopes

The hydrogen and oxygen isotopes in the water molecule can be used to show the value of stable isotopic studies. Hydrogen is present in two forms: ^1H, which is the common hydrogen atom and constitutes more than 99.9 percent of all the hydrogen atoms, and ^2H or deuterium, which is heavier and much less abundant. Oxygen occurs in three forms: ^{16}O, ^{17}O, and ^{18}O. ^{16}O is the lightest and most abundant isotope, making up over 99.7 percent of all oxygen atoms.

The vapor pressure of water molecules composed of the lighter isotopes, ^1H and ^{16}O, is higher than if one of the heavier isotopes (^2H, ^{17}O, ^{18}O) were substituted in the molecules. Because their vapor pressure is higher, it is easier for the molecules containing lighter isotopes to be evaporated from the surface waters of the ocean. Under conditions of evaporation the surface waters will show a decrease in their lighter isotope components and will have an increase in the number of heavier isotopes relative to the evaporated water. Latitude plays an important role, since there is more evaporation in equatorial areas (increase in heavier isotopes) than in the high latitude areas where, besides there being less evaporation, there is also melting ice that has a relatively small quantity of the heavier isotopes.

If an isotopic difference exists between waters, it can be utilized to study mixing processes. H. Craig in 1961 examined oxygen isotope data and arrived at the conclusion that most of the deep water in the Atlantic Ocean originates by mixing processes occurring in the Arctic region. I. Freedman in 1953 determined the relative isotopic abundance of waters from many areas of the ocean as well as from rain water, rivers, and glaciers. His results confirm that surface waters contain more deuterium than deeper waters, and that waters from the higher latitudes are usually lighter (relatively smaller quantities of heavier isotopes) than equatorial waters. S. Epstein and T. Mayeda in 1953 noted that the observed differences in the oxygen isotope composition of sea water were higher than theoretically expected, and they concluded that vaporization from the ocean is a multiple-staged process.

The shell-forming animals and plants that live in the surface waters will reflect the temperature differences of the water in the ratio of Oxygen-18 to Oxygen-16 ($^{18}O/^{16}O$) within their shells. After they die, their shells settle to the ocean bottom and become incorporated into the bottom sediments. A core or sample of these shells produces a continuous record of temperature changes in the surface waters; this record is read by determining the oxygen isotope composition in the sample. If radioactive isotopes are also used the record can be dated and compared with events on land. C. Emiliani used this tech-

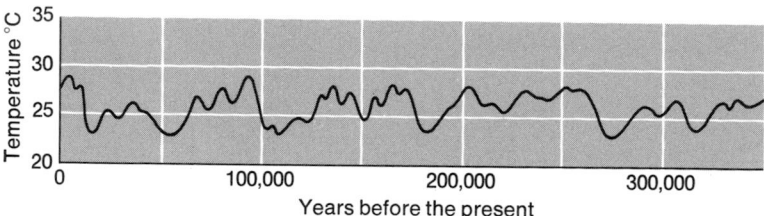

Figure 5-13   A proposed and generalized temperature curve for the surface waters of the ocean. The temperatures are based on $^{18}O/^{16}O$ ratios, the ages, in part, by ^{14}C and $^{231}Pa/^{230}Th$ ratios. (After Emiliani, 1964.)

nique to determine the temperature of the surface waters that planktonic Foraminifera lived in. By examining long deep-sea cores, he has produced a record of the climatic history of the surface waters of the ocean for about the last 300,000 years (Figure 5-13). The results have been questioned, in part, by some scientists who argue that the variations in isotopic composition could be caused mainly by changes in the isotopic ratios in the ocean during glacial periods, because more of the light isotopes would be contained in the glaciers. If the second interpretation is correct, these ratios indicate glacial events rather than strictly ocean surface temperatures; however, in either case they are valuable indicators of past conditions within the ocean.

Sediments collected from the Red Sea show an abrupt increase in ^{18}O at a depth of about 180 cm below the surface sediment (Figure 5-14). This depth, which has been dated by Carbon-14, has an age that corresponds to the last retreat of the glaciers and rise of the sea level. These results have been interpreted as indicating that at one time the Red Sea was isolated from the ocean due to lowered sea level, and that it underwent extensive, if not almost complete evaporation (which increased the amount of ^{18}O relative to ^{16}O remaining in the water).

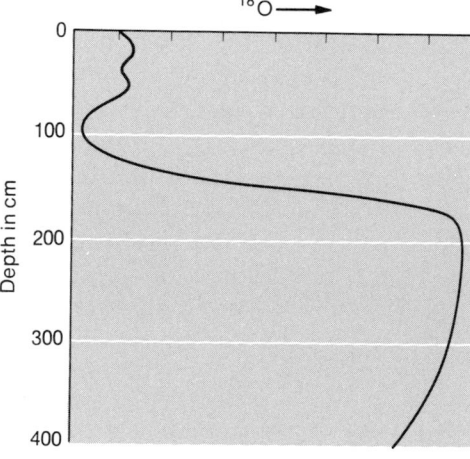

Figure 5-14   Changes in ^{18}O with depth in a core from the Red Sea. Arrow indicates direction of increasing ^{18}O. (After Deuser and Degens, 1969.)

This period was followed by the rise in sea level (see Figure 2-2) which flooded the Red Sea, thereby decreasing the relative amount of heavier isotopes left in the water.

There is also a fractionation of isotopes in the biological environment, where numerous scientists have noted an increase in the heavier isotopes of oxygen in the oxygen-minimum zone. Apparently marine plankton and other organisms that utilize organic material in oxidation processes selectively remove the lighter isotopes of oxygen, leaving the heavier isotopes behind.

Studies of stable isotopes will probably become more important in the future. The examination of the dissolved organic material of sea water and its influence on the biological productivity of the sea may become an especially fruitful field of study.

Radioactive Isotopes

Radioactive isotopes are very valuable to the oceanographer because they allow him to understand the changes that occur in the ocean over a long period of time. These isotopes are especially useful in the study of deep-sea sediments that are deposited at very slow rates. Besides being able to use the isotopes in determining the absolute rate of deposition, the marine geochemist can establish correlation or time-equivalencies of events over large areas of the ocean and even correlate them with events on land.

Radioactive isotopes in the ocean and sediment have three origins:

1. Material formed when the earth was created
2. Cosmic and solar reactions with the atmosphere
3. Atomic reactions produced by man.

I discussed the first group in Chapter 2, and only mention here one use of isotopes of that origin: that of estimating sedimentation rates of the very slowly deposited deep-sea sediments. Potentially valuable for dating are some members of the uranium decay series, ^{231}Pa (protactinium) and ^{230}Th (ionium). There are two sources for these isotopes in sediments: precipitation from solution in sea water (most important) and decay of uranium in the sediment. Although the content of these isotopes is very small in sediments (generally measured in parts per billion or less), the concentrations appear to be closely related to sedimentation rates as determined from other techniques. The uranium decay series is useful mainly for dating material younger than about 300,000 years.

One way of dating older material is by using the potassium argon system. Potassium-40 decays (with a half-life of 1.3×10^9 years) to

Argon-40, which is a gas. If this gas is trapped, as it might be in a volcanic rock or mineral, a measure of the Potassium-40/Argon-40 ratio would indicate the age of the material. One must be careful when using this technique to see that no argon is lost (which would indicate a younger age) and that no argon from some other chemical process is added (which would indicate an older age). The potassium-argon method is particularly useful on layers of volcanic material that are found interbedded with deep-sea sediments. Because the volcanic layer was molten, one can assume that any relict argon was removed and that all argon present is due to decay of Potassium-40.

Another method of determining the age of old sediments is possible because the earth's magnetic field has reversed periodically during the geological past. In other words, the north and south magnetic poles of the earth have reversed. When a volcanic rock that contains magnetic minerals cools, these minerals will retain the magnetic field of the earth at the time of the cooling. Dating volcanic sequences on land with radioactive isotopes has provided a chronology of these reversals. The last reversal, which gave us our present magnetic situation, occurred about 700,000 years ago (see Figure 8-50). Fortunately,

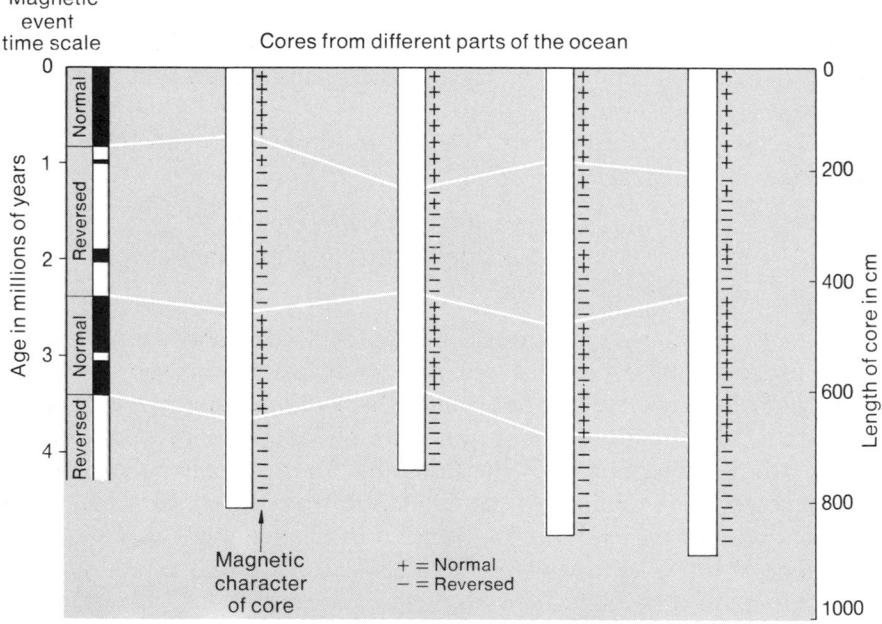

Figure 5-15   Use of the effects of the reversal of the earth's magnetic field to correlate deep-sea cores taken in different parts of the ocean. The magnetic time scale was established by dating the reversals on land; by measuring the magnetic character of the cores they can be correlated with the time scale and to each other.

deep-sea sediments also contain magnetic minerals that will align themselves with the prevailing magnetic field at the time the minerals are deposited. By examining the magnetic orientation of these minerals, we can assign them to one of the magnetic periods and thus date them. This technique is especially useful since it permits easy correlation of cores over large areas (Figure 5-15). The dating of magnetic reversals is also important in the recent sea-floor spreading hypothesis concerning the origin of the ocean basin (see Chapter 8).

The isotopes produced by cosmic and solar reactions with the atmosphere are sometimes of value to oceanographers because of the relatively short half-lives of these isotopes (Table 5-5). Short half-lives permit measurement of events having time scales within the range of certain oceanographic phenomena, such as circulation processes and sedimentation rates.

TABLE 5-5 SOME RADIOACTIVE ISOTOPES, THEIR HALF-LIVES, AND SOURCES

Isotope	Half-Life	Source
^{14}C	5,560	Cosmic rays and nuclear bombs
^{32}Si	500	Cosmic rays
^{3}H	12	Cosmic rays and nuclear bombs
^{90}Sr	28	Nuclear bombs
^{137}Cs	30	Nuclear bombs

Probably the most useful isotope is Carbon-14 (^{14}C). It is formed by the interaction of cosmic rays with the atmosphere, which produces higher-energy neutrons, most of which in turn are captured by Nitrogen-14 to form Carbon-14. The ^{14}C combines with oxygen, producing CO_2, which then enters the ocean, by exchange with the atmosphere, to be utilized in life processes. The ^{14}C decays at a constant rate: its half-life is 5,560 years.

The ^{14}C in organisms or surface waters is in equilibrium with the environment. After death of organisms or sinking of the water, however, the ^{14}C ratio will start to decrease with time (50 percent decrease every 5,560 years). Therefore the measurement of this ratio will indicate how long the material has ceased to be in equilibrium with its environment. For water, the resulting age will also reflect the degree of mixing with waters of differing ^{14}C ages.

The ^{14}C is only used to date material having an age of less than about 50,000 or 60,000 years. This is due to its relatively short half-life and the difficulty of detecting the small amounts present after this period of time. Two corrections must be made to the ^{14}C stable carbon ratio before it can be used: one for the recent increase in carbon in the atmosphere due to the burning of fossil fuels, the other for the ^{14}C produced by nuclear explosions.

An application of ^{14}C is the dating of sediments, a technique especially valuable in understanding the recent glacial history of the oceans. Carbon-14 has also been used to calculate the age (or how long the water has been away from the surface) of various water masses. These calculations are based on numerous assumptions and usually depend on models of differing complexities. Ages will vary with the model, but it is generally agreed that the age of deep Pacific water is between 1,000 and 1,600 years and of deep Atlantic water about half that.

The use of most other radioactive isotopes depends on improved techniques of detection and a better understanding of their modes of introduction into the ocean. Radium-226 has an interesting potential use, because it is released into the ocean from the sediments and could be used to crosscheck Carbon-14. Silicon-32 could be useful in studying water mixing problems, but it is present in small and difficult-to-detect quantities.

SUGGESTED FURTHER READING

Barnes, Harold, *Apparatus and Methods of Oceanography, Part I. Chemical.* New York: Interscience, 1959.

Degens, Egon T. *Geochemistry of Sediments; a Brief Survey.* Englewood Cliffs, New Jersey: Prentice-Hall, 1965.

Harvey, H. W., *The Chemistry and Fertility of Sea Waters.* Cambridge, England: Cambridge University Press, 1960.

Hill, M. N., ed. "The Composition of Sea-Water, Comparative and Descriptive Oceanography." In *The Sea; Ideas and Observations on Progress in the Study of the Sea,* Vol. 2. New York: Interscience, 1963.

Kort, V. G., ed. "Chemistry of the Pacific Ocean," *The Pacific Ocean.* Moscow: Izv. Akad. Nauk SSSR., 1966.

Riley, J. P., and Skirrow, G., eds. *Chemical Oceanography,* Vol. I and II. New York: Academic Press, 1965.

Sverdrup, H. V., Johnson, M. W., and Fleming, R. H. *The Oceans: Their Physics, Chemistry, and General Biology.* New York: Prentice-Hall, 1942.

Chapter 6
BIOLOGICAL
OCEANOGRAPHY

INTRODUCTION

Perhaps of all aspects of oceanography, biological oceanography has most intrigued and fascinated man. All the myriad species of ocean life and their distribution in the sea are not yet known. Rarely does a day or two pass without some new life-form being found. The anticipation of finding new sea monsters is a favorite subject of newspapers and magazines. One expedition has spent several years looking for a Loch Ness monster.

Biological oceanography is not always glamorous. Scientists spend long periods of time at sea collecting and studying specimens. Because it is very difficult to simulate oceanographic conditions in the laboratory, many important laboratory studies are made under conditions different from those of the "real ocean." As our understanding of the sea and its response as a biological environment increase, we are better able to simulate it in our laboratories.

A report of the Panel on Oceanography of the President's Science Advisory Committee in 1966 suggested that biological oceanography, or marine biology, be regarded in broad terms. The Panel defined four major areas of research:

1. Animal and plant populations and their interaction with each other and the ocean
2. The unique characteristics of diverse marine organisms that enable them to exist in the ocean
3. Utilization of marine organisms as unique experimental material for investigations of biomedical problems
4. The processes and factors involved in food production from the sea.

In this chapter I emphasize all but the utilization of marine organisms in biomedical research, a subject that is beyond the scope of this book. The following sections of this chapter consider the history of biological oceanography, the sea as a biological environment, the animals and plants of the sea and their interaction with each other and the ocean, and the processes involved in the production of organic matter (food) in the sea. I discuss the biological resources of the sea in Chapter 9.

History of Biological Oceanography

Prehistoric man certainly knew something of the food to be obtained from the sea. Ancient dwellings frequently are found to have large quantities of shells of marine organisms and other evidence that "sea food" was popular then.

While some early marine scientists were concerned with the depths of the ocean, others were interested in the distribution of life —especially its existence at great depths in the ocean. Samples of bottom life were usually obtained with the devices used in deep-sea soundings and from dredgings.

One important early marine biologist was C. G. Ehrenberg (1795–1876). Ehrenberg noted that many of the siliceous rocks he studied on land were composed of skeletons of microscopic organisms such as diatoms, radiolarians, and sponges, and that similar organisms could be found living in the ocean. He thus concluded that many of the rocks found on land must have been formed on the bottom of the sea.

Edward Forbes in 1844 divided the ocean into eight zones on the basis of marine organisms. He observed that animal life existed, although in decreasing amounts relative to the surface water, to a depth of 300 fathoms; below this depth he thought no life existed. Forbes' observation was somewhat surprising, considering that animal life had been brought to the surface from greater depths. The controversy that resulted was beneficial to the blossoming science of oceanography, because it stirred interest in the field and helped launch the Challenger Expedition of 1872 to 1876.

Another incident that helped spark interest in oceanography was the amusing "Bathybius" mystery. Deposits of calcareous ooze raised from the sea floor were found to contain a strange gelatinous substance believed by some scientists to be a primitive form of life, called Bathybius, and actually classified according to genera and species. The mystery came to an inglorious end when people associated with the Challenger Expedition found that Bathybius was the result of the interaction of the alcohol preservative and the sample collected.

The important voyage of the BEAGLE, with Charles Darwin aboard, took place from 1831 to 1836. Although Darwin's results were not published for many years, he significantly added to the understanding of evolution, and his work, like Forbes', stimulated others to undertake expeditions.

The Challenger Expedition was clearly one of the major advances in the field of biological oceanography. This expedition collected large quantities of data on the animals and plants in the ocean. There were, however, many other important, although not as well publicized, expeditions that made significant contributions to biological oceanography. Important studies were made by J. Vaughan Thompson, one of the first to use a net to collect plankton; Johannes Muller, a German naturalist; Sir John Murray; and Victor Hensen, who studied and named plankton. These early scientists were mainly interested in collecting, describing, and studying organisms. In later years, advances were made in understanding the intimate relationship between organisms and the chemistry of the sea water. Descriptive work continues, but as the different groups of organisms become better known, the need for these studies decreases. Emphasis is shifting to studies of the environment, interrelationships among organisms, and production of organic matter.

THE BIOLOGICAL ENVIRONMENT OF THE SEA

Marine organisms are constantly immersed in and washed by sea water. This situation has several advantages and some disadvantages. For example, any change in the chemical or physical state of the water will quickly be transmitted to the organisms. Fortunately, the physical and chemical characteristics of sea water tend to be relatively stable, and marine organisms are not exposed to sudden environmental changes as are their terrestrial counterparts. Animals living in the ocean have another advantage over land varieties in that they are free from the effects of desiccation, or drying out. Animals of terrestrial environments have had to evolve impervious skins or scales, and plants extensive root systems, to preserve or obtain more water. As discussed in Chapter 5 and subsequent sections of this chapter, organisms also influence the chemistry of the sea water by using elements in their life processes. Some of the biologically important physical and chemical characteristics of sea water are discussed in the following sections.

Biologically Important Properties of Sea Water

Water is essential for life—it is necessary for the production of food by plants. In this respect, one important property of water is its solvent or dissolving power, which allows it to carry the gases and minerals necessary for animal and plant life.

Sea water also provides support for many organisms, in some instances eliminating the need for skeletal structures. Examples of this are jellyfish and other small animals that float in the ocean. Another effect of this support is to enable the largest known animals, whales, to exist. Skeletal structures capable of supporting such a large mass do not exist among land animals. (The largest dinosaurs were also aquatic.)

Sea water is a buffered solution; this means that it will resist changes toward a more alkaline or acidic state. It is slightly alkaline, having a pH between 7.5 and 8.4. The acidity or alkalinity in water is determined by the concentration of the hydrogen (H^+) and the hydroxyl (OH^-) ions. If equal amounts are present the solution is said to be neutral. If the H^+ concentration is greater than the OH^- concentration the solution is acidic; if less, the solution is alkaline. Conventionally, the concentrations are expressed by pH (see footnote, p. 117). The alkaline state of sea water is required by organisms that secrete calcium carbonate shells. Another advantage of sea water being a buffered solution is that abundant carbon, in the form of CO_2, can be present in the water without changing the pH. The carbon is necessary for plants in the production of organic matter.

Another biologically important property of water is its transparency. Light can penetrate sea water to a considerable depth, and as photosynthesis is light-dependent, this important process is not restricted to the upper few meters of the ocean, but can perhaps take place to as deep as 200 m or more, depending on the clearness of the water.

Sea water has a high heat capacity and also a high latent heat of evaporation. Both these characteristics prevent rapid changes in temperature. Rapid temperature changes can have very harmful effects on most life.

The elements present in sea water are very important biologically (see Table 5-2). These elements and their ratios are amazingly similar to the body fluids of most marine organisms, and somewhat similar to the body fluids of land animals. This similarity between the external medium (the ocean) and the internal medium (the body fluids) is critical for osmosis. Osmosis occurs when two solutions of different concentrations are separated by a semipermeable membrane. An osmotic pressure is created when there is a difference in concentration on either side of the membrane. Water will then move through the membrane into the more concentrated solution (Figure 6-1). The greater the difference in concentration the greater the osmotic pres-

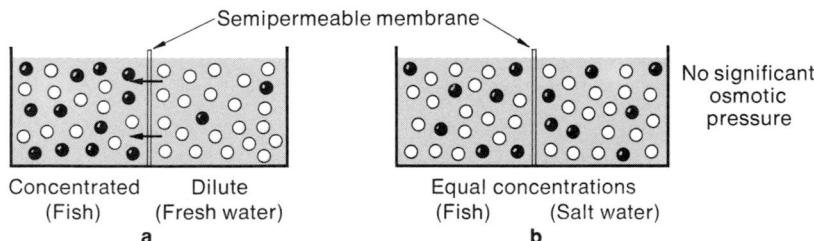

Figure 6-1 (a) Diagram illustrating the osmotic effect of an animal living in a fluid that has a different concentration than its internal fluids. This difference creates an osmotic pressure that the animal has to work against to maintain its internal composition. (b) The concentration of the body fluid and the external fluid are similar and no significant osmotic pressure results. Situation a is similar to that of a fish in fresh water, situation b of a fish in salt water.

sure. Organisms must work against osmotic pressure to maintain the composition of their internal fluids. For example, a fresh water fish in fresh water will have to work against fresh water entering his system and diluting his internal fluids. In the marine environment, the similarity of the body fluids to the external medium means that only a small osmotic pressure exists. This in turn means that these organisms need not use much energy in maintaining their body fluids. The easier control of osmotic balance in salt water, relative to fresh water, may explain why some salt water animals are larger than the largest fresh water animals.

General Characteristics of the Ocean as a Biological Environment

The temperature in the ocean ranges from almost $-2°$ C to more than $40°$ C. Salinity can vary from near zero in estuary and nearshore conditions to about 4 percent in the Red Sea. The depth reaches over 10,000 m. Pressure, which is due to the weight of the overlying water, ranges from 1 atmosphere (14.7 lb/in^2 or about 1 kg/cm^2) at the surface to over 1,000 atmospheres (atm) at great depths. There is a 1-atm increase with each 10 m of depth. Light penetration also varies, sunlight never penetrating more deeply than about 1,000 m. Even though the range of these conditions is extensive, many large areas have uniform conditions. Temperature, for example, is fairly similar over large parts of the ocean (Figures 6-2, 7-3, and 7-4). Salinity actually is very constant in the surface waters of the open ocean and ranges between 3.3 percent and 3.7 percent, and only in isolated areas does it get higher. The salinity of the deeper water is even more uniform, having a normal range of 3.46 percent to 3.5 percent. Even though pressure clearly does have an effect on animal life, many organisms, through special functional adaptations, are able to range over considerable depths; whales, for example, can dive to depths of 1,000 m (a pressure of 100 atm). However, even though most organisms live within a very small range of conditions, many live in different conditions during different periods of their growth.

A commonly-held misconception is that a fish brought to the surface from great depths, and found to be dead, has "exploded," because one of its internal bladders is observed protruding from its mouth. In most instances, however, death is due to the large changes in temperature the fish experienced in being brought to the surface.

The motion of sea water is biologically very important. This motion will move the nutrients necessary for plant growth from the deeper water to the surface water where they can be utilized by plants. The motion also provides a dispersal mechanism for waste products, eggs, and larvae or adult forms of life. Water motion can

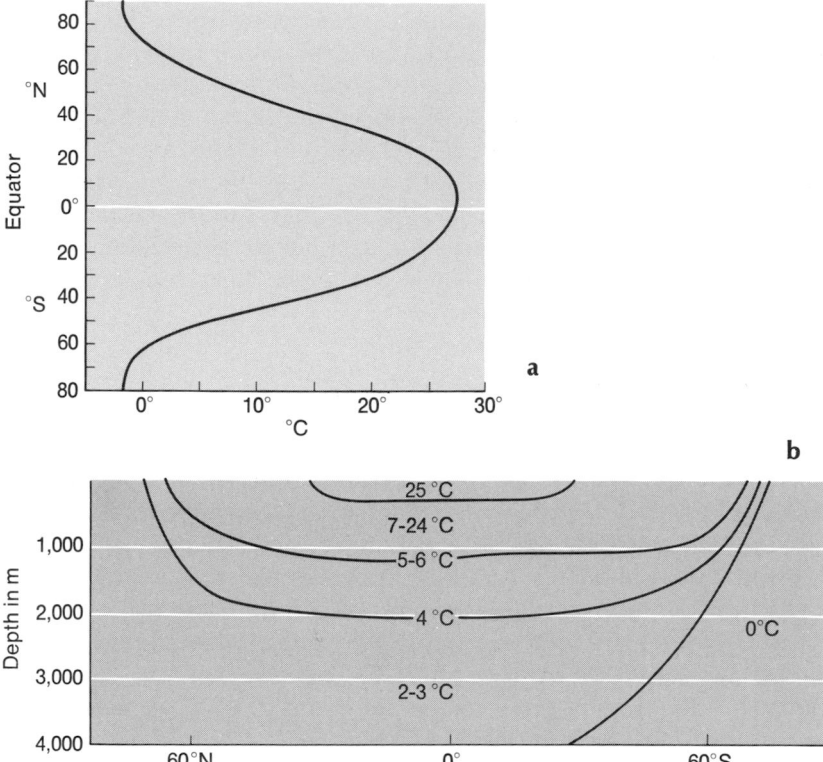

Figure 6-2   (a) The average surface temperature of the ocean as a function of latitude. (After Wüst and others, 1954.) (b) The range of temperature with depth and latitude in an idealized ocean. (After Raymont, 1963.)

also have some nonbeneficial results, such as when animals are carried out of their natural environment into an unfavorable one. This can happen where warm water is brought into contact with cold water or vice versa.

The Divisions of the Marine Environment

The marine environment can be divided into two major realms: the **benthic,** which refers to the ocean bottom; and the **pelagic,** which refers to the overlying water (Figure 6-3). The pelagic realm can be subdivided into the **neritic** environment (the water that overlies the continental shelf) and the oceanic environment (the water of the deep sea). The pelagic realm can also be subdivided on the basis of depth. The benthic realm is usually divided into a **littoral** (area out to a depth of 200 m) and a deep-sea system. A more detailed division is possible for the nearshore region. The depth ranges of these different environments are given in Table 6-1. Note that similar terms can be used for

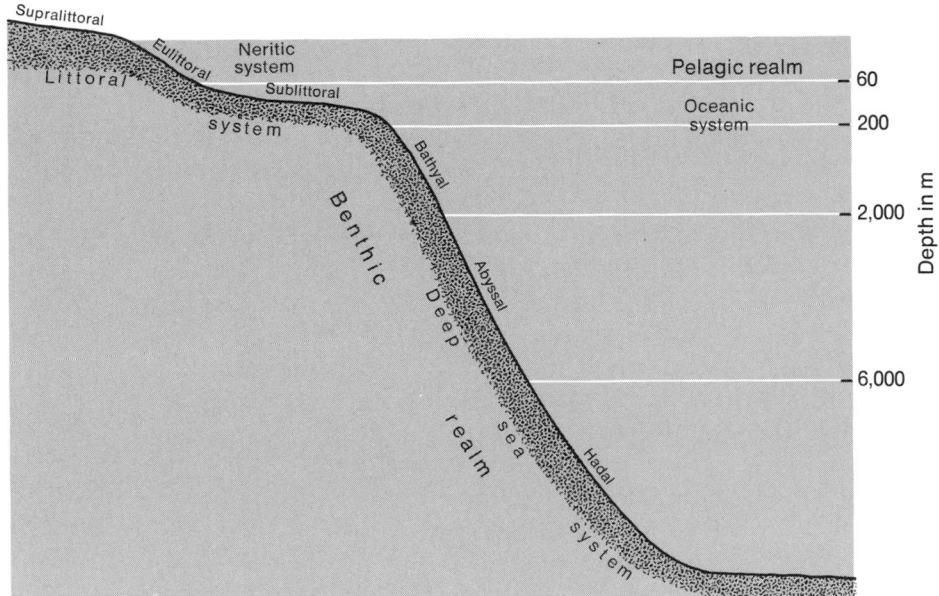

Figure 6-3   The divisions of the marine environment.

both the benthic and pelagic realms, and that the depth divisions are not absolute figures, but, being dependent on life forms, can vary somewhat in meaning. Therefore, if one wanted to talk about the water at a depth of 7,000 m he would speak of the **hadal** pelagic environment; the bottom at 4,000 m would be the **abyssal** benthic environment. The oceanic province of the pelagic environment can also be divided into two zones on the basis that most light doesn't penetrate much deeper than 200 m. This upper lighted area is called the **euphotic** zone, and it is within this region that photosynthesis by plants occurs. The deeper, darker region is called the **aphotic** zone.

TABLE 6-1   DEPTH RANGES OF THE DIFFERENT ENVIRONMENTS OF THE OCEAN

Depth	Benthic Environment		Pelagic Environment	
above high tide		Supralittoral		
high tide to 40 to 60 m	Littoral system	Eulittoral	Neritic system	
60 to 200 m		Sublittoral		
200 to 2,000 m		Bathyal		Bathyal
2,000 to 6,000 m	Deep-sea system	Abyssal	Oceanic system	Abyssal
greater than 6,000 m		Hadal		Hadal

Benthic Environments Benthic environments (Table 6-1 and Figure 6-3) cover a wide range of oceanographic conditions, from the exposed supralittoral areas to the hadal environment. Obviously then, the benthic organisms (those that live on the ocean bottom) will vary in the different environments and no one type will be found in all environments.

The supralittoral environment is extremely rugged. Animals living there are almost continuously exposed, being immersed only during periods of extremely high tides, storms, and by the spray from breaking waves. These organisms, then, besides being able to resist drying out must also be strong enough to withstand breaking waves. Animals of this environment are usually similar the world over: generally small gastropods and lichens on rocks, and crabs and amphipods on beaches.

The eulittoral environment includes the tidal region, which is periodically exposed at low tide, and extends to a depth of 40 to 60 m. The width of the intertidal region depends on the tidal range of the slope of the bottom. Animals living in this region also must withstand the effect of breaking waves. Many animals accomplish this by burrowing into the bottom, thus also removing some of the harmful effects of exposure at low tide. The outer limit of the eulittoral is at about the depth where attached plants can grow on the bottom; they cannot grow in deeper water because of the absence of sufficient light. Thus only a small portion of the sea is available for the growth of attached plants, and even within this area large parts cannot be utilized because the bottom may be muddy or otherwise unsuitable for plants.

The eulittoral is probably one of the best studied marine biological environments, especially since it can be observed by divers. The animals and plants of this environment are very numerous and varied.

Outermost of the littoral system is the sublittoral zone, the outer limits of which extend to 200 or even 400 m. This limit is based on the maximum depth where algae (plants) can live, and is principally controlled by light and temperature. Proceeding seaward from the eulittoral to the sublittoral there is a decrease in plant life and an increase in animal life. The outer part of the zone, which generally conforms to the edge of the continental shelf, is an area extensively exploited by commercial fishermen.

The deep-sea system, composed of the bathyal, abyssal, and hadal divisions, is not as well known as the shallower littoral system. The deep-sea system is devoid of higher plant life, but bacteria can live at this depth.

Oceanographic conditions of the deeper part of the ocean are uniform: temperature decreases slowly with depth, salinity is relatively constant, and pressure increases 1 atm with each 10 m of depth. As most organisms are composed in large part of water, with few if any air spaces, and because water is not very compressible, deep-sea pressure itself is not an excluding factor for life there. Pressure does, however, have other effects which can affect the life processes of deep-sea animals.

The uniform conditions of the deep-sea system suggest that seasons would have little biological importance in the deeper part of the ocean, as compared to the numerous seasonal phenomena, such as breeding, affected seasonally in the shallower waters. Oceanographers from Florida State University have recently found that perhaps some seasonal effects do extend to deeper waters. They noted that some deep-sea animals were spawning off North Carolina only during August to November, and in the Antarctic only during July to October. This presents two interesting problems: how do the animals recognize the seasons, and why are the breeding periods similar in both hemispheres (remember that when it is winter in the northern hemisphere it is summer in the southern hemisphere).

Because the deep-sea floor is usually muddy, surviving benthic animals must have adapted to this condition. Food is not as abundant as in the littoral system. Animals in the deep sea generally are thought to receive their food from organic material falling from near surface waters down to the ocean bottom. The production of organic matter in surface waters is usually higher over the littoral system and decreases with distance from land, becoming rather small over the deep sea. Thus the amount of food reaching the deep ocean bottom is small, and this quantity is further reduced by its disintegration and decay while sinking through the water. It follows, therefore, that the animals of the deep sea should be small scavengers rather than large predators.

Many animals of the deep sea are bizarre in appearance (Figure 6-4). However, their size is generally small. Actually, one should exercise caution in making comments about conditions in the deep sea, because we do not have many observations on which to base our conclusions. Our information is derived from underwater photographs, deep-sea dredgings, and occasional glimpses of the bottom made from submersibles. The latter have been restricted mainly to depths of 2,000 m or less. My own observations, from ALVIN, generally showed more fish and other animals at depths of 1,500 to 1,600 m than I would usually see while skin diving in shallow water (Figure 6-5). This observation should also be taken with caution—the point is that we simply don't know enough about the biological environment of the deep sea.

a

b

Figure 6-4 Some animals of the deep sea. (a) Taken at a depth of 1,600 m on the continental slope off Massachusetts. The animal on the right is a fish, about 2 ft long, commonly called "rattail." On the left is a small eel. Note the numerous burrows and depressions, which were made by animals that live in the bottom. (b) Also a rattail, taken at a depth of 4,000 m on the continental rise south of Nova Scotia. In this picture the camera has fallen over and is taking a picture while lying on its side. (Photograph 6-4b courtesy of C. D. Hollister.)

a

b

Figure 6-5 Some bottom photographs taken from ALVIN. (a) Shows some sea urchins and a squid. (b) Shows a small fish. Note the track marks in the central part of the picture made by some bottom-crawling animal.

The density of life in the different areas of the ocean can be expressed by the **biomass** (the quantity of substance in live organisms in grams per square meter of the ocean bottom). The biomass clearly decreases going from the littoral region into deeper water (Table 6-2).

TABLE 6-2 AVERAGE BIOMASS IN DIFFERENT PARTS OF THE OCEAN (DATA FOR THE NORTHWEST PACIFIC, FROM BIRSTEIN, 1959 AS REPORTED IN MADSEN, 1966)

Area	Biomass (in grams per square meter)
Coastal zone	100–5000
50–200 m depth	200
about 4,000 m	about 5
Central part of ocean floor	0.01
Kuril-Kamchatka Trench	
about 6,000 m	1.2
about 8,500 m	0.3
Tonga Trench 10,500 m	0.001

Pelagic Environments The pelagic environment is divided into the nearshore neritic system and the offshore open-sea oceanic system. The border between these two areas is not very definite, and generally is set at the edge of the continental shelf.

The neritic pelagic environment shows large diversity of conditions, because of the fresh-water discharge from rivers. Organisms living in this environment must therefore be able to withstand wide ranges of salinity. Nutrients are brought into the sea by upwelling due to coastal winds (see Figure 7-13) and by river waters. This nutrient supply sustains the abundant growth of plankton, the basic food of the sea. The supply of food attracts other forms of life, and as a result, the neritic area is generally the most biologically productive area of the sea. This is where most fish and other types of food from the sea are caught.

The oceanic system can be divided as shown in Table 6-1 or, as previously mentioned, into a light (euphotic) and dark (aphotic) zone, with the boundary at a depth of about 200 m. Compared to the neritic environment, the salinity of the oceanic area is relatively constant. Temperature decreases with depth, the greatest change occurring at a depth of about 100 m at the **thermocline** (see Figure 7-3). The surface waters have a temperature variation that is a function of latitude (see Figure 6-2). Nutrients are usually low in the surface waters and increase to the upper lighted zone.

In the deeper layers currents are slow or almost nonexistent; this

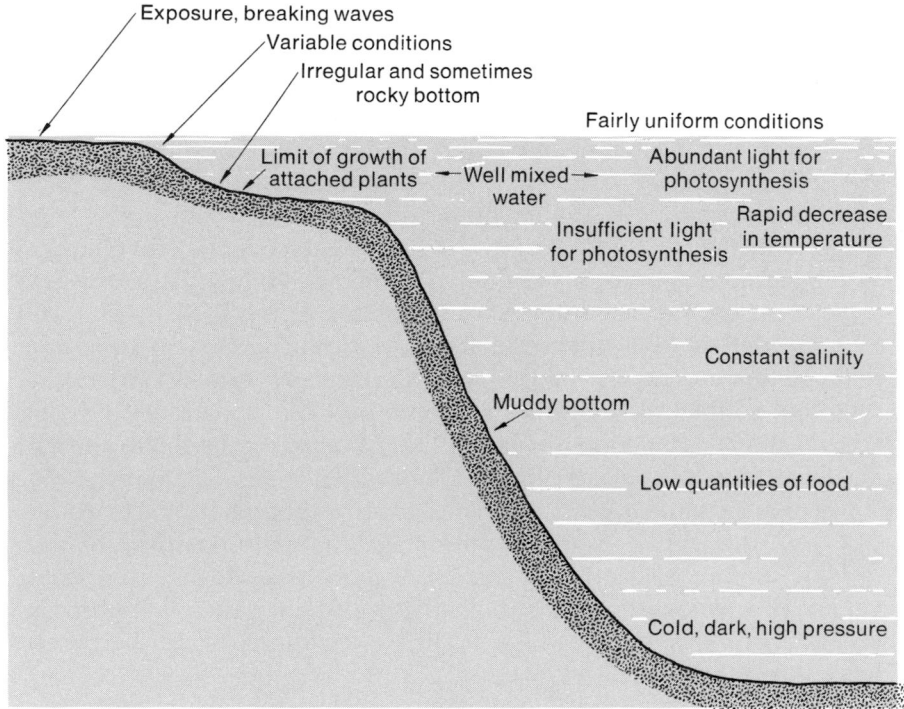

Figure 6-6   General characteristics of the marine environment.

is an area of complete darkness that apparently undergoes few seasonal changes. Many higher forms of animal life here are blind. The abyssal pelagic area is the world's largest ecological unit: about three-quarters of the total volume of the ocean lies within this zone.

Little is known about the deep hadal zone. Very little work has been done to collect animals from this zone; the benthic fauna have been better sampled and more than 350 species have been identified.

A general summary of some of the important characteristics of the marine environment is shown in Figure 6-6.

The Biological Community

The preceding discussion has shown that the biological environment of the sea can be divided on the basis of water depth, light, and pressure. In these rather large-scale divisions, characteristic types of organisms may prevail. However, within these large divisions, many different types of conditions are possible. These conditions can be due to many factors such as the character of the bottom or some physical-chemical condition of the water. Ecologists (biologists who study the relationship of the organisms to the environment) classify the environment according to **biotopes** or niches. A biotope is an area where the principal habitat conditions and the living forms adapted to them are uniform. Life in a biotope is not static; some animals may wander freely from one to another. It follows from the definition that as the living conditions of the environment become more specialized, so will become the inhabitants. It is generally thought that the more rigorous the condition, the fewer the number of different species and the greater the numbers of individuals of those species. This situation is, for example, typical of marsh environments. A similar situation was thought to be true in the deep sea, but studies by R. R. Hessler and H. L. Sanders in 1966 suggest that this may not be the case and that many different species may inhabit the deeper parts of the ocean. One sample they obtained from a depth of 4,700 m had 196 different species of life, a number similar to that obtained from shallower and apparently less rigorous biotopes. One should remember that the biotopes change more rapidly in shallow water (because the conditions change). The above example only refers to a comparison of two specific biotopes. Clearly the shallow water areas will have a greater variety of species per unit area than the deeper parts of the ocean. Biotopes in the deep sea will generally cover a larger area than those in shallow water.

When speaking of the inhabitants of a biotope, the concept of a biological community should be applied. A community is composed of organisms, occurring together, that appear to be dependent upon each other or perhaps upon the common environment. The community may just represent the animals that live on the leaf of a particular plant, or it may include a more extensive relationship such as that between plankton and the animals that consume them—a dependency primarily based on the need for food. The food chain in the ocean is a complex system involving several levels, starting with phytoplankton (the producers), then different kinds of herbivores (plant eaters), carnivores, and finally scavengers and bottom feeders. These relationships are developed in later sections; now it is appropriate to consider the population of the ocean.

THE POPULATION OF THE OCEAN

As you can imagine, one chapter or even one book is inadequate for anything but a very brief description of the animal and plant life in the sea. Two methods of description are used: first, a discussion of the organisms based on their mode of locomotion and their type of habitat; second, a discussion based on taxonomic classification.

Considering the first, the organisms of the sea can be divided into three large groups: the benthos, the nekton, and the plankton.

Benthos

The term **benthos** comes from the Greek word for deep or deep sea. The benthos (Figure 6-7) are those organisms that live on or below the ocean bottom. Some of these organisms, such as barnacles and oysters, have planktonic larval forms that eventually settle and attach themselves to the bottom for their adult lives. Other types of benthic life (the term benthic life refers to those organisms living on the bottom and is essentially equivalent to benthos) such as worms and clams may burrow into the bottom, while other animals such as starfish and echinoids may creep slowly over the bottom. In shallow water, plants form part of the benthos.

Benthos have geologic importance because they will, during their lives on the sea floor, modify and change some physical and chemical properties of the sediment. Also, many of the fossils in the sediments are the remains of benthic organisms. Bacteria, which constitute a small part of the benthos, may be very important in the food chain in the deep sea.

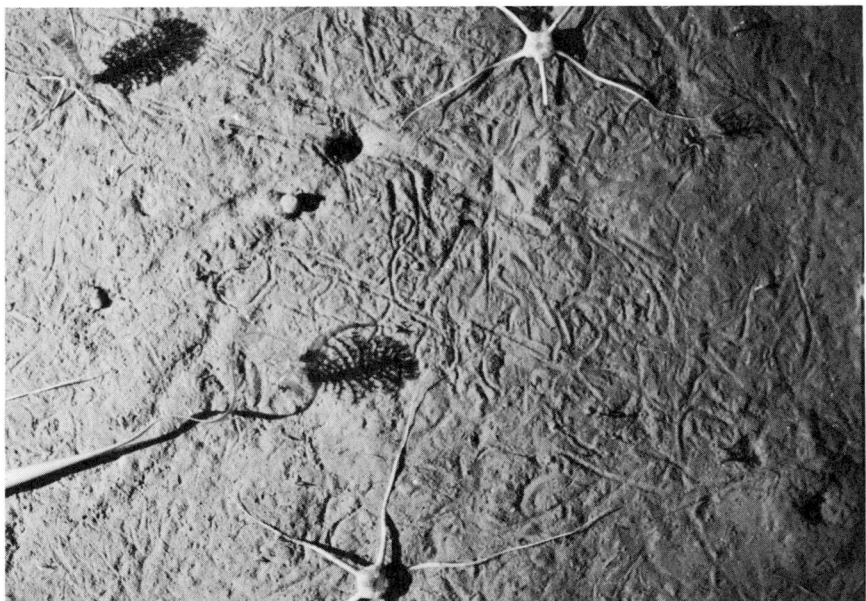

Figure 6-7 Bottom photograph showing some benthic forms of life, depth about 1,300 m. Note the numerous tracks on the bottom. (Photograph courtesy of Woods Hole Oceanographic Institution.)

The number of benthic individuals usually decreases with depth. Many studies have been made of benthic organisms and several different types of communities have been recognized. One special and interesting community is the coral reef, which I treat later in greater detail.

Nekton

Nekton (the term derives from the Greek word for swimming) include those animals that are able to swim freely, independent of current movement (Figure 6-8). This group (plants are not included) encompasses many advanced forms of animal life such as fish, whales, and other mammals.

Nekton have the ability to search actively for food and avoid

Figure 6-8   Nekton. Some porpoises playing on the surface of the ocean. Note their blow holes through which they breathe. (Photograph courtesy of R. K. Brigham.)

predators. These animals can also migrate extensively throughout the oceans.

Nekton are commercially important for man and, because of their feeding habits, are important for other forms of life. Since nekton feed mainly on plankton, they can limit and control the phytoplankton population. Decomposition products of nekton are important sources of raw materials for the producers of organic material and bacteria.

Nekton are generally the least restricted form of animal life in the sea. Although they can inhabit different parts of the pelagic environment during their lives, their distribution is limited by temperature and pressure. The influence of these and other environmental factors is not as well understood as for the benthic and planktonic forms of life.

Plankton

Plankton, from the Greek word for wandering, are the third large group of marine organisms. These organisms are usually small (Figure 6-9) with very weak powers of locomotion, and are moved mainly by ocean currents. Some forms have a limited ability to move for themselves. Plankton can be either animals (zooplankton) or plants (phytoplankton). Most are microscopic, but the group includes some large floating forms such as jellyfish and sargassum weed. Plankton comprise the largest group of organisms in the ocean. Many animal forms in the ocean have a planktonic stage, usually at birth, when they float freely in the ocean.

Phytoplankton is probably the most important individual form of life in the sea. These organisms, which by photosynthesis convert water and carbon dioxide into organic material, are at the base of the oceanic food chain.

The distribution and growth pattern of phytoplankton (as plants they must live in the euphotic zone) shows pronounced vertical and seasonal variations. The vertical distribution is due to the depth that the light can penetrate, a depth that can be as shallow as 1 m in nearshore waters to as much as 200 m in the open ocean (Figure 6-10). The seasonal changes are due to complex relationships between light, nutrient supply, temperature, and herbivores, among other factors. The growth rate of phytoplankton can be very high, sometimes as much as six cell divisions per day (each cell division produces a new organism).

Zooplankton include representatives from almost every group of marine organism. These plankton may be one of two types: holoplankton (permanent plankton) which spend their entire life as plankton, or meroplankton (temporary plankton) which spend only a portion of their life (usually the larval stage) as plankton. Meroplankton

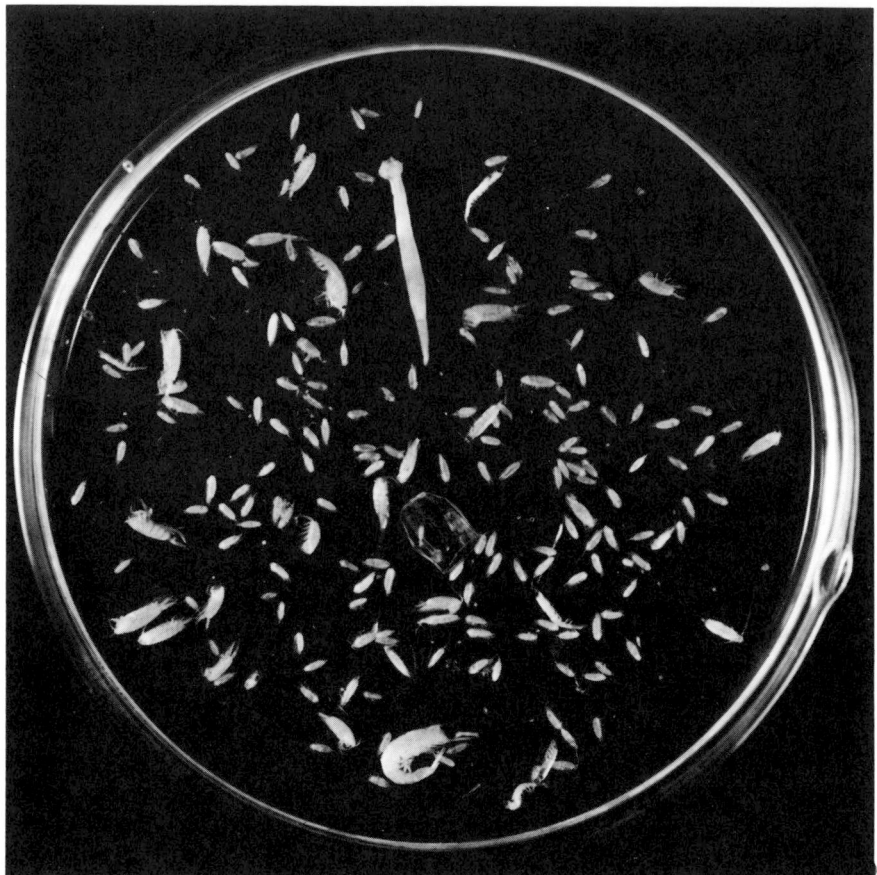

Figure 6-9 A mixed collection of zooplankton. Near center is transparent *Trachomedusa,* above which is pencil-shaped chaetognath. To left of chaetognath is an amphipod recognized by its spherical black eye. At bottom of dish is a partially curled euphausiid. Remaining animals are mostly copepods. Diameter of dish is 10 cm. (Photograph courtesy of George D. Grice.)

become nektonic or benthic forms at other life stages. Zooplankton are very important in the economy of the sea, because they eat and thereby concentrate phytoplankton, making the phytoplankton-derived energy more easily available for the higher forms of life (when they eat, in turn, the zooplankton).

Some plankton are especially valuable for oceanographers, because certain species are characteristic of particular bodies of water. These species, called indicator species, can be used to point out the origin and movement of the water body. Many areas of the sea floor are covered with the shells or tests of planktonic organisms. Geologically, perhaps the most important of these organisms is the protozoan,

Figure 6-10 Percentage of total incident energy reaching different depths of the ocean for different types of water. Note that the degree of light penetration varies with water type, and that for some water types only 5 percent of the light penetrates to a depth of 20 m. (After Jerlov, 1951.)

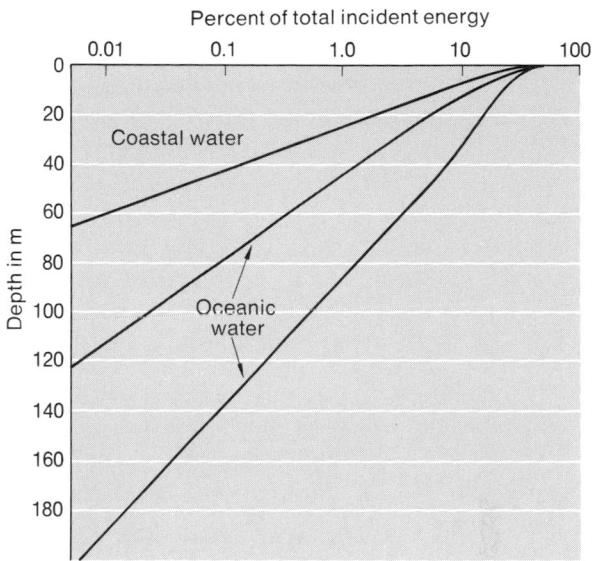

Foraminifera, whose tests provide valuable information about the history and climate of the ocean at the time these organisms lived.

The organisms living in the ocean belong to one of two major kingdoms. This simple system of just two major divisions, the animal and plant kingdoms, has been challenged by some biologists who argue, quite possibly correctly, that the evolutionary relationship between the organisms is better represented by a new and more complex classification. However, the traditional classification is used in this text because of its basic simplicity and wider present-day acceptance by scientists.

In the following pages, I briefly mention some of the more common life forms present in the sea.

Plants of the Sea

The plants in the ocean are very different from land plants. Sea water can be compared with soil water in that it carries the nutrients necessary for plant life. On land the plants had to develop extensive root systems to obtain water and food, and leaves to obtain oxygen and carbon dioxide. However, in the ocean the plants are completely surrounded by nutrient-carrying water. In the ocean, plants have difficulty receiving enough light to carry on photosynthesis. Some plants that live in shallow water can be attached to the bottom and receive sufficient light, but only a small portion of the sea floor, probably less than 2 percent, is shallow and solid enough for attached plants.

Since only a small portion of the ocean is available for attached plants, most plants are planktonic. They are small, single-celled organisms that in some instances are very similar to animals. These microscopic plants, which produce the bulk of organic material in the ocean, occur in almost unbelievably large quantities. All the ocean's creatures either directly or indirectly (by eating animals that feed on plants) feed on these plants; yet, one should remember that the phytoplankton are restricted—because of their dependence on light—to the thin surface layer of the ocean, while the consumers of the organic matter produced by plants occur throughout the ocean.

The plant kingdom can be divided into four major divisions:

1. Spermatophyta—seed and flowering plants
2. Pteridophyta—ferns
3. Bryophyta—mosses
4. Thallophyta—algae and fungi.

Only spermatophytes and thallophytes are found in the ocean. Spermatophytes are considered to be the highest type of plant. Apparently these plants did not originate in the sea, but entered it from the land or fresh water. Only a few marine species are found. Perhaps the most important form is *Zostera,* or as it commonly is called, eelgrass. This plant (Figure 6-11) possesses true roots attached to a stem or rhizome. It can reproduce by seeds or by sending up new leaves from its rhizome. Eelgrass grows in water usually less than 4 or 5 m deep, where wave action is not very strong. When the plant dies and is broken, its pieces may be carried out to sea and become an important source of food in some areas. Where it produces a thick growth, *Zostera* provides protection for many forms of animal life. An entire biological community, ranging from small diatoms to nearshore animals, is dependent on the eelgrass environment. In the early 1930s a disease killed most of the eelgrass on the Atlantic Coast. This caused

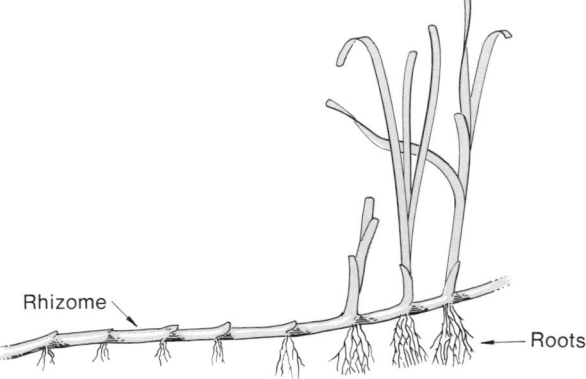

Rhizome

Roots

Figure 6-11. *Zostera,* a nearshore Spermatophyta.

considerable damage to the scallop population, because of the latter's dependence on eelgrass for refuge. Fortunately for the scallop fisheries, the eelgrass recovered and has repopulated most of its original habitat.

The more common thallophytes have no true roots, stems, or leaves. Most important of this division are algae (Figure 6-12), which H. U. Sverdrup and others in 1942 divided into five groups based mainly on their color:

1. Blue-green algae (Myxophyceae)
2. Green algae (Chlorophyceae)
3. Brown algae (Phaeophyceae)
4. Red algae (Rhodophyceae)
5. Yellow-green algae.

The first four are usually attached plants, and the yellow-green algae are mainly planktonic.

Blue-Green Algae Blue-green algae are most abundant in rivers and lakes, and are not too common in the ocean except near some rivers and tropical regions. These organisms are generally very small and poorly developed, and some are floating forms. Even though they are called blue-green algae, some may be other colors due to accessory pigments within the plant. A dramatic example of this is the floating

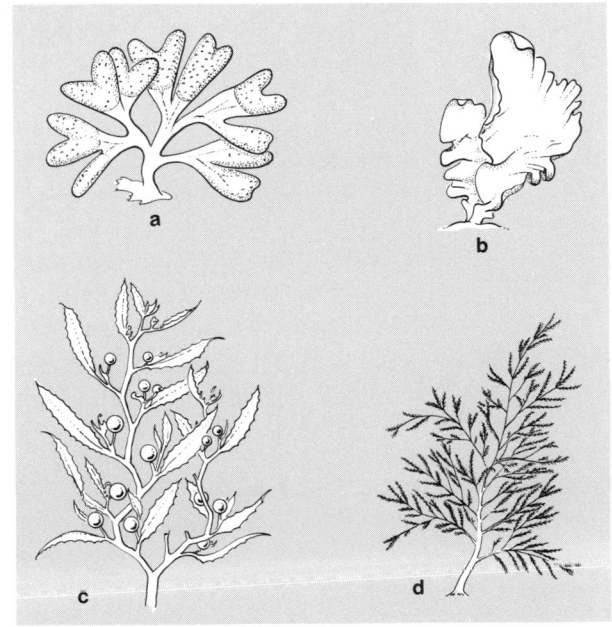

Figure 6-12   Some common forms of marine algae: (a) *Fucus,* a brown alga; (b) *Ulva,* a green alga; (c) *Sargassum,* a brown alga; (d) *Polysiphonia,* a red alga. (H. U. Sverdrup, Martin W. Johnson and Richard H. Fleming, *The Oceans: Their Physics, Chemistry, and General Biology,* © 1942. Reprinted by permission of Prentice-Hall, Inc., Englewood Cliffs, N.J.)

form *Trichodesmium,* which has a red color. It is this plant which often gives the Red Sea the color that earned this body of water its name.

Because of their limited distribution, blue-green algae are not very important in the overall picture of the ocean.

Green Algae Green algae are mainly found in fresh water, where fresh water and salt water are mixed, and in the shallower parts of the littoral system. They rarely occur below a depth of 10 m and are thus restricted to the well-lighted part of the ocean. A common form is the alga *Ulva* or sea lettuce.

Green algae can sometimes impart a distinct green color to the water. Some ponds can have a green "cover" due to the growth of these algae. Sometimes they also form an algal slime on boats and other submerged objects.

The green alga *Halimeda* can become encrusted with calcium carbonate, and when it dies forms a carbonate deposit on the sea floor. *Halimeda* is common in the lagoons of some atoll areas.

Brown Algae Brown algae are found mainly in the ocean environment. These algae, which include kelp and *Sargassum,* are the largest of the marine algae; one, *Nereocystis,* may be as much as 80 m long. This plant forms kelp beds that commonly grow near some coasts. These algae are sometimes harvested from boats, by cutting off their top layers. The harvest is valuable as a food and a source of iodine, potash, and iodine-based drugs.

Brown algae are considered the most advanced of the thallophytes. The large forms that make up the kelp beds are attached to the bottom by a holdfast, a branched structure that attaches to a rock (Figure 6-13). From the holdfast extends a long tube (stipe) which ends in a large circular ball. Both the ball and the stipe are hollow and filled with gas. The gas gives the plant buoyancy, permitting it to float. At the end of the bulb are long thin fronds, which have the appearance of leaves. The plant reproduces by dropping reproductive bodies from its fronds. These bodies settle and form small plants on the ocean bottom. The small plant looks very different from its parent, the large kelp. The small plants germinate, producing a fertilized egg which grows into the brown kelp. Thus, in this type of reproduction there is an alternation of generations.

There are other forms of brown algae; some are small delicate branching plants, others big and broad like *Fucus* (see Figure 6-12). One brown alga, *Sargassum,* is found far from land on the open ocean. *Sargassum* actually grows in tropical areas, but when torn loose by waves it will float and drift with the currents. It also grows and multiplies while it is drifting. Large quantities of these algae have been

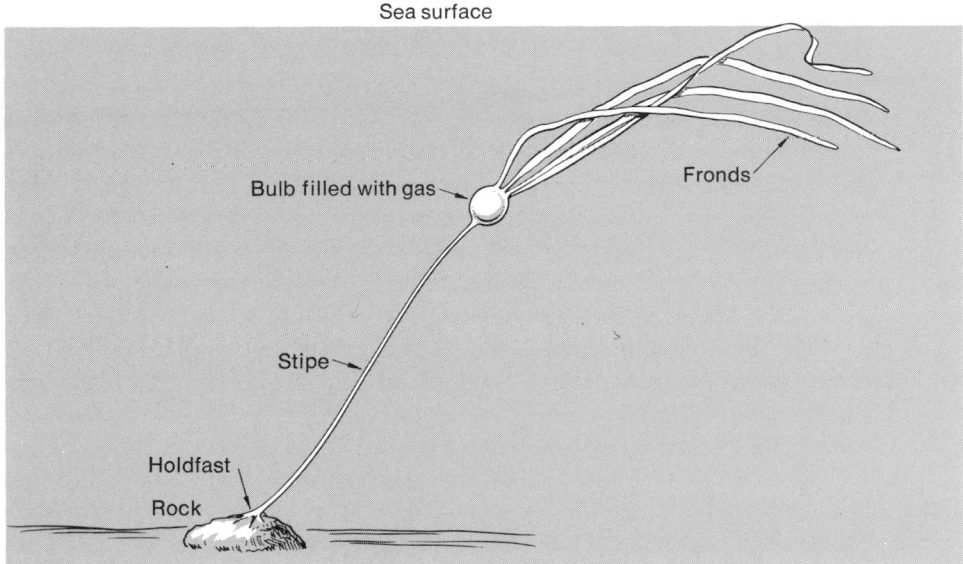

Sea surface

Bulb filled with gas

Fronds

Stipe

Holdfast

Rock

Figure 6-13   General structure of a large brown alga. The length of these plants can exceed 40 m.

accumulated by currents in an area of the North Atlantic that is called the Sargasso Sea. Before the plant dies and sinks, it forms a unique environment that provides shelter for many different kinds of animals.

With some exceptions, for example, *Sargassum,* brown algae tend to be best developed in cooler parts of the ocean, especially in near-shore, rocky-bottomed areas.

Red Algae Red algae are considered to be among the prettiest organisms in the sea. They are red colored (although some are purple, brown, or green) because of the abundance of red pigments. Like other plants, red algae contain green chlorophyll pigment, but the green color is masked by other pigments. Red algae extend further out to sea than the other forms (with the exception of *Sargassum* after it is broken off from its original habitat). In some areas, red algae have been observed at depths of over 100 m. Thus, proceeding out from shore into deeper water one would successively observe green, brown, then red algae, with some overlap.

Red algae can be an important producer of organic matter, especially on the outer areas of the continental shelf. Some species are commercially valuable because they are a source of agar, which is used, among other things, as a thickening agent for ice cream and other products.

Red algae are widely distributed throughout the ocean, but they tend to be more abundant in warmer waters. Some forms such as

Lithothamnion, an alga that lives with coral, have the ability to precipitate calcium carbonate.

Yellow-Green Algae The yellow-green algae are a group of several different types of organisms. Whatever their classification, the yellow-green algae are a very important group of plants in the ocean. They are mainly planktonic organisms containing chlorophyll and capable of photosynthesis. Because they can float, they are found in the surface waters of all the oceans and are not restricted to the nearshore areas, as are the other species of algae.

Perhaps the most important of this group is the diatom, a small microscopic organism found both in salt and fresh water. Diatoms are single-celled organisms that can combine with other individuals to form long chains or groups (Figure 6-14).

In some areas of the ocean, the production and growth of diatoms is especially high. Diatoms can multiply in a geometric manner (that is, 2 become 4, 4 become 8, and so on) and their numbers can become very large in a short period of time (days). Diatoms have siliceous shells, and if enough of them accumulate on the ocean bottom after death, they can form a deposit called diatomaceous ooze. There are large areas of the ocean (see Figure 8-42) that are covered with this type of deposit.

Diatoms have the ability to form resting spores, when the environmental conditions become unfavorable. They can remain in this

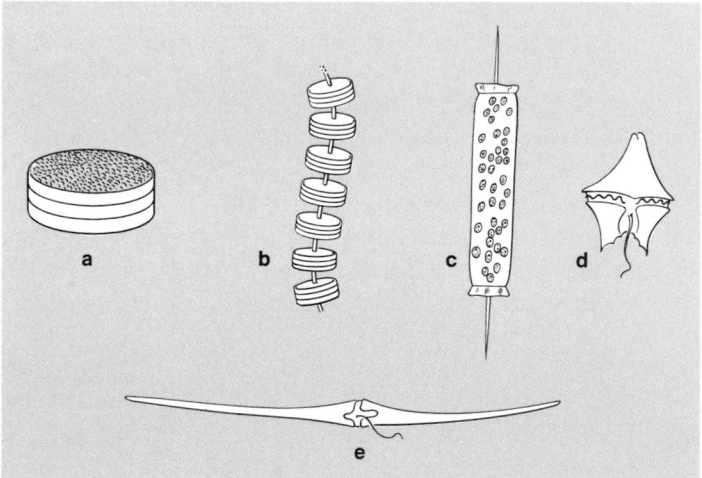

Figure 6-14 Some common diatoms (a,b,c) and dinoflagellates (d,e). (H. U. Sverdrup, Martin W. Johnson and Richard H. Fleming, *The Oceans: Their Physics, Chemistry, and General Biology,* © 1942. Reprinted by permission of Prentice-Hall, Inc., Englewood Cliffs, N.J.)

configuration for long periods of time; and when conditions improve, they start reproducing again.

Another important member of the yellow-green group is the dinoflagellate (Figure 6-14). Some of these organisms are animal-like (as determined mainly by the food they eat, that is, rather than photosynthesizing), and others are definitely plants. Dinoflagellates have flagella, or "tails," that they can use for locomotion and to search for nutrients or better environmental conditions. Many of these organisms are luminescent, and when excited impart a glowing color to the water.

Dinoflagellates tend to be more abundant in warmer waters, and diatoms in colder waters. A large sudden growth, or bloom, of dinoflagellates will discolor the water, causing a "red tide." Humans can be poisoned if they eat mussels or clams that have fed on certain species of dinoflagellates and diatoms during a red tide period.

The tests, or shells, of dinoflagellates are easily destroyed after death; thus these organisms do not form extensive deposits on the sea floor.

Another group of yellow-green algae consists of the smaller Coccolithophoridae, organisms that are about 5 to 10 μ in diameter (see Figure 8-41b). These organisms were first recognized by geological oceanographers who noted their calcareous shells in deep-sea sediments. They were not observed in the samples obtained by plankton nets because they were small enough to pass through the holes of the net. The contribution by the Coccolithophoridae and other small yellow-green algae to the economy of the sea is not adequately understood at present.

Bacteria, although poorly understood, are important organisms in the ocean for the production of organic material. There are two types of bacteria, the **heterotrophs** and the **autotrophs.** The heterotrophs use organic material obtained from other organisms for their nutrition. This group is probably the more common one. Autotrophic bacteria use inorganic material and carbon dioxide to form organic material, and in this respect are similar to plants. The amount of organic material produced by bacteria in this manner is relatively very small when compared to that produced by plants, but this small quantity may be important in the deep sea where other sources of food are not available.

In summary, the plants of the sea are quite different from those of the land. In the ocean there are few areas where attached plants can grow and receive enough light for photosynthesis. Therefore, the organic producers in the ocean must be microscopic floaters that can utilize the light available in the upper 200 m of the ocean. Even though the plant life is microscopic its numbers are sufficient to feed the remaining population of the ocean.

Animals of the Sea

The animal kingdom can be divided into the following general categories (given in descending order):

Phylum

   Class

      Order

         Family

            Genus

               Species

In the following pages, I mention some of the more important representatives of the animal kingdom in the sea. The number of phyla included in the animal kingdom varies with the classifier. Whatever the number, one point is obvious: all the phyla have marine representatives, whereas some do not have a terrestrial representative. The ocean is the area where animals have had their best development and land is the area where plants have had their best development.

There is one fundamental difference between plants and animals. Plants have chlorophyll and can produce their own food; animals do not have chlorophyll and must eat plants or other animals to obtain their necessary food.

The different animal phyla are described in order of one interpretation of their increasing biological complexity. For a more detailed discussion of individual animals of the sea, consult a good biology text. For illustrations of some animals see the color plates in this chapter.

Protozoa This phylum consists mostly of single-celled microscopic organisms. The two classes of this phylum that are important in oceanography are Sarcodina and Mastigophora. Included in Sarcodina are the orders Foraminifera and Radiolaria (see Figure 8-41). Tests of these animals cover large areas of the ocean bottom (see Figure 8-42). They live in the surface waters of the ocean, and when they die their shells settle to the bottom. Foraminifera are also valuable in that isotope concentrations in their tests can indicate some conditions of the environment that they lived in. Fossil tests, therefore, can give information about ancient environments. Radiolaria and Foraminifera can also be used to date and correlate sediments, because certain species are characteristic of different geological time periods. The tests of most Foraminifera are composed of calcium carbonate; the Radiolaria tests are siliceous. Some Foraminifera are benthic, that is, they live on the bottom.

The class Mastigophora includes the dinoflagellates, some of which, as previously discussed, are more typical of plants. The "animal" dinoflagellates are also important; these small organisms reproduce very rapidly, and as voracious feeders, they can consume a large quantity of phytoplankton.

Also included in this phylum are two animals that may be more familiar to you: the amoeba and *Paramecium*. However, neither of these animals is particularly important in the ocean.

Porifera This phylum is composed of those multicellular animals commonly known as sponges. Sponges are benthic animals that occur in many different forms. They are classified on the basis of composition of their internal skeletons. Sponge skeletons may be composed of calcareous, siliceous, or spongin material. The last is what the commercial sponges are composed of.

Sponges grow attached to the ocean bottom, and can be found at all depths. Siliceous sponges are more abundant at great depths than other sponges, apparently because it is easier to precipitate siliceous material than calcareous material in the deep sea.

Sponges feed by passing large quantities of water through their body walls and filtering out microscopic organisms and organic detritus.

Ctenophora These animals resemble jellyfish, and are similar to the coelenterates. Ctenophora are exclusively marine pelagic animals and are important since they are voracious feeders.

Coelenterata This phylum is more complex in that it shows the development of tissue. Individuals also have stinging cells called nematocysts which can be used in immobilizing some animals. These nematocysts are usually on tentacles which can then bring the victim into position for ingestion. This phylum also shows a high degree of polymorphism, that is, individual species may occur in a variety of forms. Usually there is an alternation of generations between benthic polyps (attached to the bottom) and floating medusae.

Three classes of this phylum are worthy of mention here. The class Hydrozoa includes some jellyfish such as *Physalia,* more commonly known as the Portuguese man-of-war. Poison carried in the nematocysts can cause its sting to be fatal to humans. The tentacles of *Physalia* can be as long as 10 m. Large jellyfish, sometimes as much as 2 m in diameter, belong to the class Scyphozoa. The third class, Anthozoa, contains most corals, sea anemones (Figure 6-15), and alcyonarians. Corals are important because their calcareous skeletons can form the core of large coral reefs (see Figures 6-26 and 6-27). Alcyonarians

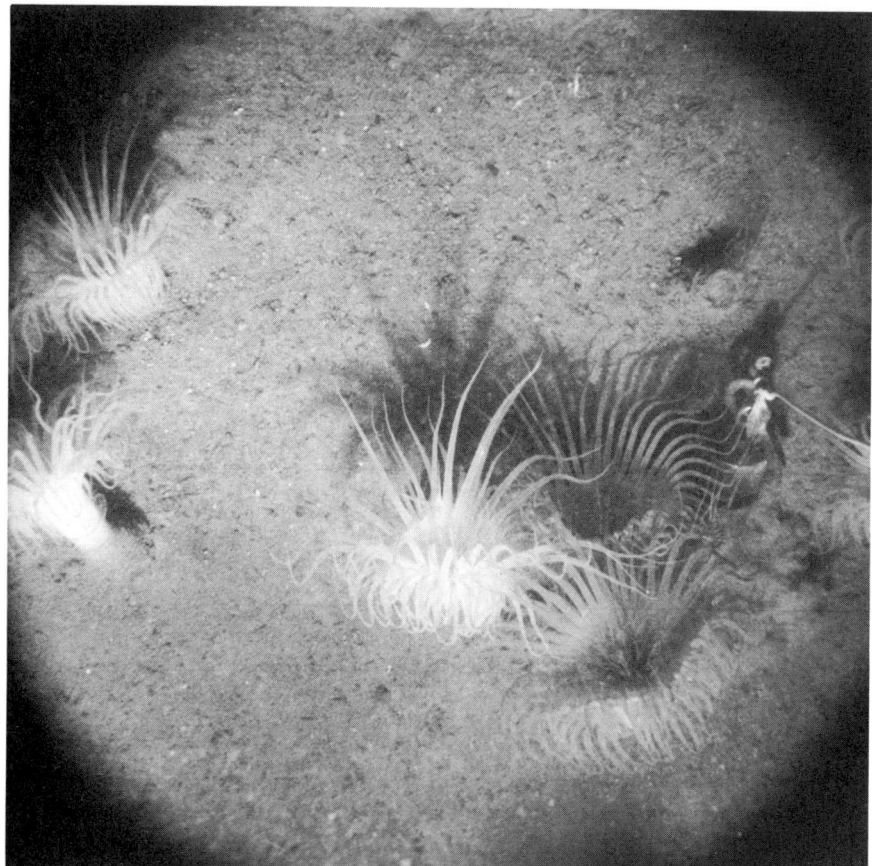

Figure 6-15   Some anemones photographed in the Gulf of Maine at a depth of 194 m.

include sea pens which skin-divers sometimes observe growing on the sea floor. An extraordinary picture of a sea pen is shown in Figure 6-16.

Platyhelminthes, Nemathelminthes, and Trochelminthes These three phyla include the unsegmented varieties of worms. The Platyhelminthes are flatworms. They include *Planaria,* the "cross-eyed" worm commonly studied in high school or college biology, and the tape worm found in humans, only one of the many parasitic genera in this phylum. There is a wide range of size for adult individuals in this phylum, from as small as 0.5 cm to as large as 25 m. Some of the larger forms have been called sea monsters; however, even though they are long they are very thin and not really up to the standards of a "Loch Ness sea monster."

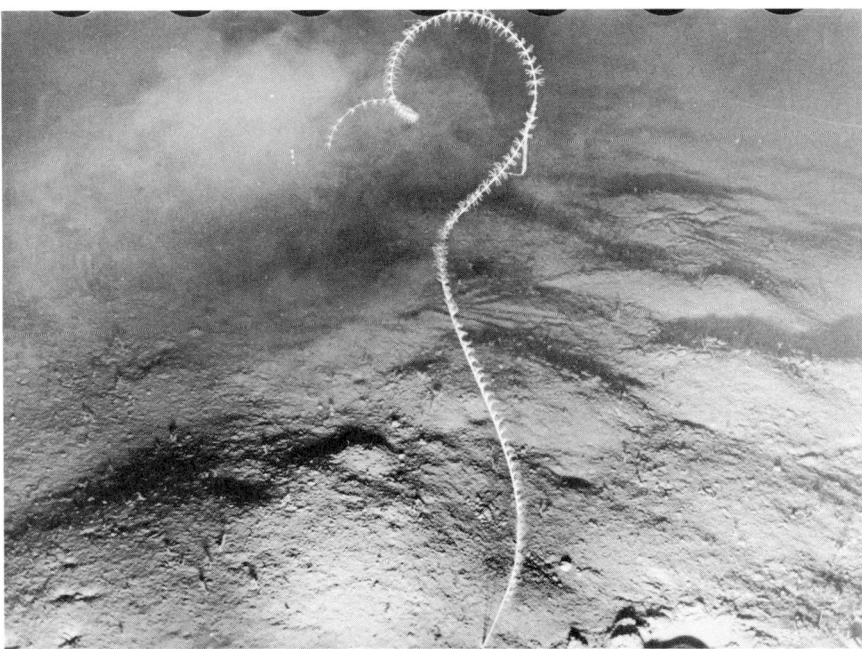

Figure 6-16   Pennatula or sea pen photographed at a depth of 3,000 m on the continental rise off New York. (Photograph courtesy of David W. Folger.)

The Nemathelminthes are the round, or thread, worms. Most forms are parasites. One land variety, hookworm, or *Trichinella,* is a parasite dangerous to humans.

Trochelminthes are the so-called wheel worms. Although most examples of this phylum are fresh-water inhabitants, some occur as marine plankton.

These phyla have sessile and mobile benthic forms, often found at great depths, and parasitic and planktonic forms floating at all depths in the ocean.

Bryozoa These animals can form rigid calcareous mats or coatings on kelp and other objects. Because their skeletons are calcareous, they are preserved after death and are abundant as fossils.

Brachiopoda This group of benthic animals is especially valuable to geologists because of its widespread fossil representation. Brachiopods have two calcareous hinged shells that superficially resemble some pelecypods. Brachiopoda are generally found in the littoral part of the ocean.

Chaetognatha This is a relatively small phylum, for which few genera are known. Chaetognaths, which are very voracious and can quickly consume an entire spawn of small fish, are small, transparent creatures that resemble worms; they are commonly called arrow or glass worms (Figure 6-17). They occur throughout most parts of the ocean.

Figure 6-17   *Sagitta,* a chaetognath.

Annelida These are the earthworms, leeches, and sand worms. They have segmented, elongated bodies. Most marine annelids are benthic, many of them living in burrows. Those burrowing forms are important because of their incessant churning and mixing of the upper 10 cm of bottom sediment.

Arthropoda This is the largest phylum in the sea, both in numbers and total mass. Arthropods have an external skeleton and numerous jointed appendages. This phylum includes three very important classes: Insecta, Arachnoidea, and Crustacea. Insects, which form a very large and important class of land animals, are almost totally absent from the sea. Only *Halobates,* a water strider, spends its entire life in the sea, living on the water surface.

Arachnoidea includes horseshoe crabs and sea spiders or pycnogonids. The last are not true spiders, which also belong to this class. The arachnids, like insects, form a relatively minor group in the ocean.

The most important class of animals is the Crustacea. Crustaceans are divided into several subclasses. One subclass, Cirripedia, includes barnacles. Adult barnacles generally have hard shells and live as attached forms on the ocean bottom, on fixed objects (pier pilings, for example), or on other animals. They have a pelagic larval stage which accounts for their occurrence on some rather strange objects such as whales or ships. Their growth on ships causes a fouling problem, and they must be removed from most vessels periodically.

The most numerous of the crustaceans are members of the order Copepoda. Copepods are important because they eat phytoplankton and concentrate it in their bodies for other larger animals to eat. In this manner they form an essential link in the food chain of the sea. Most copepods are pelagic zooplankton (see Figure 6-9).

Another order, Euphausiacea, also is a common zooplankton. These animals are somewhat larger than copepods and are more advanced in their development. Euphausids, along with some copepods, are capable of extensive vertical migrations, sometimes traveling several hundreds of meters within a day. Euphausids are the favorite food of some whales.

Another similar order, Mysidacea, has individuals that often live near the sea bottom. They are more commonly found in the neritic zone, but there are some bathypelagic species.

The order Amphipoda consists of mainly benthic organisms with some pelagic forms. Some amphipods are parasitic.

The animals of the order Isopoda also live near the sea bottom. Others are parasitic and live in the gills of fish, while still others burrow into wood and can cause extensive damage to piers and ships.

Probably the most commonly known order of crustaceans is the order Decopoda; it includes shrimps, crabs, and lobsters. Most of these animals are benthic, and only a few are pelagic forms. This group of animals is rather important to man, who fishes and traps for them. They are not, however, very important in the overall picture of the ocean.

Mollusca Mollusks have a soft body covered in most genera by a hard shell. This shell may have one or two parts or eight segments. Five classes are noteworthy: Amphineura, Scaphopoda, Gastropoda, Pelecypoda, and Cephalopoda. The amphineurans are the chitons, which are small, flat benthic animals having eight segments in the outer shell. Scaphopods are the so-called tooth- or tusk-shelled mollusks. Their shells have been found on most parts of the ocean bottom. They are hard to observe on beaches, because they generally live below the sediment surface. Shells of these animals were used as wampum by many tribes of Indians.

Gastropods are terrestrial and benthic-living snails, slugs, and floating forms such as pteropods. These animals, like scaphopods, have a "foot" that is used in movement on the bottom. In most forms the foot is attached to a hard spiral convolute shell, which can be absent from some of the planktonic species. Pteropods, one of these planktonic forms, may settle on the bottom and form extensive sea floor deposits after death.

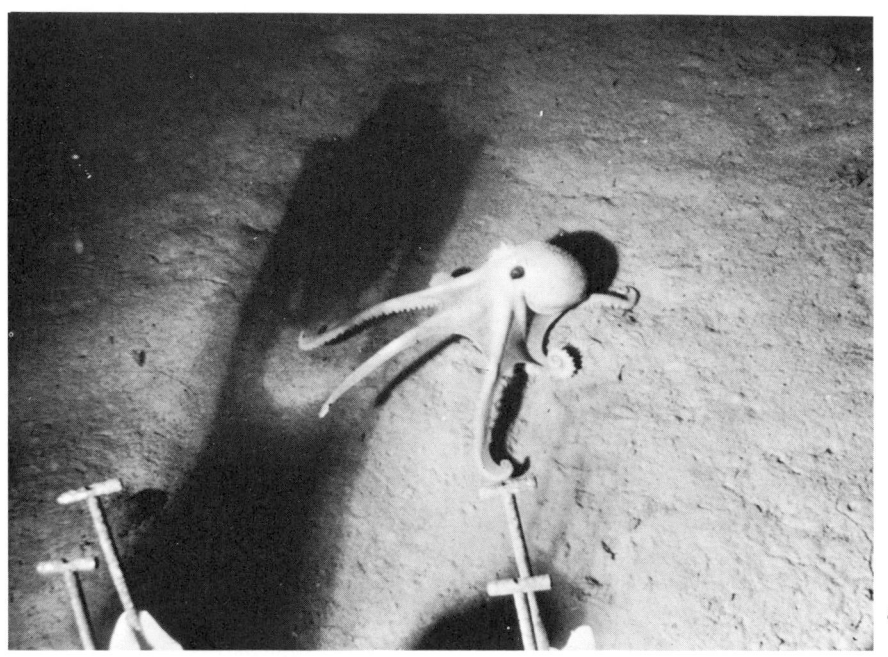

a

b

Figure 6-18

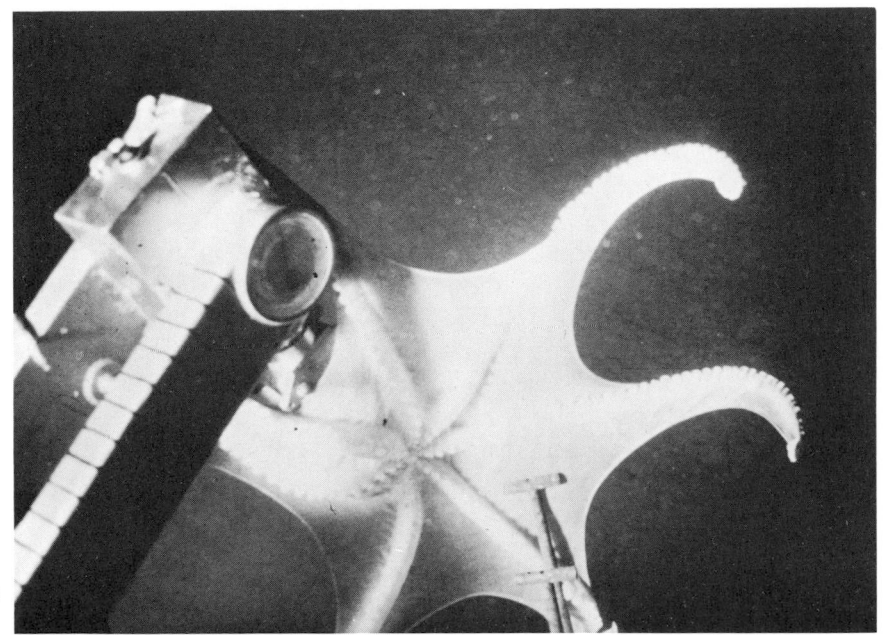

c

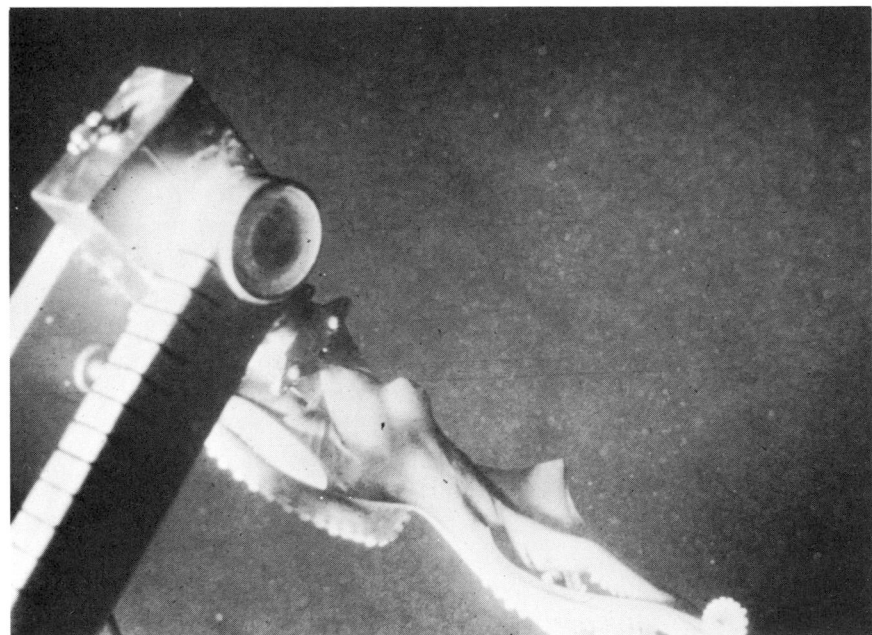

d

Figure 6-18 A pugnacious octopus, which when annoyed by the submersible ALVIN decided to attack its mechanical arm. (Photographs courtesy of Woods Hole Oceanographic Institution.)

Pelecypods are the clams, oysters, scallops, mussels, and the like. These are the typical bivalved mollusks. Most marine animals of this order live either attached to or burrowed in the bottom. Some forms burrow into wood; these wood borers can cause extensive damage. Two genera, *Teredo* and *Bankia,* have pelagic larval forms that can bore holes up to a foot long into wood. Pelecypods constitute an important source of food to man. The settlements of early man can often be identified by large piles of empty shells, mainly pelecypods.

The cephalopods include squid, octopus (Figure 6-18), and nautiloids. In these animals the solid foot typical of the other classes is divided into arms or tentacles. Squid is a very common animal in the ocean and an important source of food to many other creatures. The giant squid, which can be as long as 15 to 20 m, is the largest living invertebrate animal known. Invertebrates are animals without backbones, and include all the phyla mentioned in this chapter except the last one, Chordata.

Echinodermata This is an exclusively marine phylum; it includes sea stars, sea urchins, and sea cucumbers. These animals have a five-sided pseudosymmetry and an internal skeleton. Most of the forms are benthic. Four classes are worthy of note here.

The class Holothuroidea includes sea cucumbers (Figure 6-19), animals that live in all depths of the ocean. The five-sided symmetry typical of echinoderms is visible only in the skeleton of this animal. Sea cucumbers have one very peculiar ability: they can eviscerate. In times of danger, they can discharge their internal organs, leaving a meal for their tormentors, and later regenerate another set of organs.

The class Asteroidea, which includes the sea stars, is well-represented the world over. Sea stars are frequently seen in the littoral regions, but also occur in the deeper parts of the ocean. The five-sided pseudosymmetry is obvious with these animals. Starfish, as they are commonly called, feed on oysters and clams and can cause considerable damage to these valuable food resources. In the past, when fishermen caught starfish they would cut them in half, thinking they had killed the animals, and throw them back into the ocean. Unfortunately for the fishermen (and clams), starfish can regenerate their lost arms, so that by cutting them in half, the fishermen were actually doubling their numbers. Today more effective control of starfish population is practiced.

The class Ophiuroidea includes the brittle stars, animals which resemble starfish, but which have a more distinct central area. These animals live in the deepest parts of the ocean.

The class Echinoidea includes sea urchins (see Figure 6-5a) and sand dollars.

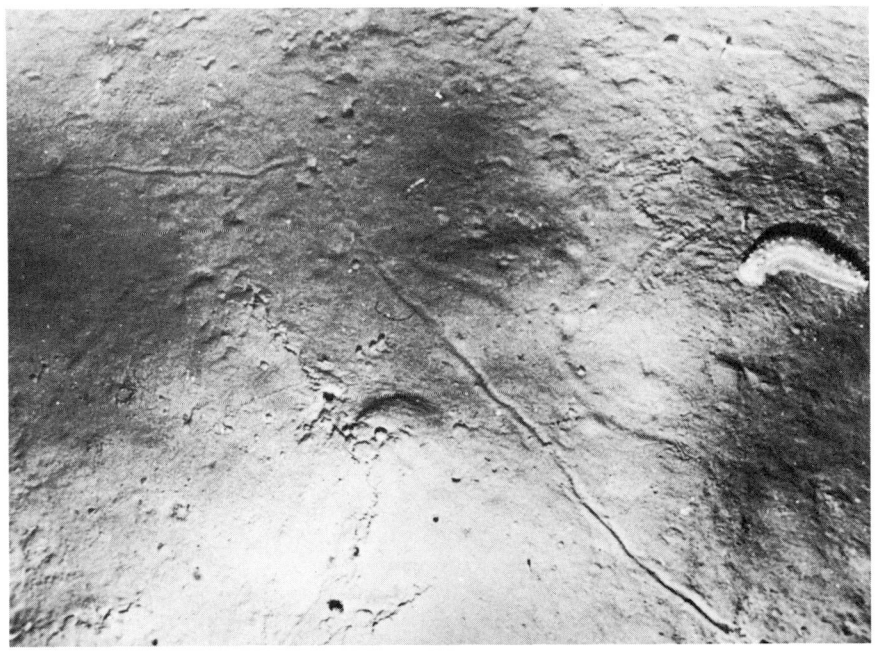

a

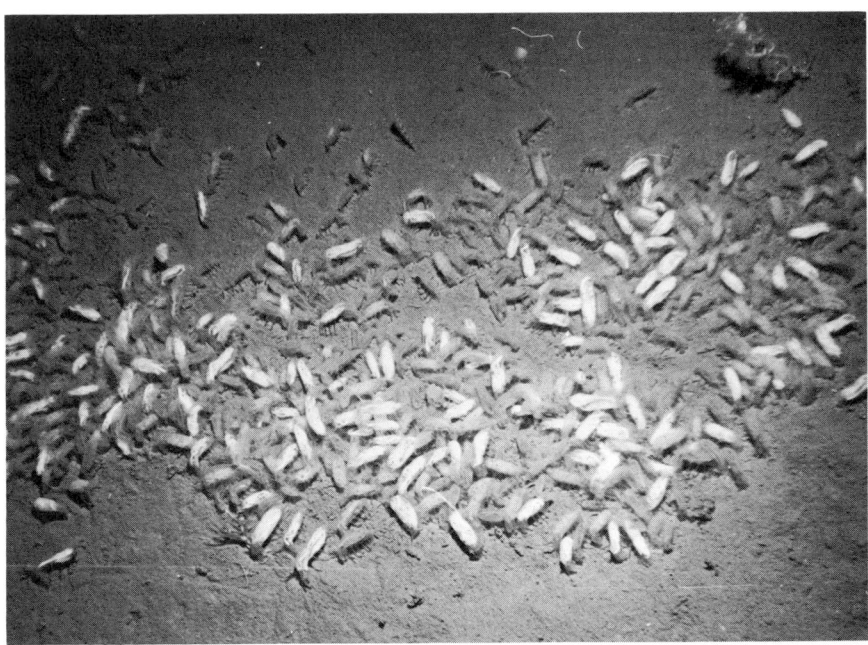

b

Figure 6-19 (a) Picture of a holothurian (sea cucumber), center right, taken at a depth of 4,165 fathoms in the Peru-Chile Trench. Note the numerous track marks. (From Heezen and Hollister, 1964.) (b) A large group of holothurians photographed on the continental slope off Virginia at a depth of 1,615 m.

Chordata This is a large and very important phylum. The chordates all possess a notochord, a series of elements that forms an axial supporting structure to the animal's skeleton. This phylum has been divided into four subphyla: Hemichordata, Cephalochordata, Tunicata, and Vertebrata. The Hemichordates are mainly certain worm-like organisms, such as acorn worms (Figure 6-20). Cephalochordates are also a worm group. Both these subphyla are of minor importance in the ocean.

Tunicates are marine filter feeders, animals that feed by filtering out organisms and detritus from the water. Some are attached to the bottom, and others are planktonic forms. These animals can develop in large numbers and then feed on similar food that small fishes and other animals eat, thus depriving them of their food.

Vertebrates include all animals having vertebrae, and are considered to be the most highly developed form of life. Vertebrata includes six important marine classes: Cyclostomata, Elasmobranchii, Pisces, Reptilia, Aves, and Mammalia.

Primitive fish such as lampreys and hagfish comprise the group Cyclostomata. They have neither articulated jaws nor scales. Most members of this class are parasites or scavengers. The lamprey attaches

Figure 6-20   An abyssal acorn worm photographed at a depth of 4,735 m in the Kermadec Trench. The worm's body ends shortly past the first bend, and the rest is its track. Note another set of tracks in the upper left hand corner of the photograph. (From D. W. Bourne and B. C. Heezen, *Science,* Fig. 2, **150** [October, 1965]: 60–63; Copyright 1965 by the American Association for the Advancement of Science.)

itself to the side of another fish, makes a hole through the body wall, then sucks out the fish's body fluids, killing it.

Elasmobranchii are the cartilaginous fish such as sharks (Figure 6-21), skates (Figure 6-22) and rays, and chimaera (Figure 6-23). They have scales which do not overlap, as in bony fish. Their mouths are not located at the head (anterior) but somewhat in front of and under it. Sharks are the largest of these fish, some being over 15 m long. At one time sharks used to be fished for extensively because of the nutritional value of their liver.

Figure 6-21 A large Lemon shark. Note the attached remora or sucker fish. (Photograph courtesy of Marineland of Florida.)

Figure 6-22 A small skate traveling along near the ocean bottom. (Photograph courtesy of Woods Hole Oceanographic Institution.)

Figure 6-23　A long-nosed chimaera photographed from ALVIN at a depth of about 1,600 m.

The class Pisces is characterized by overlapping scales, an anterior mouth, and a bony skeleton. Of all the animals in the sea, Pisces are the most important to man. Many billions of pounds of fish are caught and consumed by man each year. There are over 25,000 different species of fish. Most fish are pelagic, living in all depths of the ocean; however, there are many species which prefer staying near the bottom (Figure 6-24), while others carry out most of their activities near the surface.

In the ocean the commonest members of the class Reptilia are turtles and snakes. None of these is very important to the overall economy of the ocean. As air breathers, they must live in surface waters.

The class Aves (birds), along with Mammalia, are warm-blooded animals, and thus have the ability to maintain a certain body temperature. Birds actually don't live in the ocean, but many are dependent on the ocean for food, and only return to land to breed. Guano, the accumulated fecal waste product of birds and other animals, occurs on some nesting areas forming valuable fertilizer deposits.

The class Mammalia is the most advanced group of organisms living in the sea. These animals are warm-blooded and air-breathing. There are three orders with marine genera worthy of note here: Carnivora, Pinnipedia, and Cetacea. The carnivores include the sea otter and polar bear, and the pinnipedes include seals, sea lions, and walruses. Cetacea are the dolphins, porpoises, and whales. Whales are the largest creatures known on earth; the blue whale can be over 35 m long and weigh 150,000 kg. Some whales are quickly becoming ex-

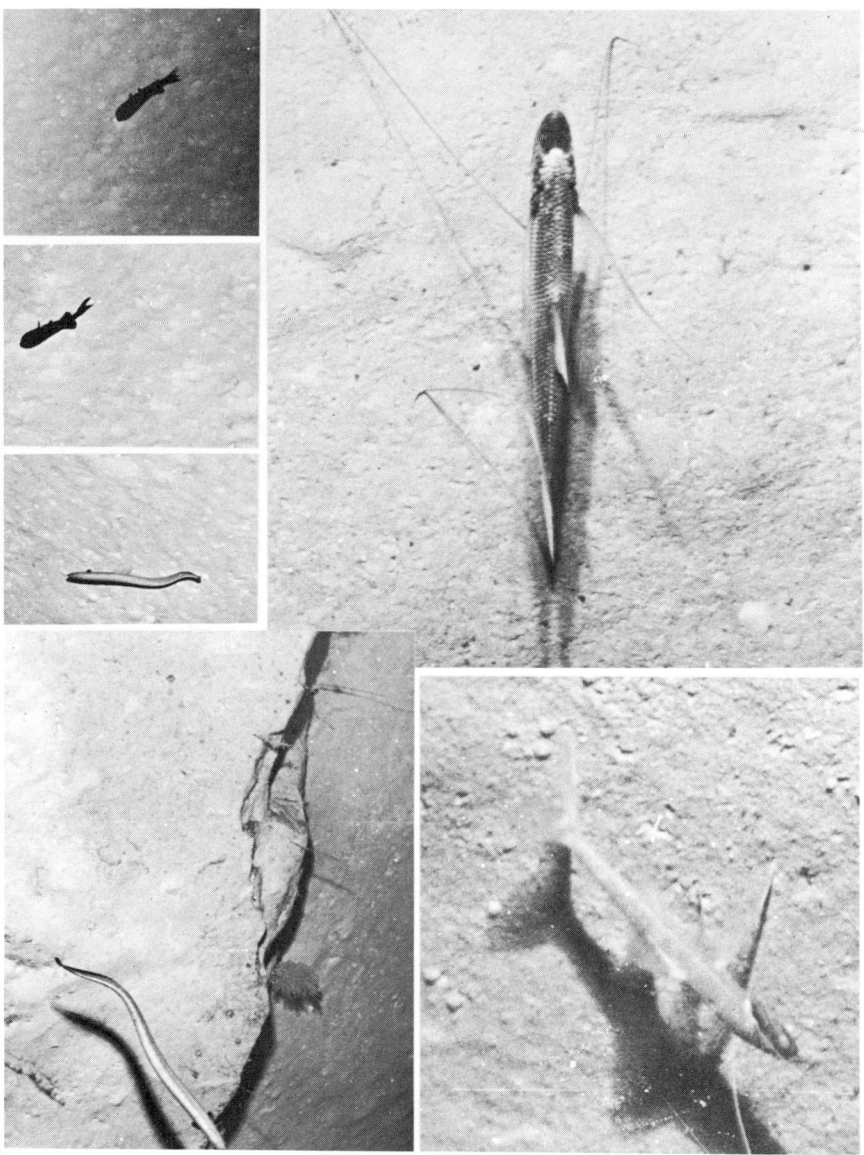

Figure 6-24 Some bottom-living fish photographed near Bermuda. The one in the upper left is from a depth of about 1,300 m. (Photograph courtesy of C. D. Hollister.)

tinct because of man's extensive hunting of them for food and their oils and fats. Some whales are filter feeders whose diet consists mainly of plankton; others, such as the sperm whale, have teeth and feed on organisms like squid.

Man belongs to the class Mammalia but as yet cannot really be considered as an inhabitant of the sea. However, man, through his activities, has had a considerable influence, mostly bad, on the ocean. He has been guilty of polluting the nearshore waters and destroying or severely changing the living environment of many marine organisms. Also, through indiscriminate fishing methods he is causing several species to be in danger of extinction.

Coral Reefs and Atolls

Coral reefs and atolls are two of the more interesting biological environments in the ocean. These environments, which may be located a thousand or more kilometers from the nearest continental land mass, represent a delicate balance between the forces of the ocean and the strength of the reef.

A reef is a biological community on the sea floor that forms a solid limestone (calcium carbonate) structure strong enough to withstand the force of waves. The predominant organisms in most of these communities are the corals and algae. The algae tend to grow over the coral, encrusting it, giving it strength, and forming a solid structure. Since most reefs grow at about sea level they must be strong enough to withstand the eroding power of breaking waves.

Coral reefs require definite limited conditions for growth, such as a water temperature of about 70° F. For this reason most reefs today are found in the tropics. Corals cannot tolerate low salinities, and are killed by fresh water. The most active growth of the coral is in water shallower than 35 m. In some instances, the reefs must be able to grow fast enough to keep up with the rise in sea level or, in some cases, with the slow sinking of the islands that they are growing on. The recent rise in sea level of about 120 m in the last 20,000 years (see Figure 2-2) required that most reefs grow very fast to maintain their favorable growth position near sea level.

There are three basic types of reefs (Figure 6-25): the fringing reef, the barrier reef, and the atoll. The fringing reef grows out from a landmass but is attached to it. An example is the reef that borders the Florida Keys. A barrier reef is separated from the land mass by a lagoon. This type of reef, as exemplified by the Great Barrier Reef of Australia, can be a very imposing structure. An atoll (Figure 6-26) is an oval-shaped reef surrounding a lagoon; it is not associated with an obvious land mass. Atolls commonly are found rising abruptly from the deep sea, and some are very large. Kwajalein, for example, in the Pacific, is about 65 km long and 30 km wide.

The conditions on a reef vary from the quiet of the lagoon to the breaking waves of the outer part of the reef and are reflected by the different types of coral growing in these areas (Figure 6-27). In areas

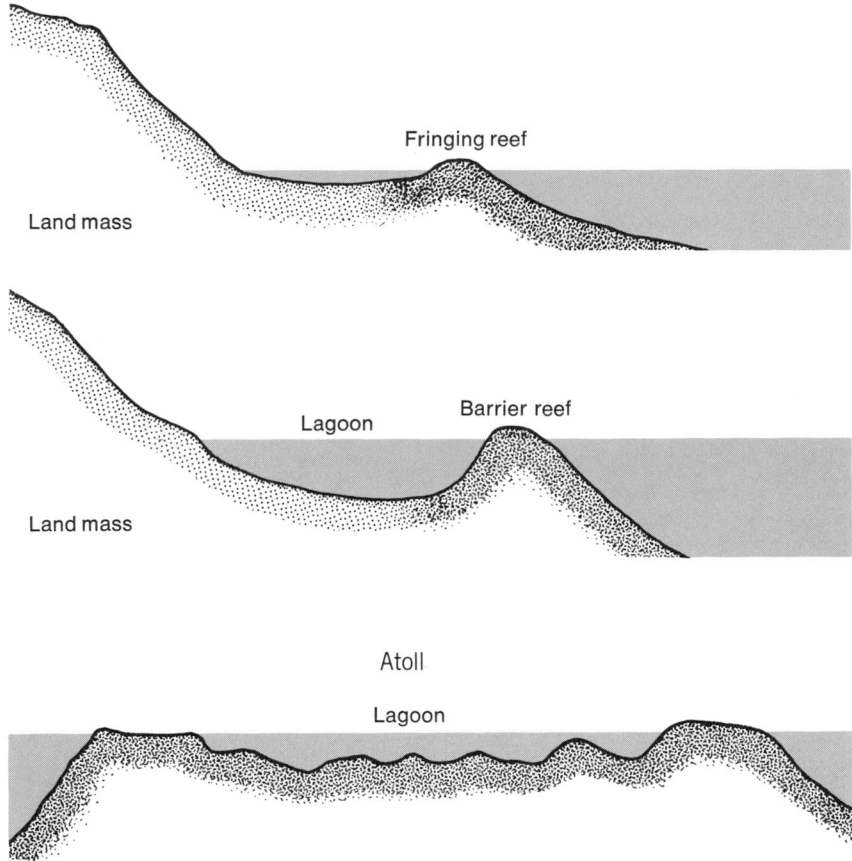

Figure 6-25   Different types of coral reefs.

of intense wave action, the coral must be strong enough to withstand the waves; more delicate forms can grow only in the quiet areas.

The finding of numerous coral atolls in the middle of the deep ocean, without any visible land mass, puzzled many early scientists. How could these shallow-water animals have established an existence in water several kilometers deep? During his voyage on the BEAGLE, Charles Darwin saw a few reefs and atolls, and on the basis of this trip he formulated a hypothesis to explain their origin. His theory, as shown in Figure 6-28, is very simple. He suggested that a volcanic island initially provided a shallow-water base for the growth of a fringing reef. Then there was a slow subsidence of the island, during which time the reef continued to grow. Eventually the island and the reef became separated by a lagoon, similar to a barrier reef. Further subsidence then buried the volcanic island, resulting in an atoll.

It wasn't until almost 100 years later that Darwin's hypothesis was

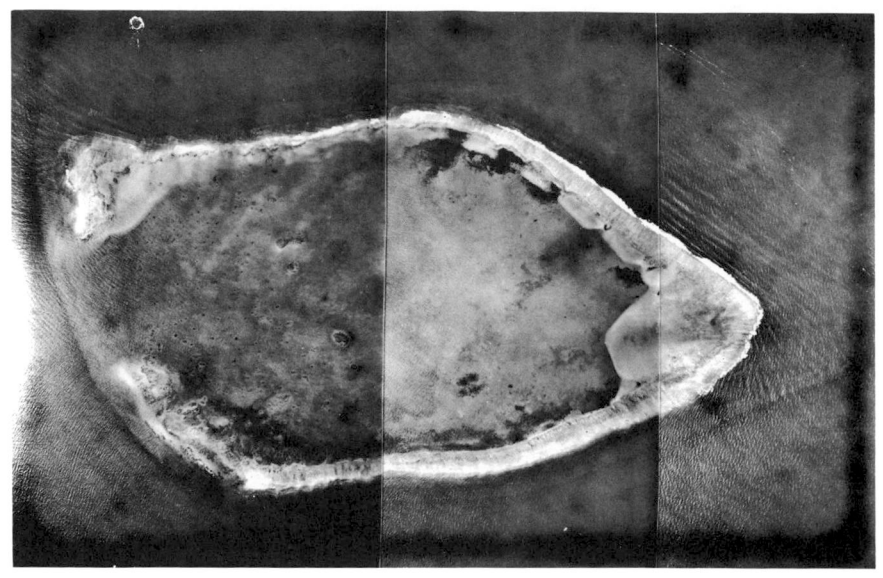

a

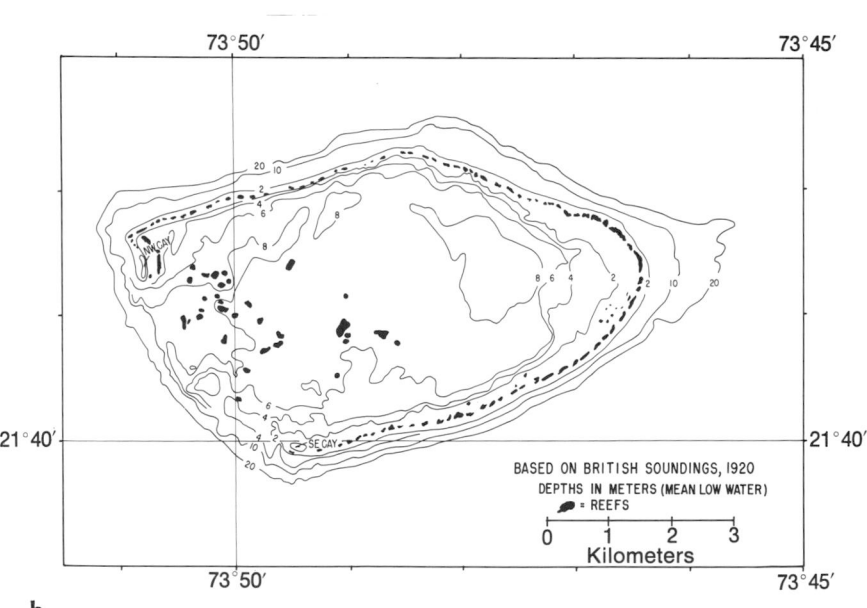

b

Figure 6-26 (a) Hogsty Reef, an atoll in the Bahamas. (Official U.S. Navy photograph.) (b) Chart of the lagoon and shallow-water area of Hogsty Reef. Depth in meters. (From J. D. Milliman, 1967.)

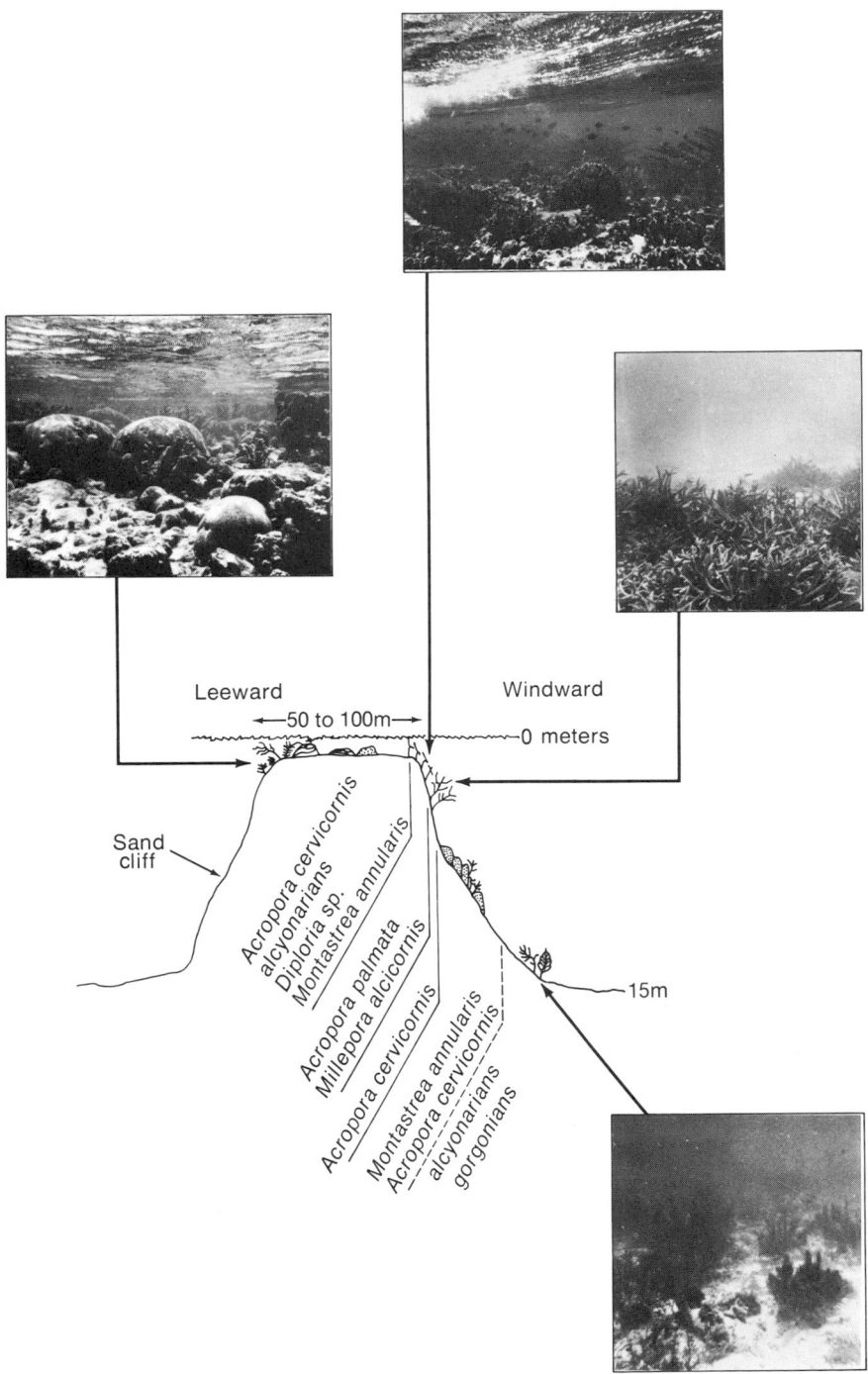

Figure 6-27 Illustration showing the different forms of coral that grow on the various parts of a reef. (Photograph courtesy of J. D. Milliman.)

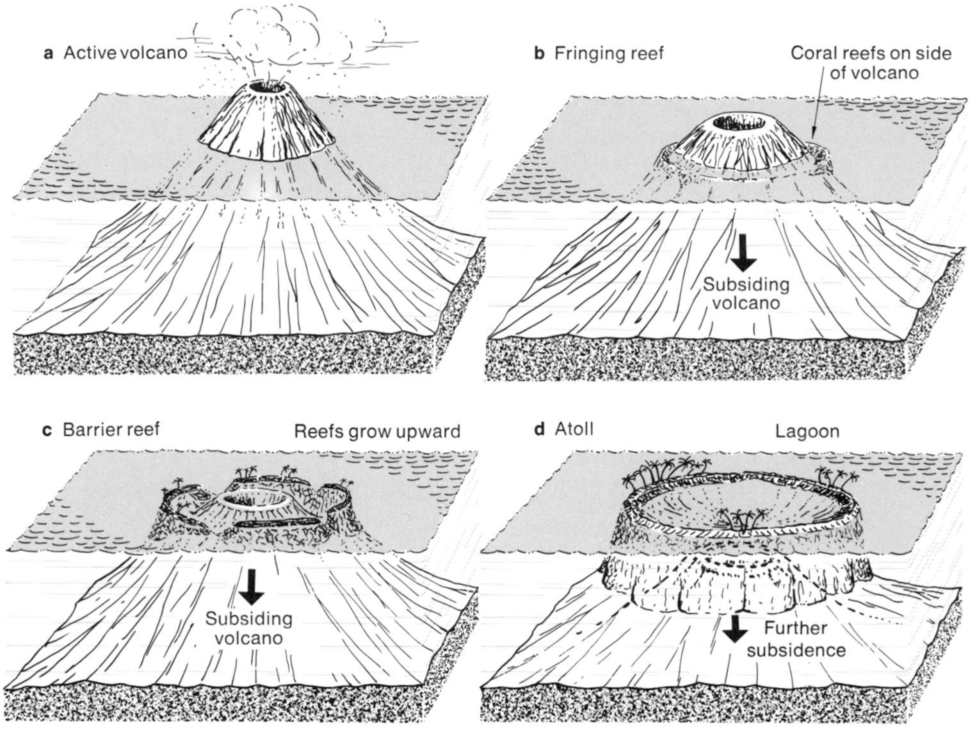

Figure 6-28 Darwin's theory of the formation of an atoll.

found to be essentially correct. The evidence came from drillings on Eniwetok and Bikini atolls. These drillings found over a thousand meters of coral underlain by volcanic rock.

THE ORGANISMS AND THE OCEAN

Plants and the Ocean

Now that I have presented some of the different plants and animals that inhabit the ocean, we can consider the importance of different aspects of the marine environment and their effects on the organisms.

Plants are the key to life in the oceans. These organisms are the primary producers of organic material, and almost all other forms of life are dependent on them for food. This process of organic production is called photosynthesis; it is a process common to all plants whether they are floating in the ocean, attached to rocks in the shallow parts of the ocean, or rooted on land.

Photosynthesis is dependent on the plants being able to receive light. The photosynthetic reaction is an endothermic reaction; that is, it requires energy.

$$CO_2 + H_2O + nutrients + solar\ energy \rightarrow organic\ matter + O_2$$

Plants contain chlorophyll, a green pigment that allows them to utilize energy from sunlight. This energy, used with carbon dioxide, water, nutrients, and vitamins, produces the organic matter. The reverse of this reaction, where the organic matter is consumed, is called respiration. This process uses oxygen and ultimately returns the nutrients back to the water. These two processes together make up the organic cycle in the ocean (Figure 6-29).

Light is necessary for plants; it determines the depth to which they can live in the ocean. This depth varies with latitude, time of day, location, weather, and other factors. As seen from Figure 6-10, generally little light is present below a depth of about 200 m; for plants to survive they must live above this depth. Plants that are attached to the bottom thus are restricted to only a small portion of the ocean. Most plants in the ocean, therefore, are planktonic: they float.

For plants to float is not as simple as it sounds. The density of living protoplasm is generally greater than sea water; the shells are even denser. Plants have evolved several adaptations to enhance their floating ability, the most common of which is to increase their surface area. The frictional resistance of the plant to the water is increased as the surface area to volume ratio is increased. A large surface area,

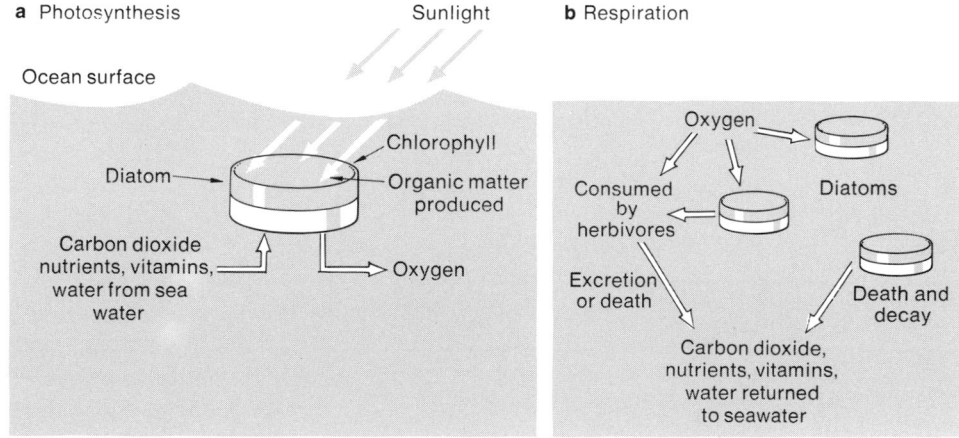

Figure 6-29   The organic cycle in the ocean—photosynthesis (a) and respiration (b).

besides helping the plant to float, has another advantage: it brings the plant in contact with a larger amount of nutrients. Other adaptations for flotation include special shapes of some shells that retard sinking, thin shells, and secreted oils or fats that lower the bulk density of the plant.

Once a plant sinks to a depth where there is insufficient light for photosynthesis, it is in danger of dying unless carried up by a current. There is a certain point, called the **compensation depth,** where the oxygen produced by photosynthesis equals the amount the plant needs for itself. This is not the lowest depth where photosynthesis can occur, but below the compensation depth the plant cannot really be considered a producer. The depth of the compensation zone is a function of the intensity of the light, which is affected by factors such as suspended material in the water and turbulence. In coastal water the compensation depth is generally around 20 to 30 m. In the open ocean it can be as deep as 100 m.

The amount of photosynthesis can be closely related to light available (Figure 6-30). In the upper few meters of the ocean there can be an inhibition of photosynthesis—apparently due to too much light. Another requirement of the photosynthesis equation is CO_2 (carbon dioxide), which, because of its usual abundance in the sea, is rarely a limiting factor.

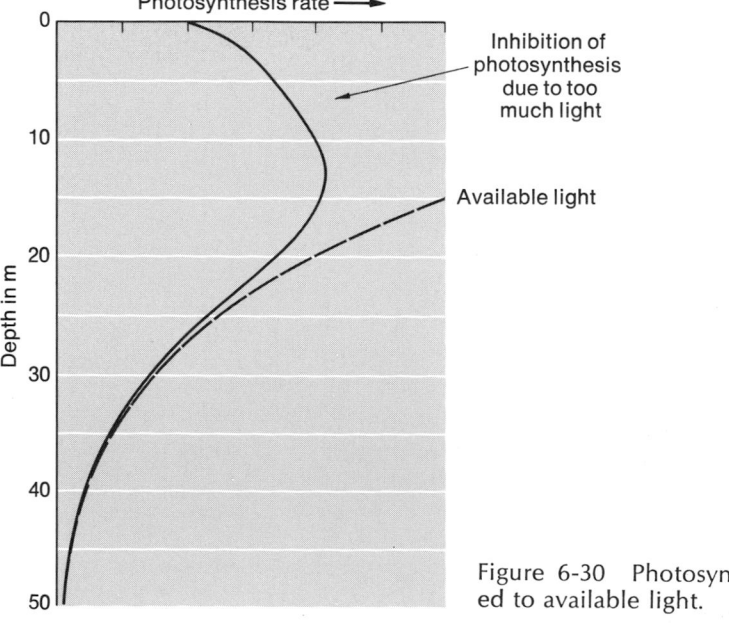

Figure 6-30   Photosynthesis as related to available light.

Plate 1 A sea spider (*pycnogonid*) photographed from ALVIN. Photograph courtesy of Woods Hole Oceanographic Institution.

Plate 2 Millions of these small (two- to three-inch long) lantern fish were observed in the Deep Scattering Layer from ALVIN.

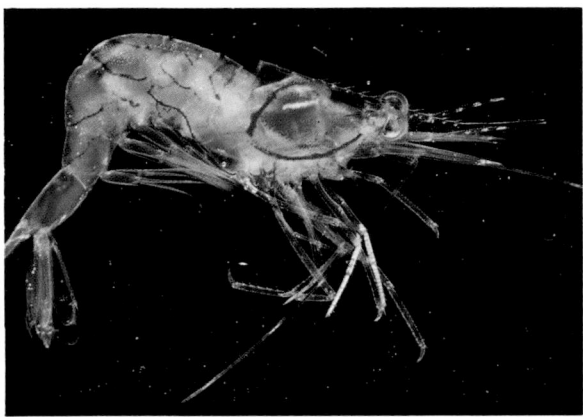

Plate 3 A crustacean (*pandalus*). Photograph courtesy of P. A. Shave, Systematics-Ecology Program, Marine Biological Laboratory.

Plate 4 A ctenophora (*pleurobrachia*). Photograph courtesy of P. J. Oldham, Systematics-Ecology Program, Marine Biological Laboratory.

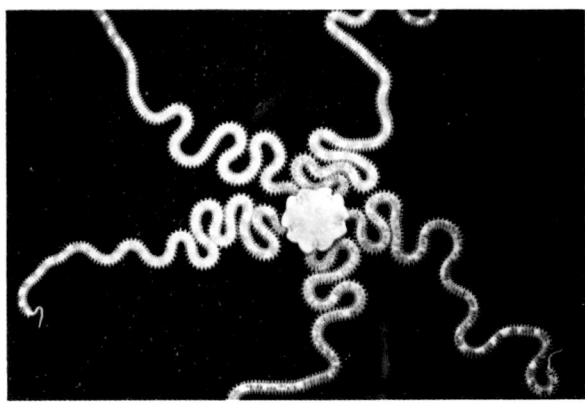

Plate 5 An echinoderm (*amphioplus*). Photograph courtesy of P. J. Oldham, Systematics-Ecology Program, Marine Biological Laboratory.

Plate 6 A crustacean (*byblis*). The specimen has been stained. Photograph courtesy of P. J. Oldham, Systematics-Ecology Program, Marine Biological Laboratory.

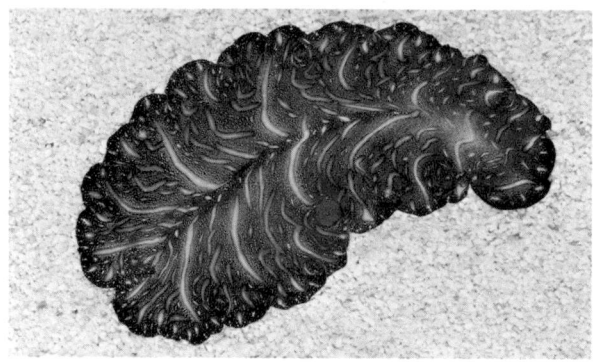

Plate 7 This is a turbellarian from the Great Barrier Reef (Heron Island). Turbellarians avoid daylight and crawl about on the undersurface of corals. They are extremely fragile, fragmenting immediately when handled. Photograph courtesy of Ederic Slater.

Plate 8 A giant jellyfish common to the eastern seaboard of the United States. Photograph courtesy of George Lower.

Plate 9 This annelid lives in a tube secreted by its own body. The appendages are used as paddles to keep the water circulating through its tube, thus bringing in oxygen and small animals upon which it feeds. It is luminescent, which seems strange since there is no opportunity for any other animal to appreciate its beauty. Photograph courtesy of George Lower.

Plate 10 The hermit crab removed from its shell. Its habit of living in an abandoned snail shell has resulted in the loss of the heavy exoskeleton characteristic of other crabs. Photograph courtesy of Ederic Slater.

Plate 11 This is a small shark embryo removed from the uterus of the mother. The long umbilical cord is attached to the half empty yolk sac, which supplies nourishment to the embryo during its early life. Photograph courtesy of George Lower.

Plate 12 This colorful annelid lives in a tube among the corals of the Great Barrier Reef. The feathery heads extend when feeding and are quickly retracted into the tube when disturbed. Photograph courtesy of Ederic Slater.

Plate 13 An acorn barnacle (*balanus*). Photograph courtesy of P. J. Oldham, Systematics-Ecology Program, Marine Biological Laboratory.

Plate 14 An anemone (*metridium*). Photograph courtesy of P. J. Oldham, Systematics-Ecology Program, Marine Biological Laboratory.

Plate 15 A nudibranch. Photograph courtesy of P. J. Oldham, Systematics-Ecology Program, Marine Biological Laboratory.

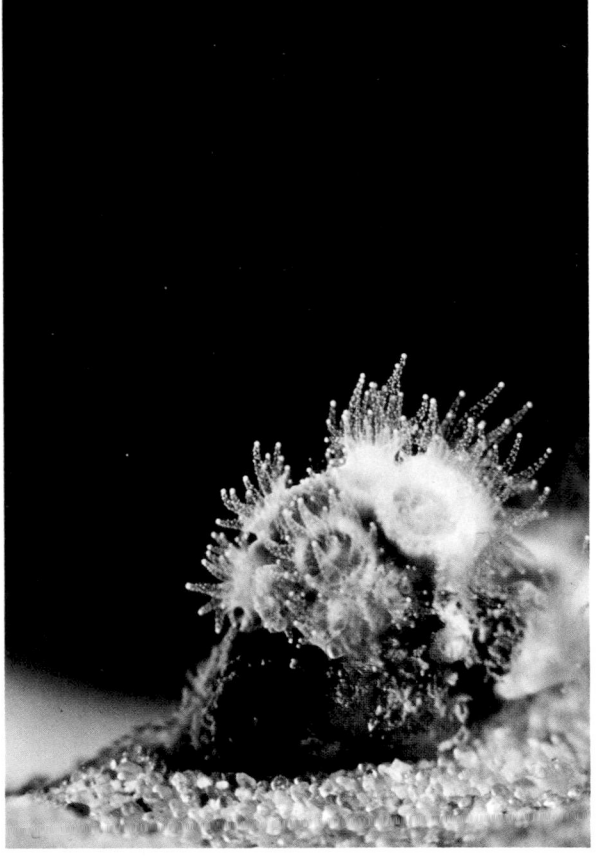

Plate 16 A coral (coelenterate). Photograph courtesy of P. J. Oldham, Systematics-Ecology Program, Marine Biological Laboratory.

Plate 17 A bryozoan (*bugula*). Photograph courtesy of P. J. Oldham, Systematics-Ecology Program, Marine Biological Laboratory.

Plate 18 A squid (*loligo*). Photograph courtesy of P. J. Oldham, Systematics-Ecology Program, Marine Biological Laboratory.

Plate 19 A tiny shrimp lives in the mantle folds of the Blacklip Pearl oyster where it is nourished by the organisms brought to it as the oyster feeds. Photograph courtesy of Ederic Slater.

Plate 20 A sea vase (tunicate). Photograph courtesy of P. J. Oldham, Systematics-Ecology Program, Marine Biological Laboratory.

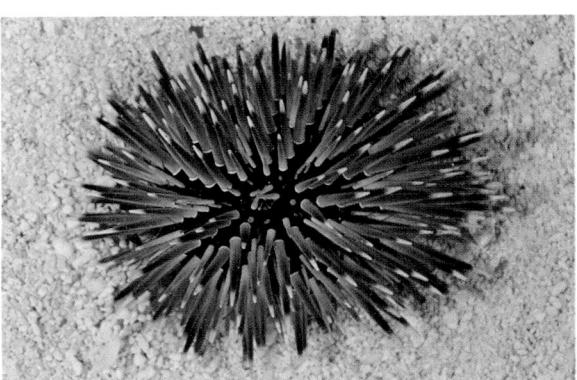

Plate 21 A basket star. The five principal arms are divided into a great many smaller branches. This is a ventral view. Photograph courtesy of George Lower.

Plate 22 A sea urchin from the Great Barrier Reef. Photograph courtesy of Ederic Slater.

Plate 23 A nudibranch from the Great Barrier Reef. This one is called "Spanish dancer" because of its agility when swimming. Other varieties only crawl. Photograph courtesy of Ederic Slater.

Plate 24 The HERO, an Antarctic oceanographic research vessel operated for the National Science Foundation. Photograph courtesy of William R. Curtsinger.

Plate 25 A Satellite photograph taken over the Pacific Ocean from a height of 22,240 statute miles. A low pressure area extends over southwestern United States and Mexico; a large storm area occurs west of South America. Photograph courtesy of NASA.

Plate 26 A Satellite photograph taken over the Atlantic Ocean from a height of 22,240 statute miles. A low pressure storm area can be observed just west of the Mediterranean Sea. Photograph courtesy of NASA.

Plate 27 The tanker TORREY CAN-YON lying off the coast of England. Note the oil (dark area) leaking from the vessel.

Plate 28 Pair of Black Skimmers, nesting. Photograph courtesy of Karin Engstrom.

Plate 29 Artemisia and bird tracks. Photograph courtesy of Karin Engstrom.

Figure 6-31 Seasonal changes in phosphate concentration as measured in the surface waters and at a depth of 70 m in the English Channel. (After Atkins, 1926.)

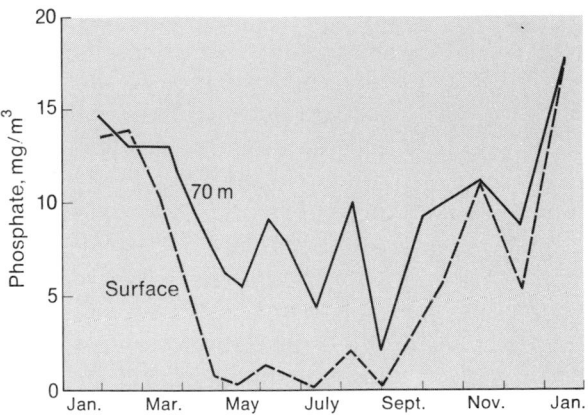

The supply of nutrients can be a critical point for photosynthesis. Some of the elements known to be essential for plant growth, such as potassium, sulfur, and magnesium, are usually found in sufficient quantities. Other important nutrients, like nitrogen, phosphorus, and iron, are present in smaller amounts; in some instances the low amount may be a limiting factor for photosynthesis. These small quantities can be utilized by the phytoplankton because of their large surface area which aids in the absorption of the nutrients. Land plants would not be able to exist in a situation where the essential nutrients were in such small supply.

A detailed discussion of the nutrient distribution in the ocean was presented in Chapter 5. One point that should be emphasized is that the nutrient distribution in the ocean is not uniform. There are seasonal changes (Figure 6-31) that relate to nutrient use by phytoplankton during their periods of extensive growth and reproduction. There are also geographical differences (Figure 6-32) due to variations in concentration and growth of phytoplankton in separate areas. For example, in the Arctic the yearly production of organic matter by phytoplankton is relatively low because of the ice cover which limits the penetration of light. In the Antarctic there is a strong water circu-

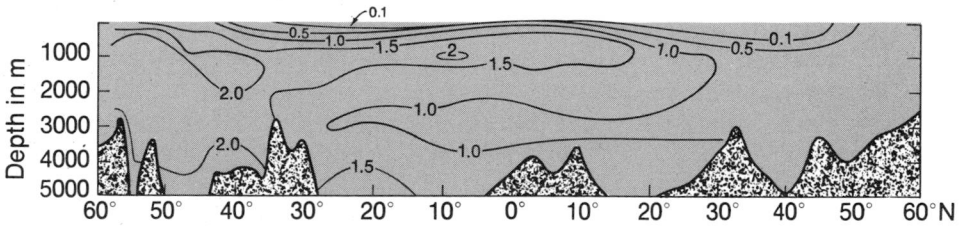

Figure 6-32 Distribution of phosphate (μ gram atoms/liter) along the central Atlantic. (After Sverdrup and others, 1942.)

lation pattern that supplies large quantities of nutrients to the surface waters; the supply is so large that it is not depleted despite areas of high productivity.

Nutrient distribution also shows vertical changes. Generally their concentrations are low in the surface waters, where they have been utilized by the phytoplankton, and relatively high in deeper waters due to their subsequent decay or consumption (see Figure 5-11). This difference is also a seasonal phenomenon, the contrast generally being greater during periods of rapid growth.

In some instances the phytoplankton production decreases even though the nutrients are present in apparently sufficient quantities. In these instances, growth of the plants is limited by perhaps another essential element. Many elements are found in very small quantities in plants, but their significance is not fully understood; vitamins must also be important. Elements such as copper, zinc, and manganese have been shown to be beneficial to the growth of some phytoplankton. Silicon is important to many plants, especially the diatoms, which require it for shell production. In areas where the supply of silicon is low, diatoms tend to have thinner shells, apparently reflecting the scarcity of this element.

Up to now I have stressed factors that are important to the growth of plants; there are other factors, somewhat less obvious, that affect the metabolism of plants and the density of their distribution.

Salinity is important in that it influences the osmotic pressure between the plant and the environment. In this respect salinity can limit the type of plant that can grow in a particular environment.

Temperature can affect the metabolism and distribution of plants. For example, a two- or three-fold increase in metabolism may occur with a 10° C rise in temperature. Certain species of plants are common to polar areas, others to temperate or equatorial regions. Temperature also affects water viscosity, thus causing some plants to sink.

Light and, to a lesser degree, temperature, influence the seasonal changes in the phytoplankton population. In the temperate and high latitudes, phytoplankton blooms usually occur sometime in the spring, and after quickly reaching a peak number, the population rapidly decreases. This decrease is usually accompanied by a decrease in nutrient concentration. In many areas a similar, though usually smaller, increase in phytoplankton growth will occur in the autumn, followed by a decrease extending over the winter, in turn followed by the spring bloom (Figure 6-33). The exact time of high growth varies according to local conditions. It has recently been suggested by some scientists that the spring bloom is caused by an increase in the incident radiation and the development of a stable upper layer. When the wind-mixed upper layer becomes shallow enough so that the phytoplankton are

Figure 6-33 Diagrammatic representation of seasonal changes in light, nitrate and phosphate, and phytoplankton in a typical northern hemisphere temperate sea. (From Raymont, 1963.)

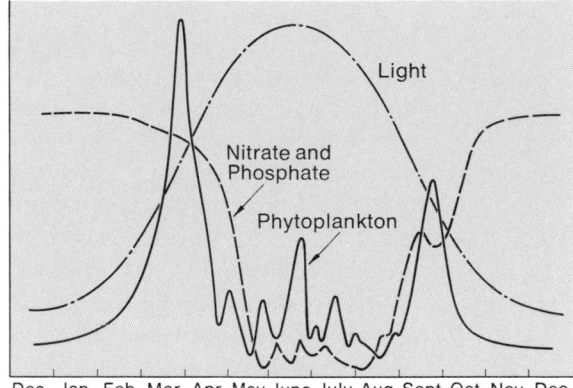

Dec. Jan. Feb. Mar. Apr. May June July Aug. Sept. Oct. Nov. Dec.

kept within the well-lighted region, a bloom occurs. If the mixing extends too deep, the phytoplankton, which are at the mercy of the current, are carried down below the aphotic zone and have insufficient light to bloom. With the advent of spring, the increase in water temperature in the upper layers causes a thermal stratification which suppresses deep vertical mixing. In regions of ice and high runoff, a sharp salinity gradient, due to the overlying fresher water, suppresses deep vertical mixing in a similar manner. This means that the plants are confined to the upper sunlit area and thus have a chance to bloom.

A high concentration of nutrients is necessary for rapid growth. The nutrients in the surface waters which were depleted by the spring and autumn blooms are replenished over the winter by mixing of the water, especially during storms. During the summer months the surface waters are heated, producing a thermocline (see Figure 7-3), or temperature stratification. This stratification restricts the transport or movement of the nutrient-rich bottom waters into the surface-water layers where they can be utilized in photosynthesis. Thus the thermocline can act as a break holding back the growth of the phytoplankton. During autumn and winter, storms and the cooling surface waters tend to break the thermocline and permit mixing of the water layers. In this manner a supply of nutrients is carried to the surface waters, sometimes resulting in the autumn bloom. This bloom is generally smaller than the spring one because less light is available.

In some areas of the ocean, enough of the nutrient-rich bottom waters are moved to the surface by various types of vertical water motion to support a large phytoplankton population. These motions include upwelling, divergence, turbulence, and convection (see p. 218). Thus, the regions of vertical motion may also be areas of high organic production.

One area, the equatorial divergence, where deeper water is brought to the surface along the equator, shows the effect of this productivity by the large quantity of shells found in the bottom sediment (see Figure 8-42). Areas of upwelling can occur along a coast where the winds blow away the surface water that, in turn, is replaced by nutrient-rich deeper water (see Figure 7-13). Some areas of high biological productivity, such as the California coast and along the west coast of South America, are due to this phenomenon. Turbulence is especially important in shallow areas characterized by strong tidal action, such as the Bay of Fundy. Convection occurs in areas having strong seasonal temperature changes. In the winter the water is cooled, becoming denser, and may eventually sink, to be relaced by nutrient-rich deeper water.

In conclusion, the growth processes of marine plants are similar to those of land plants: both must have enough light and nutrients, and an otherwise hospitable environment. The difference between marine and land plants is the result of the smaller concentration of nutrients in the ocean, and the fact that plants in the ocean have to float in the surface waters to avoid being carried to the depths where the available light is insufficient to sustain plant life. The growth of these floating plants is of paramount importance in the ocean, since all forms of animal life are dependent on them for food.

Organic Production

Organic production can vary considerably with time, location, and other factors. In the polar regions, for example, production is very high in the summer months because the light shines almost throughout the entire day. In the winter the days are essentially dark and production is very low. Production in the temperate regions was previously discussed. In the tropics, where light reaching the sea is fairly constant, production proceeds at a relatively constant rate throughout the year.

When a marine biologist talks about organic production he is referring to the amount of organic matter produced in a unit area or volume (square meter or cubic meter) during a unit time (day or year, for example), and the amount synthesized from inorganic salts by the plants. The gross production is the total amount produced, some of which will be utilized by the plant itself during its respiration process. The **standing crop** is the actual number of organisms. This number is not an absolute measure of productivity but may be related to it. One reason for this is that the production can be high but the standing crop can be kept low due to consumption of the plants by herbivores.

Organic production can be measured by several techniques, mostly based on the photosynthetic equation. Other methods include measuring the amount of nutrients going through the organic cycle and the amount of chlorophyll in the water. The latter is an indication of the number of plants present.

Another method for determining organic production consists of lowering sealed bottles containing phytoplankton and water collected from an area back into the ocean. After a specified period of time, the bottles are retrieved and the oxygen content is measured (it was also measured before the bottles were lowered). The difference in oxygen content before and after lowering can be related to photosynthesis. These measurements usually show an increase in oxygen content in the upper layers. With greater depth, a point is reached where the oxygen content in the bottles shows no further change during the experiment (Table 6-3). This depth is the compensation depth, where the amount of oxygen produced during photosynthesis equals the amount used by the plants in respiration. Below this depth, the oxygen content in the bottles can decrease. The amount of oxygen produced can be used to give an estimate of organic production. This method does not measure respiration, whereby oxygen is consumed, and therefore does not give an actual measure of organic production.

TABLE 6-3 OXYGEN CONTENT IN LOWERED BOTTLES MEASURED OVER A 24-HOUR PERIOD (DATA FROM GAARDER AND GRAN, 1927)

Depth Lowered meters	Oxygen cm^3/liter (difference)
0	+0.20
2	+0.19
5	+0.13
10	0.0 compensation depth
20	—0.03
30	—0.05
40	—0.07

To measure respiration the experiment needs to be slightly modified. Two bottles containing the phytoplankton and sea water are lowered to various depths; one bottle is covered with opaque material, the other is left clear. The change in oxygen content in the dark bottle is due to respiration by plants and bacteria. Thus the amount of oxygen lost in the dark bottles added to the amount produced in the clear bottles will indicate the gross organic production. Sources of error in these experiments include the accidental inclusion of some zooplankton in the bottles and the rapid reproduction rate of some bacteria, both of which will affect the oxygen concentration in the bottles.

One of the most widely used techniques of measuring organic production involves Carbon-14. A known amount of carbon dioxide containing Carbon-14 is added to sea water containing a known amount of normal carbon dioxide and phytoplankton. The amount of carbon fixed by the plant can be calculated by measuring the amount of Carbon-14 in the plants at the end of the experiment. An estimate or measurement of the Carbon-14 lost by the plant during respiration must be made.

The standing crop can be measured by filtering sea water and collecting the plankton. This method leaves much to be desired, as many small forms, such as coccolithophores, can flow through even the finest nets. Thus only when the phytoplankton population is composed of larger forms will filtering give an accurate estimate of the standing crop. Another method requires measurement of chlorophyll, which must come from the plant cells. Some problems with this method are that the amount of chlorophyll relative to the amount of carbon in the plant can vary and that the quantity of chlorophyll present varies with different species.

Another way of measuring organic production is to monitor the change in the total quantity of nutrients within a particular area. The loss of nutrients, such as nitrogen or phosphorus, can be assumed to be due to their being added to organic matter during photosynthesis. This method has difficulties, because one cannot accurately estimate losses due to inorganic precipitation or recycling of dead material.

In summary, essentially all methods of measuring organic production have some drawbacks. They can, however, be used to give a fairly good estimate of relative organic production in different parts of the ocean.

Variations in organic production such as latitudinal variations have been previously mentioned. There are other causes of variation. J. H. Ryther and C. S. Yentsch in 1958 compared organic production in inshore waters (less than 50 m deep), intermediate waters (100 to 200 m deep), and offshore waters (deeper than 1,000 m). They found that the daily range of the rate of production in these areas is similar, but that over a period of time such as a year, there is a considerable difference in total production (Figure 6-34). Organic production in the nearshore waters will generally exceed that of the intermediate waters and offshore waters, and intermediate waters usually exceed the offshore waters. The most reasonable explanation for this observation is that the nearshore waters are richer in nutrients than other waters. This factor appears to be more important than the fact that light penetration is less in nearshore regions than in deep-water regions, because

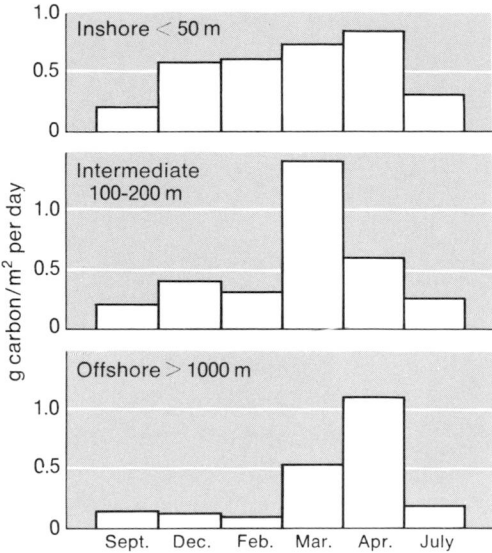

Figure 6-34 Comparisons of the daily gross organic production for various months at inshore, intermediate, and offshore stations. The production is measured in the surface waters of these areas. (From Ryther and Yentsch, 1958.)

of increased turbidity of the waters, waves, and river runoff. Strong wave action and turbidity stir up the bottom sediments and thus decrease light penetration.

Clouds can affect productivity locally. With a massive cloud cover, little light reaches the sea surface. Winds also affect productivity because choppy water reflects more light from the sea than a smooth surface. Wind also mixes the water, providing a continuous supply of nutrients to the surface waters. Temperature, through its effect on the thickness and depth of the thermocline, is also important. Nutrients will not be recycled from deeper waters if the thermocline is well defined.

The average amount of organic production in the ocean is difficult to determine accurately. Areas of high production, such as Georges Bank, can have values as great as 300 grams of carbon per square meter per year (300 g C/m²/yr). In other areas, organic production can be ¹⁄₁₀₀ of this amount. Several estimates place the average gross production of the ocean at about 50 g C/m²/yr (Table 6-4). Areas of high productivity are shown in Figure 6-35. To determine the total mass of organic production, one must consider the thickness of the photic zone (which can be as much as 200 m thick). One estimate is that 20 billion tons of carbon is incorporated into living plant material each year.

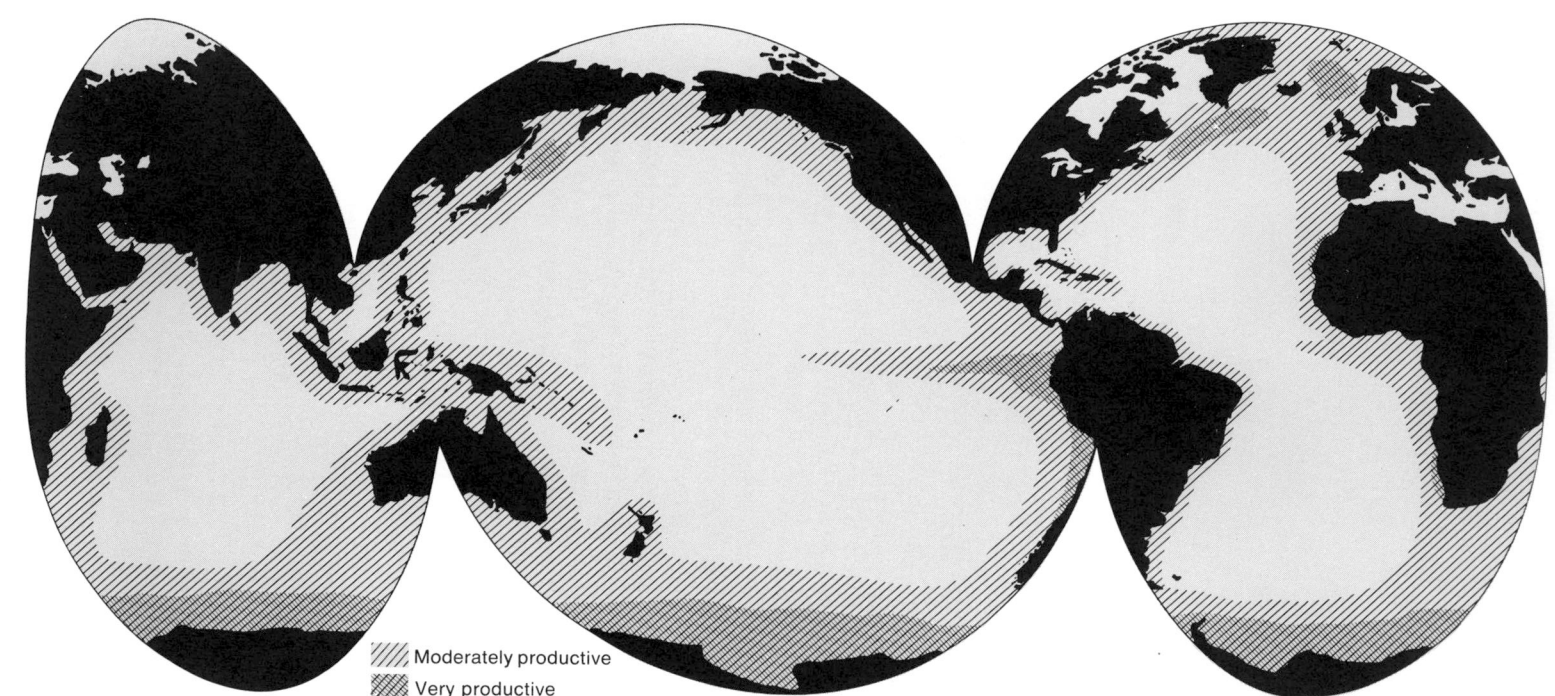

Figure 6-35 Schematic representation of the probable plant productivity of ocean areas. Light gray indicates low productive areas. (After Fye and others, 1968.)

TABLE 6-4   ORGANIC PRODUCTIVITY MEASUREMENTS FROM SOME DIFFERENT AREAS (DATA FROM RYTHER, 1963)

Area	g C/m²/day	g C/m²/yr
Open ocean waters	0.05–0.15	18–55*
Equatorial Pacific	0.50	180*
Equatorial Indian	0.20–0.25	73–90*
Upwelling areas	0.50–1.00	180–360*
Sargasso Sea	0.10–0.89	72
Continental Shelf off New York	0.33 (mean)	120
Fladen Ground, North Sea		57–82
Kuroshio Current	0.05–0.10	18–36*
Arctic Ocean	0.005–0.024	1
All oceans estimated mean:	0.137	50

* Seasonal cycle assumed negligible; annual production computed from daily rates.

Grazing In some areas an abrupt decrease in the phytoplankton population during the spring or autumn blooms does not coincide with the depletion of the nutrients. The decrease is often due to grazing (that is, the consumption of the phytoplankton by zooplankton). There is usually an inverse relationship between the numbers of zooplankton and phytoplankton in any given area. This, some scientists suggest, is because the zooplankton tend to avoid large numbers of phytoplankton. Others suggest that the plant population is kept small by the feeding activity of the zooplankton. The grazing is probably the more effective of the two. Many herbivores, such as copepods, have very large appetites for phytoplankton. Most of these animals feed by filtering water and removing phytoplankton in the process, and in this manner they can rapidly reduce a local plant population. R. H. Fleming in 1939 showed how effective their grazing can be. Assuming an initial diatom population of one million individuals, dividing at a rate of once a day, and a grazing rate by zooplankton sufficient to keep the diatom population constant, Fleming showed (Table 6-5) what would happen if the grazing rate were to double, or increase five-fold, while the diatom division rate remained unaltered. One can see from this table that it would take only a short period of time before the diatom population would be depleted.

The efficiency of zooplankton in catching phytoplankton decreases considerably as the number of available phytoplankton decreases, so some of the plants almost always survive. This is very

TABLE 6-5 THE EFFECT OF GRAZING BY ZOOPLANKTON ON A
PHYTOPLANKTON POPULATION (DATA FROM FLEMING, 1939)

| | Population | |
| | Grazing intensity doubled | Grazing intensity increased five-fold |
Time in days		
0	1,000,000	1,000,000
1	487,000	62,000
2	237,000	3,900
3	106,000	240
4	56,000	15
5	27,000	<1

important, as it permits the phytoplankton population to start increasing again when conditions become favorable.

The production of organic material is also reduced by respiration of the phytoplankton themselves. G. A. Riley in 1946 studied the effect of respiration and grazing on the rate of organic production (Figure 6-36). A model such as his can be used to predict the population of an area if the important factors like penetration of solar energy, nutrients, and quantity of zooplankton can be estimated.

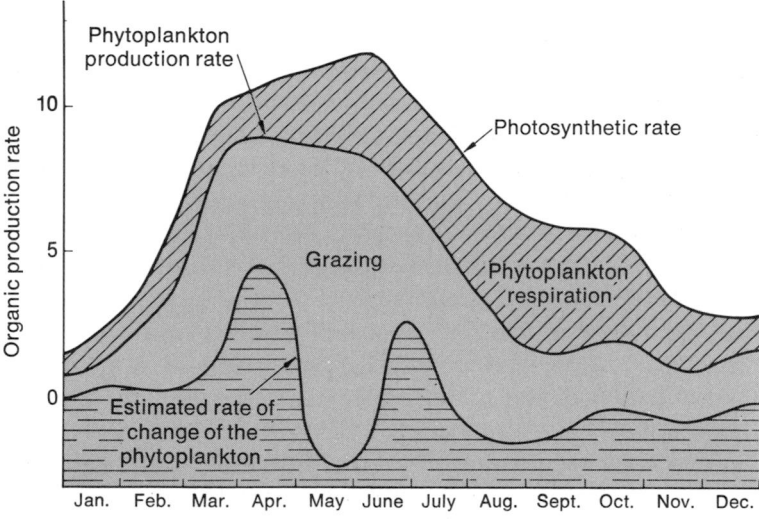

Figure 6-36 Estimated rates of production and consumption of carbon by plankton. The top curve is the photosynthetic rate. The middle curve is the phytoplankton production rate. It is obtained by subtracting the respiratory rate from the photosynthetic rate. The estimated rate of change of the phytoplankton is obtained by subtracting the zooplankton grazing from the phytoplankton production rate. (After Riley, 1946.)

Animals in the Ocean

The study of animals in the ocean has been complicated by the difficulty of sampling them adequately.

Organisms can occur in one of three different types of distribution in the ocean: even, random, or clumped (Figure 6-37). In an even distribution, each organism is an equal distance away from its neighbor. This is not a common distribution. One example is the ophiuroids, or brittle stars, that sometimes live in such proximity that each one of their arms just avoids contact with a neighbor. In a random distribution, no obvious relationship exists between the distribution of any two individuals. This distribution is very rare in the ocean. The most common type of distribution in the ocean is the clumped one, wherein animals or plants are found in patches or clumps.

The difficulties of sampling can be realized if one considers that a plankton population may have the ability to make small vertical movements in a fast-moving current. With luck one might sample such a clumped population using a plankton net, but the probability of returning to the same population and obtaining another sample is very small. The difficulty is even more pronounced with the free-swimming nekton.

Experiments show that where two similar nets are towed through the water at the same depth, but a few meters apart, the organisms caught in one net may vary greatly from those in the other net.

Organisms that live in the ocean must adapt to the conditions of their environment. Organisms living in the littoral region must withstand the large temperature and salinity changes that occur within this area. Many shelled animals must be streamlined and strengthened to withstand the crash of waves; barnacles and similar forms are strongly attached to the bottom or to rocks.

Despite the more arduous physical conditions, there are ecological advantages to living in the nearshore regions: food, oxygen, and

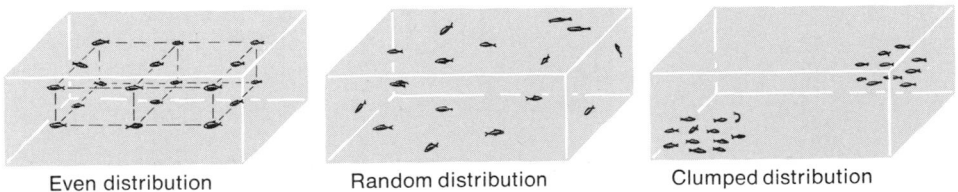

Even distribution   Random distribution   Clumped distribution

Figure 6-37   Types of distribution of animals in the sea. Most of the organisms tend to be clumped.

light are very abundant; plant growth is usually high both from floating and attached plants, producing large quantities of organic matter. These quantities are sufficient to feed the benthic population and others, as usually demonstrated by a thriving benthic community in the littoral region.

Moving out towards the deep sea, different zonations of the marine organisms can be observed. The reasons for animals inhabiting one region of the ocean rather than another are generally not fully known; however, factors such as temperature, feeding habits, and light obviously must be important.

Temperature is important, for other reasons than those previously mentioned. For example, it establishes faunal boundaries in the ocean. These boundaries exist in horizontal directions, as there are animals typical of equatorial, temperate, or polar regions, and vertically, with depth. Some nekton, however, can move freely from one area into

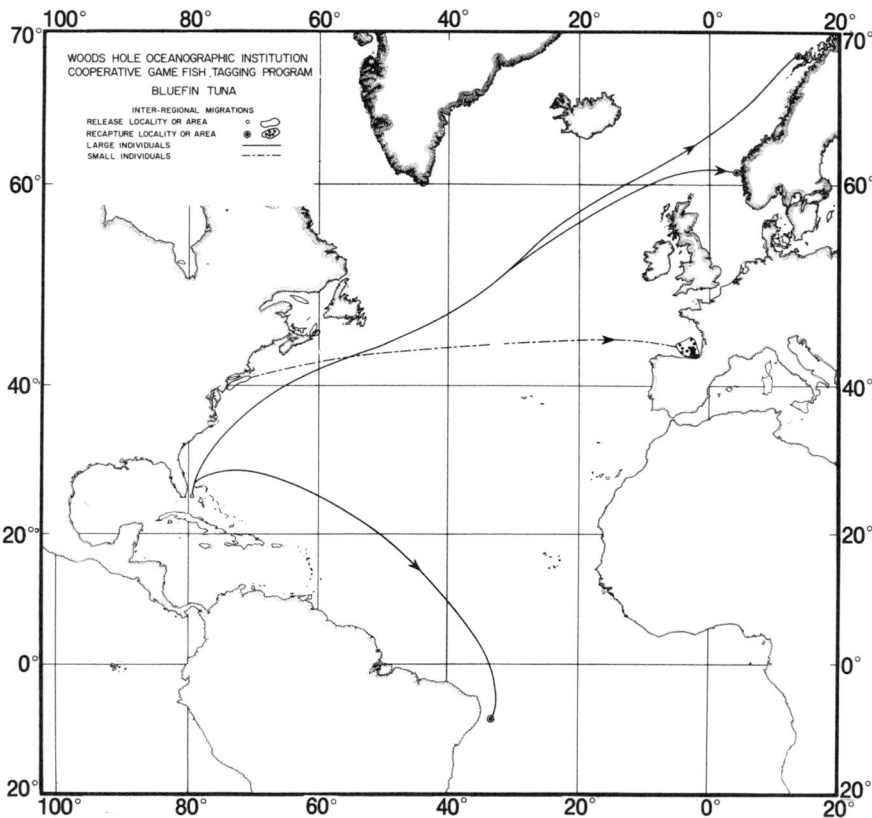

Figure 6-38 Migration of the Bluefin tuna, as determined by tagging and later capture of the tuna. (Figure courtesy of Frank J. Mather III.)

another. The migration pattern of Bluefin tuna shows that they can range over most of the ocean (Figure 6-38). Other animals are more restricted and spend their entire lives within a narrow temperature range. This is especially true of the cold-blooded animals, because they have no way of modifying their internal temperature.

Temperature also has an effect on the development of some animal forms. Fish tend to develop more rapidly and reach sexual maturity quicker in warmer regions. In colder areas the fish take longer to develop but generally grow larger.

Salinity is not an important factor in the deep ocean, because only small changes occur there. Oceanic animals generally cannot tolerate large salinity changes, and will succumb if carried by currents into an area of significantly different salinity.

If a comparison is made between similar fresh- and salt-water animals, the salt-water forms are usually larger. The reasons for this are unknown, but may be related to the greater ease of maintaining osmotic equilibrium in salt water or the greater ease with which animals respire in salt water.

Perhaps the most important factor in the distribution of animals in the sea is food. It certainly is critical in the deep sea where much of the food has to settle down through the overlying waters. It is believed that the food supply in the deep sea is very small. This probably is true in areas very far from land and areas underlying those with low organic production in the surface waters. In other localities the food supply may be adequate for the relatively small population that lives in the deep sea. Any material, such as plants or dead animals, that sinks below a depth of 2,000 m stands a good chance of reaching the bottom, because of the small number of pelagic organisms below this depth, and therefore the correspondingly small probability of the material being eaten before reaching the bottom. Bacteria can be an important source of food in the deep sea.

Almost all types of marine organisms are present in the abyssal zone; fewer are found in hadal depths. The density of life is lower in the deep parts of the ocean than in shallower areas. Animals on the deep-sea floor, as far as we know, tend to be clumped, perhaps in response to local food supplies, such as a large dead organism. The dominant benthic animals in the deep sea are the coelenterates, echinoderms (see Figure 6-19), crustaceans, and mollusks. Very little successful sampling has been carried out for abyssal and hadal pelagic forms.

An interesting question concerning the deep-sea fauna is where did they originate. One possibility is that they slowly moved down from the shallower depths. In seeking an answer one has to remember that the temperature of the ocean bottom has changed throughout geological time. There is good evidence, based on isotope studies, that the bottom water temperature may have been 7 or 8° C warmer 25 million years ago. When the temperature dropped it could have killed some earlier deep-sea forms. New animals could then have migrated down into the deep-sea area. This intriguing possibility could be checked by examining the fossil shells obtained by coring and drilling into the deep-sea floor.

Effects of Light Light is a very important factor in the ocean. The deep sea is generally thought of as being completely dark; this it is, if one only considers solar light. However, many deep-sea animals, and even some plants, have the ability to produce light, a phenomenon called **bioluminescence.** Apparently this incompletely understood phenomenon occurs in all parts of the ocean. It can be observed at sea or from beaches when certain dinoflagellates are present in the water. They can give an eerie blue color to a ship's wake or to breaking waves.

There appear to be several possible uses for bioluminescence. In the dark sea, it may help individuals of the same species to locate each other for breeding. In some deep-sea fish, light is used for feeding: these animals have evolved light organs to attract other creatures. Some squid use bioluminescence for protection: when attacked they eject a cloud of glowing material that often confuses their antagonists. But in many animals of the sea, such as the planktonic dinoflagellates, the function of bioluminescence is not understood.

An interesting phenomenon of the ocean that appears to be related to light is the **deep-scattering layer.** The deep-scattering layer was first observed as echoes on depth sounders. Observers on ships traveling in water several hundreds or thousands of meters deep would notice a broad area of sound reflection that rose toward the surface at dusk and sank at dawn (Figure 6-39). At first, the reflection was confused with the bottom. Some scattering layers appeared as even bands of faint echoes, others as dark individual inverted U-shaped echoes.

The scientists' first task was to determine what caused these layers. Net tows made in the layers would sometimes collect euphausids, other times fish or squid. Therefore, although the organically-caused, sound-reflecting deep-scattering layer occurs in many areas of the ocean, it is not always caused by the same type of organism. One type of scattering layer, called "Alexander's Acres" (Figure 6-40) has been observed by scientists in ALVIN. This type of layer appears to be related to individual schools of animals. Observations from the submersible showed that the cause of this layer was large schools of fish called myctophids or lantern fish.

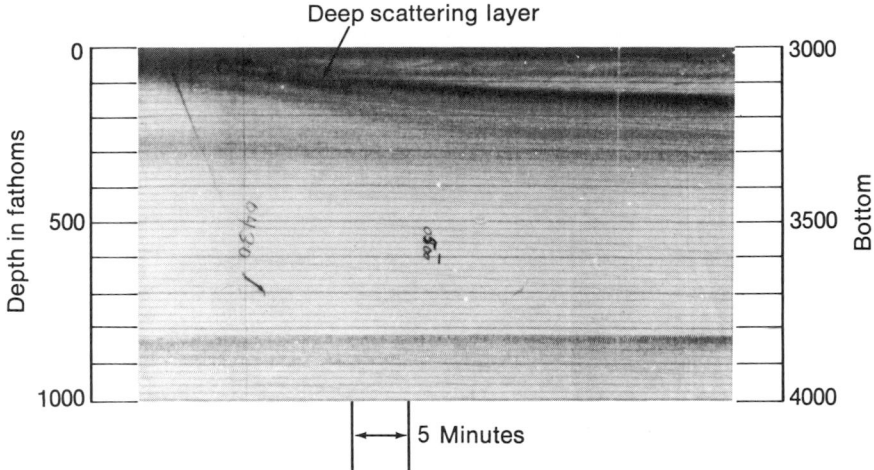

Figure 6-39 Deep-scattering layer observed in the eastern Pacific. The descent of the layer (seen on the upper left of the record) coincides with sunrise. Note that once the sun rises the layer stays at a depth of about 150 fathoms. Another layer at about 300 fathoms has remained stationary during the night and sunrise. (Photograph courtesy of R. H. Backus.)

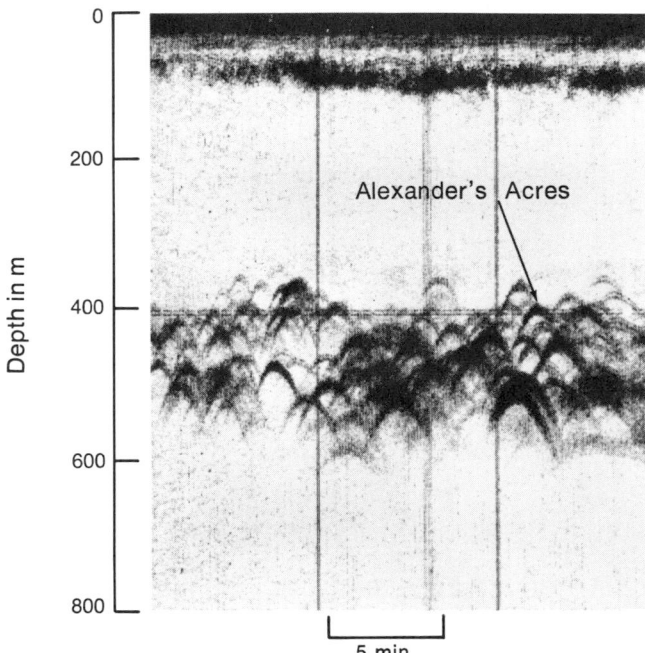

Figure 6-40 Echo-sounder record showing the deep-scattering layer called "Alexander's Acres." Note the difference between this layer and the one shown in Figure 6-39. (Photograph courtesy of R. H. Backus.)

The second question concerning deep-scattering layers is why do these animals migrate up and down, sometimes as fast as 5 m per minute. Since the layers usually move up when the sun goes down and down when the sun rises, a reasonable explanation is that the movements are in response to light. Sometimes when a bright moon is present the layers will descend slightly. The answer is probably not quite so simple—other factors such as internal physiological rhythms and feeding may also be important. With the increased use of submersibles, more definitive answers should be soon available.

THE FOOD CYCLE

Up to now we have discussed the different organisms and their responses to various factors of the environment. Here we consider the fundamental relationship in the sea, the food cycle. The cycle starts with the production of organic matter by phytoplankton. The organic matter is then consumed by herbivores, the zooplankton. The herbivores are then consumed by a higher form of animal (like sardines), which ultimately is consumed by a larger predator (like tuna). This highly simplified scheme is shown in Figure 6-41. By this method, it is estimated that 1,000 kg of plants will produce 100 kg of herbivores, which in turn produce 10 kg of filter feeders and 1 kg of the larger predators. But there are many other complex relationships that exist in the sea. A more complicated and realistic picture is shown in Figure 6-42. The diagrammatic representation shows the importance of the nutrients and bacteria in the cycle.

The oceanic food cycle differs from the land cycle, mainly because in the ocean the primary producers, plants, must be small and

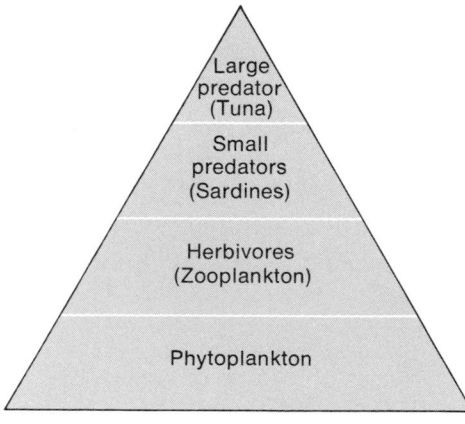

Figure 6-41 A simplified illustration showing the different feeding levels in the ocean.

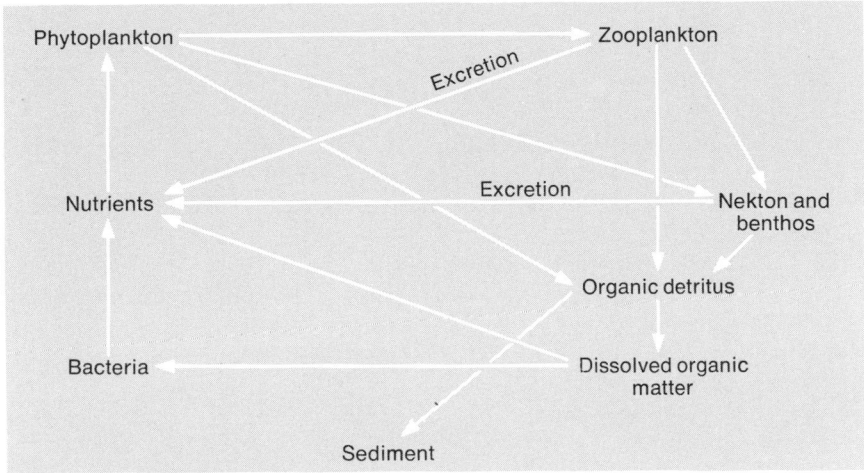

Figure 6-42   A diagrammatic representation of the cycle of life in the ocean. (After Raymont, 1963.)

must float. Animals have evolved that will feed on the microscopic plants, thereby concentrating the organic matter. Because plants are so numerous, it follows that the consumers of plants must also be numerous.

To completely understand the food relationship between the plankton, nekton, and benthos one should examine the feeding habits of all the individual species, a very large task.

The question of efficiency (does 1,000 kg of phytoplankton produce 100 kg of zooplankton?) is also very complex. The exact efficiency is variable, but each additional step in the cycle does cause a net loss of organic material. Generally, therefore, there is a low degree of efficiency in the transfer of organic matter from the phytoplankton to the fish. The point of efficiency is one that man must consider if he wants to feed the world's population from the sea. Perhaps we should either take our food from a lower part of the food cycle or find a way to make the transfer of organic matter more efficient.

SUGGESTED FURTHER READING

Berrill, N. J. *The Living Tide*. New York: Dodd, Mead, 1951.
Berrill, N. J. *The Life of the Ocean*. New York: McGraw-Hill, 1966.
Bruun, A., and others., eds. *The GALATHEA Deep Sea Expedition* New York.
    Macmillan, 1956.

Buchsbaum, R. *Animals Without Backbones*. Chicago: University of Chicago Press, 1948.

Burton, M. *Under the Sea*. New York: Franklin Watts, Inc., 1960.

Coker, R. D. *This Great and Wide Sea*. Chapel Hill: The University of North Carolina Press, 1947.

Darwin, C. *The Voyage of the BEAGLE*. New York: Harper and Row, 1959.

Duddington, C. L. *Flora of the Sea*. New York: Crowell, 1967.

Fraser, J. *Nature Adrift: The Story of Marine Plankton*. London: G. T. Foulis and Co., 1962.

Gilbert, P. W., ed. *Sharks and Survival*. Boston: Heath, 1963.

Hardy, A. C. *The Open Sea: Its Natural History*. Boston: Houghton Mifflin, 1965.

Harrison, R. J., and King, J. E. *Marine Mammals*. London: Hutchinson University Library, 1965.

Harvey, H. W. *Chemistry and Fertility of Sea Waters*. London: Cambridge University Press, 1966.

Idyll, C. P. *Abyss: The Deep Sea and the Creatures That Live in It*. New York: Crowell, 1964.

Jackson, D. F., ed. *Algae and Man*. New York: Plenum Press, 1963.

Kellogg, W. N. *Porpoises and Sonar*. Chicago: University of Chicago Press, 1961.

Lewin, R. A., ed. *Physiology and Biochemistry of Algae*. New York: Academic Press, 1963.

Marshall, N. B. *Aspects of Deep Sea Biology*. New York: Philosophical Library, Inc., 1954.

Miller, R. C. *The Sea*. New York: Random House, 1966.

Murray, J., and Hjort, J. *The Depths of the Ocean: A General Account of the Modern Science of Oceanography Based Largely on the Scientific Researches of the Norwegian Steamer MICHAEL SARS in the North Atlantic*. London: Macmillan, 1912.

Nicol, J. A. C. *The Biology of Marine Animals*. New York: Interscience, 1960.

Ray, C., and Ciampi, E. *The Underwater Guide to Marine Life*. New York: A. S Barnes, 1956.

Raymont, J. E. G. *Plankton and Productivity in the Oceans*. New York: Pergamon Press, 1963.

Ricketts, E. F., and Calvin, J. *Between Pacific Tides*. Stanford: Stanford University Press, 1948.

Sverdrup, H. U., Johnson, M. W., and Fleming, R. H. *The Oceans: Their Physics, Chemistry, and General Biology*. New York: Prentice-Hall, 1942.

Teal, J., and Teal, M. *Life and Death of the Salt Marsh*. Boston: Little, Brown, 1969.

Chapter 7
PHYSICAL
OCEANOGRAPHY

INTRODUCTION

Physical oceanography combines the study and measurements of the physical properties of the sea, and their variations in time and space, with a theoretical study of the processes that control the state of those physical properties. The first aspect is mainly a description of the distribution and motion of the ocean. The second aspect is associated with theoretical physics.

Physical oceanography is probably the field of oceanography least dependent on the others, but it cannot be wholly divorced from them. For example, understanding water chemistry is important in determining sea-water density, and variations in density, in turn, affect the circulation and currents of the ocean. Some ocean currents were first traced by means of the marine organisms living in them. Distribution of nutrients (and therefore the areas of biological activity) in the ocean is, in part, controlled by the physical conditions of the sea. Currents, either catastrophic ones such as turbidity currents, or regular ones, distribute sediment over the ocean. The bottom topography of the ocean, which may be modified by currents, can also affect the large scale oceanic circulation.

HISTORY OF PHYSICAL OCEANOGRAPHY

Man's first interest in the sea was a practical one. He wanted to know the best way of going from one place to another. Early exploration of the sea probably started with the Phoenicians and the Greeks who established lines of commerce in the Mediterranean and Atlantic several hundred years before the birth of Christ. Much of the information obtained by early sailors was not recorded, but kept as a state or family secret. It wasn't until the fifteenth and sixteenth centuries that men developed a realistic understanding of the dimensions and shape of the ocean. The voyages of Magellan, Diaz, Columbus, and, later, of Drake and Cook were of primary importance to this understanding.

The first expedition to measure the depths of the ocean was that of Sir Clarke Ross from 1839 to 1843. Early attempts at mapping oceanic currents were made by Benjamin Franklin and later by Findlay and Maury. Maury examined log books of numerous ships and noted that oceanic currents are related to the wind. His published findings (1855) combined with Findlay's of 1854, and those of the later Challenger Expedition (1872–1876), provided a basis for understanding the dynamic structure of the ocean. It was not until the German Meteor Expedition (1925–1927) that oceanographic expeditions changed from those of a world-wide and general nature to those of a more localized and detailed nature. The members of the Meteor Expedition studied the South Atlantic Ocean and deduced deep oceanic circulation by measurements of temperature and salinity. The British vessels DISCOVERY and DISCOVERY II, and the American ship CARNEGIE, also contributed to the descriptive knowledge of the ocean.

Theoretical consideration of the oceans proceeded at a slower pace than the descriptive. In 1942, Sverdrup, Johnson, and Fleming published their monumental work *The Oceans: Their Physics, Chemistry, and General Biology* which summarized most of what was known of the oceans up to that time.

PRESENT OBJECTIVES

In recent years there has been an increase in the amount of research emphasizing the theoretical causes for the observed distribution of various sea-water properties, circulation patterns, the origin of waves, and other problems. The development of new sensing devices (see Chapter 4) permits accurate and inplace measurements of temperature, salinity, currents, and other variables. Advances in data processing, especially use of modern computers, can allow meaningful results to be obtained quickly, in some instances even before the vessel has left the study area.

Several problems, such as large scale oceanic circulation, can be best solved by synoptic measurements (many measurements at the same time over a large area). Synoptic observations in the past required numerous expensive surface ships, but recently developed fixed buoys and platforms used in conjunction with airplanes, submarines, and surface vessels make the procedure today much more efficient (Figure 7-1).

Physical oceanographers are becoming increasingly interested in the interrelationships of the atmosphere and the ocean. These interrelationships are important controls in both atmospheric and oceanic circulation. Understanding and prediction of weather, both oceanic and terrestrial, await more thorough study of the air-sea interactions (Figure 7-2). Such studies can be aided by the use of unattended buoys or satellites that can transmit information directly to the laboratory.

The ability to predict in advance characteristics of the ocean is very important. At present, only tides, surface waves, and **tsunamis** (large ocean waves produced by submarine earthquakes) can be predicted. Predictability of the characteristics of the upper layers of the ocean would also be valuable for studies of sound propagation and some marine biological problems.

Many other important problems exist for the physical oceanographer. The effects of pollution, a recently recognized problem, have

Figure 7-1   Launching of a telemetering buoy from a research vessel. This buoy is used to trace currents, and it sends the data to the ship by radio. (Photograph courtesy of Woods Hole Oceanographic Institution.)

already reached the deep sea. Lead from fuel burned by boat engines and radioactive isotopes from explosions of nuclear devices can be measured in the ocean. The interactions of ocean bottom sediments and the sonar beams bounced off them are relatively unknown and have defense implications, because sonar, besides being used in echo sounding, is also used in searching for submarines. Mixing processes in the ocean, which are turbulent processes, are also poorly understood, but detailed measurements of temperature and salinity have begun to reveal an interesting microstructure in the ocean.

Figure 7-2 Waterspouts (photographed off the Bahamas) provide an excellent example of the interaction between the ocean and the atmosphere. (Photograph courtesy of Captain G. Stephen Gwin.)

GENERAL CHARACTERISTICS OF THE OCEAN

Salinity

Three very important properties of sea water are salinity, temperature, and density. Salinity is defined as the total amount of dissolved material, in parts per thousand by weight, in one kilogram of sea water when all the bromine and iodine have been replaced by the equivalent amount of chlorine, all the carbonate has been converted to oxide, and all the organic matter has been oxidized. It generally is impractical to analyze for every component of sea water; usually just a single element related to salinity, such as chlorine, is measured. This technique is possible because the major components of sea water have an essentially constant ratio to each other (Forchhammer's Principle, see p. 102). Salinity is now determined mainly by measuring the electrical conductivity of sea water, a method accurate to $0.002^0/_{00}$.

The salinity of surface waters depends mainly on the difference between evaporation and precipitation. Other less important factors are freezing of ice (which increases the salinity of sea water because the salts are left behind), runoff from land, and melting of sea ice. In areas of high evaporation, such as the Red Sea, salinity can be as high as $40^0/_{00}$. However, in most parts of the ocean the salinity range is from 33 to $37^0/_{00}$, with an average value of about $35^0/_{00}$. The higher salinity values occur near the arid equatorial areas, the lower values near the polar regions.

The vertical distribution of salinity, which is very similar to the temperature distribution, can be expressed as three or four zones (Figures 7-3 and 7-4):

1. A well-mixed surface zone, 50 to 100 m thick, of generally uniform salinity

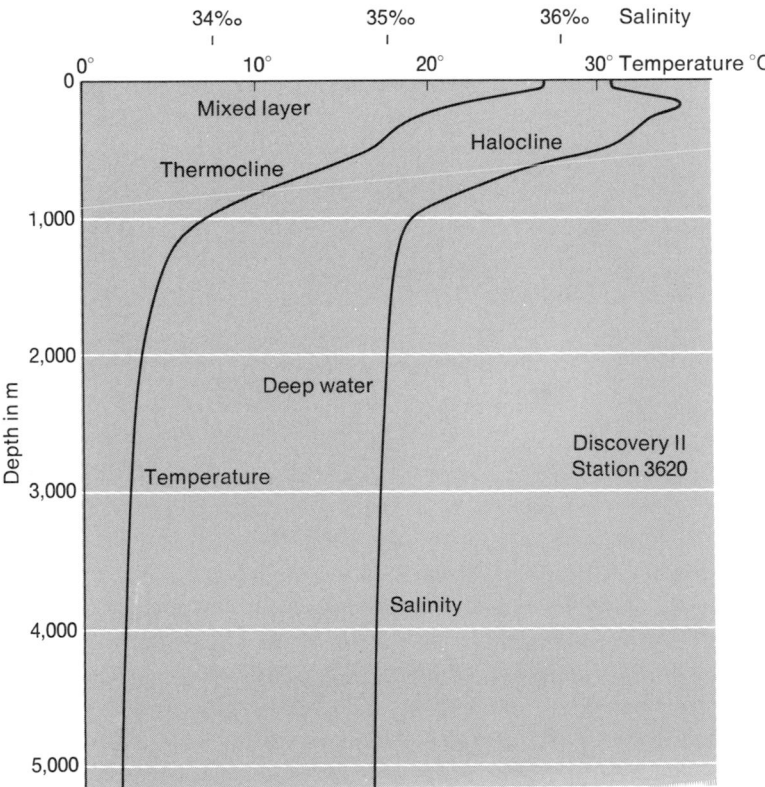

Figure 7-3 Typical salinity and temperature profiles. Data from DISCOVERY II, Station 3620. (After Fuglister, 1960.)

2. A zone with a relatively large salinity change, called the halocline
3. A thick zone of relatively uniform salinity, extending to the ocean bottom
4. A zone at a depth of 600 to 1,000 m in some areas, where there is a pronounced minimum salinity.

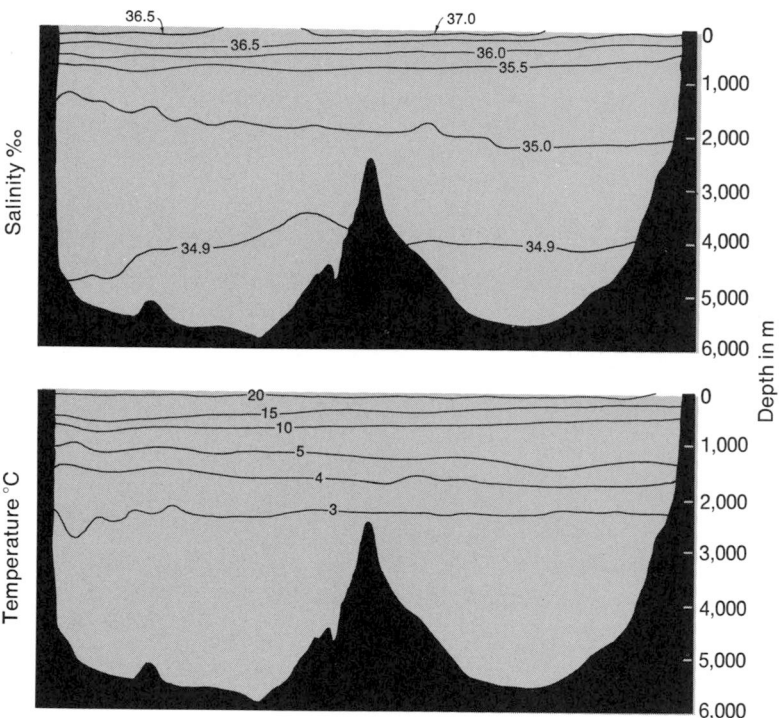

Figure 7-4   Salinity and temperature section across the North Atlantic. Section runs west to east at about 24° N. (After Fuglister, 1960.)

Temperature

Temperature is probably the most commonly measured oceanographic variable. It is usually measured with mercury thermometers that are mounted on water sampling devices, such as Nansen bottles (Figure 7-5). The water obtained in the Nansen bottle is generally used for salinity determinations, as well as for oxygen and nutrient measurements. Usually two thermometers are used with each Nansen bottle. When the bottles are overturned by a "messenger" sent down the wire, which tips the bottle over, the thermometers are inverted, breaking the mercury column in the thermometer and preserving the tem-

Figure 7-5 Nansen bottle being used on a hydrographic station. Scientist's left hand is on the container that holds the two reversing thermometers. (Photograph courtesy of Woods Hole Oceanographic Institution.)

perature reading at that moment. One of the thermometers is protected against water pressure while the other is exposed to the pressure. The pressure will affect the reading on the exposed, or unprotected, thermometer and the resulting difference in readings between the two thermometers will indicate the pressure.

The lowering of numerous Nansen bottles (usually spaced from 5 to 400 or 500 m apart) with their attached inverting thermometers constitutes a hydrographic station. Set up as early as the Challenger Expedition, hydrographic stations have produced much information about the internal structure of the ocean.

Recently devised instrumentation, using numerous temperature sensors and transmitting devices, permits continuous measurements of temperature to be made. New instruments easily allow electronic processing and direct reading of the data. Devices such as infrared radiometers can, when used from an airplane, give instantaneous readings of the temperature of the sea surface.

The surface of the ocean is heated by (1) radiation from the sky and sun, (2) conduction of heat from the atmosphere, and (3) condensation of water vapor.

The sea surface is cooled by (1) back radiation from the sea surface to the atmosphere, (2) conduction of heat back to the atmosphere, and (3) evaporation.

Below the sea surface horizontal currents can transfer heat from one area to another. Currents can bring bodies of water having different temperatures in contact with each other.

The surface temperature of the ocean is closely related to latitude and time of year, more heat per unit area being received at the equator than at the poles (Figure 7-6), and in the summer than in winter. The usual temperature distribution with depth (see Figures 7-3 and 7-4) consists of three layers:

1. A warm, well-mixed surface layer, from 10 to perhaps 500 m thick.
2. A transition layer, below the surface layer, called the main thermocline, where the temperature decreases rapidly. The transition layer can be 500 to 1,000 m thick.
3. A layer as much as several kilometers thick which is cold and relatively homogenous and where the temperature slowly decreases toward the bottom.

The main thermocline is a layer of water having a steeper vertical temperature gradient than that of the water above or below it. This thermocline is virtually absent in polar regions, where most of the ocean surface is covered with ice in winter and where solar radiation is small in summer. In areas such as the tropics, the thermocline may rise to near the surface. Areas having a strong seasonal warming also have a temporary or seasonal thermocline in the surface layers.

Temperature and salinity values below the thermocline usually show a very close relationship. This relationship can be used to define different water types or masses. Temperature-salinity relationships can

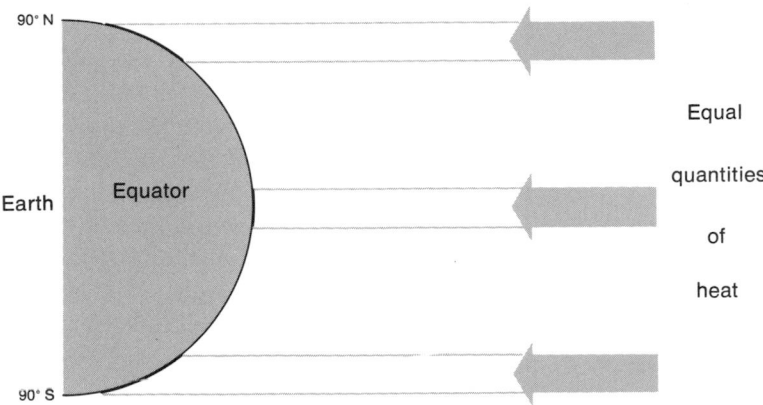

Figure 7-6   The difference in heat received per unit area for polar and equatorial regions.

also indicate the source and mixing of water masses. They are especially important in studies of deep-ocean circulation.

Density

A third important property of the ocean to the physical oceanographer is density. The density of sea water (the mass per unit volume) ranges from about 1.02 to 1.07 g per cm³. It is determined by three variables whose interactions are complex: salinity, temperature and pressure.[1] In general, density increases with increasing salinity, increasing pressure or depth, and decreasing temperature. The colder, deeper, more saline water is also usually the densest water. Density of sea water can be calculated if the three variables are known precisely.

Changes in sea-water density result from processes such as evaporation or heating that occur at the sea surface. We see in subsequent sections that the deep, or thermohaline, circulation of the ocean is due to density differences in the ocean.

There is a tendency, because of gravity and buoyancy forces, for denser water to sink and less dense or lighter water to rise to the ocean's surface. This movement will produce a stable density stratification (increasing density with increasing depth) of sea water. About the upper 100 m of the ocean are influenced by wind and waves and therefore are well mixed and relatively uniform. Below this surface layer, large changes in temperature (the thermocline) and salinity (the

[1] Pressure in the ocean is expressed in decibars (a decibar is approximately ⅒ normal atmospheric pressure). A decibar is nearly equal to the weight of a column of sea water one meter high acting on a surface of one square centimeter.

halocline) produce a corresponding change and increase in density (the pycnocline). Below the pycnocline are the deep, dense waters of the ocean.

The large density differences defining the stable pycnocline effectively isolate the surface waters from the deep waters of the ocean, except in the polar regions. There the thermocline, halocline, and pycnocline are absent and a strong density stratification does not exist. The absence of the stratification allows exchange between the atmosphere and the deep ocean water (see next section). The increase in oxygen concentration in deep waters (see Figure 5-11) is generally thought to be due to exchange processes occurring in polar areas. These polar areas apparently are the source of the deep waters of the ocean.

INTERACTION OF THE ATMOSPHERE AND THE OCEAN

Interactions between the atmosphere and the ocean are complex, and in many instances it is difficult to establish cause and effect. The circulation of the ocean is dependent mainly on two atmospheric factors, wind and heating of the ocean. The ocean, which can store heat much better than the atmosphere or land, absorbs more heat per unit area at the equator than at the poles (Figure 7-6). This heat will be transferred to the colder areas of the ocean by convection, or movement

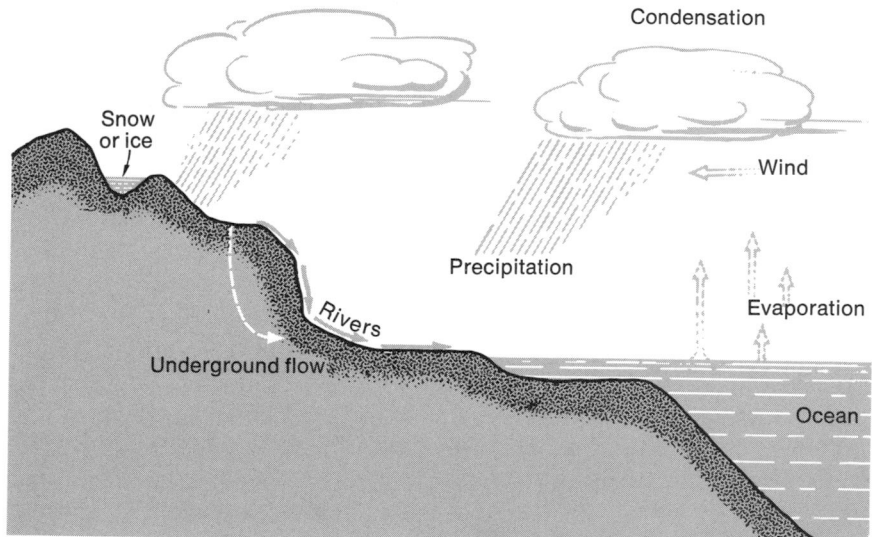

Figure 7-7 The hydrological cycle. For simplicity, biological utilization by plants and animals is not shown.

of the water. The heat-storing capacity of the ocean is very important in modifying and influencing the continental climate. This influence can be noted on the west coasts of land in intermediate latitudes of the northern hemisphere, such as California and England, where the dominantly onshore winds transport warm air from the sea to the land.

The wind blowing on the ocean generates waves, mixes the surface waters, and removes water vapor from the sea surface. The water vapor is taken into the atmosphere by evaporation and is eventually transferred to the land as precipitation. This cycle, called the hydrological cycle (Figure 7-7), is completed when the water is returned to the ocean.

Near coasts the wind may cause the surface waters to move offshore and be replaced by colder, nutrient-rich, deeper waters. This upwelling, can, because it supplies nutrients to the surface waters, produce rich fishing areas.

The interaction of the atmosphere with the ocean produces two main types of circulation: a wind-driven circulation, and a thermohaline or density circulation. The wind-driven circulation is stronger than the density circulation; its major importance, however, is restricted to the upper 1,000 m. The thermohaline circulation, on the other hand, is mainly a deep-sea circulation.

Wind-Driven Circulation

The atmosphere, like the ocean, receives a larger quantity of solar radiation per unit area in the equatorial regions than in the polar regions. To maintain the earth's heat balance some of this heat is transferred to the higher latitudes by the atmosphere. If the earth were not rotating a simple circulation would probably exist between the equator and the poles (Figure 7-8). The air at the equator is heated, expands, and rises, and because of expansion, it creates a low pressure area. Cooler air from the surrounding area will move toward the low pressure area at the equator and will in turn be heated, expand, and rise. At the poles the air is cooled, contracts, and sinks, creating a high pressure area. The polar air moves toward the equator (from high to low pressure), resulting in a steady wind from the north in the northern hemisphere.

This simple, theoretical one-cell model of atmospheric circulation should be developed into a more complex three-cell model for a rotating earth, because the air movement will have an apparent deflection due to the earth's rotation. This deflection, known as the **Coriolis force** (Figure 7-9), will apparently cause the air to turn toward the right in the northern hemisphere and toward the left in the southern hemisphere. Thus, instead of the wind flowing in a straight

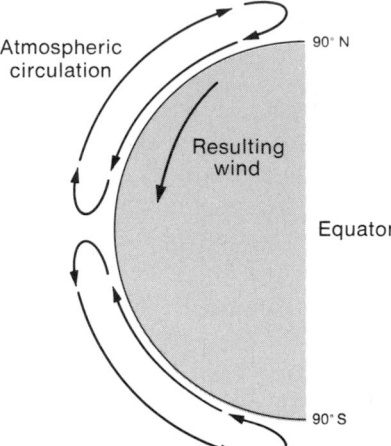

Figure 7-8 Possible atmospheric circulation and resulting winds for a non-rotating earth.

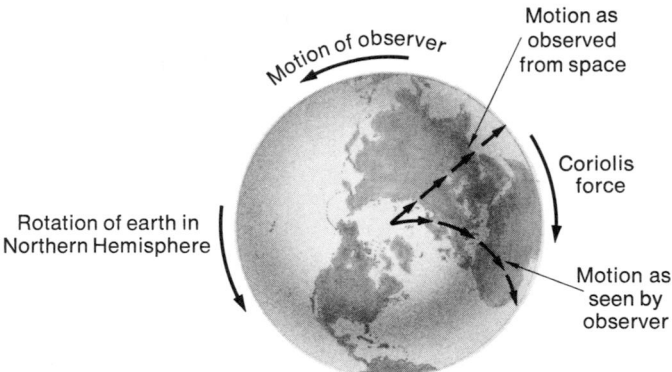

Figure 7-9 Deflecting or Coriolis force due to the earth's rotation.

line along the pressure gradient from high to low pressure, it will appear to be deflected into curved paths. In the northern hemisphere in the three-cell model, rising warm air from the equator will start to flow north toward the pole. As it leaves the equator it is deflected toward the right and cools and eventually descends at about 30° N latitude. Part of this air completes the gyre, or circular trip, and heads south toward the equator and another part continues northward toward the pole. The air traveling toward the pole is warmed and again deflected to the right, forming another cell. In the polar region the air moves downward at the pole and travels south until it is heated sufficiently to rise again at about 60° N. The resulting winds and circulation cells are shown in Figure 7-10. Areas of rising or sinking air generally are areas of calm winds, such as the doldrums along the equator and the horse latitudes at about 30° N and S. Air traveling

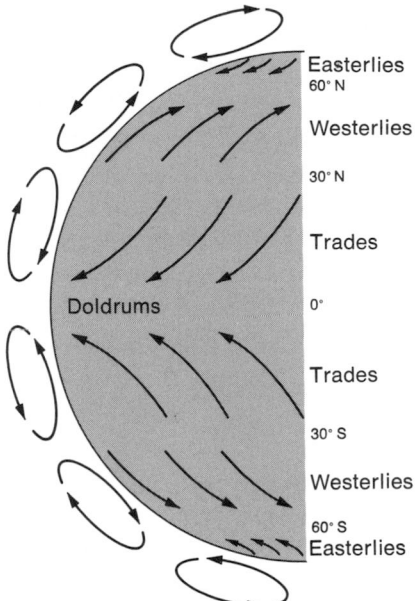

Easterlies
60° N

Westerlies

30° N

Trades

0°

Doldrums

Trades

30° S

Westerlies

60° S
Easterlies

Figure 7-10   Atmospheric circulation
and resulting winds.

along the earth's surface generally produces steady and intense winds, such as the westerlies[2] and the trades.

The wind system described above exerts a stress on the ocean's surface and produces the wind-driven circulation of the ocean (Figure 7-11). The easterly trade winds form the equatorial currents common to all oceans. In the Atlantic and Pacific Oceans these currents are intersected by land and are deflected to the north and south. These deflected currents travel along the western parts of the oceans and are sometimes called the western boundary currents. They are among the largest and strongest currents in the ocean. One, the Gulf Stream (Table 7-1), transports more than 100 times the combined out-flow of all the rivers of the world. The western boundary currents are in large measure due to the variation of Coriolis force with latitude. The currents are driven across the ocean by the westerly wind and form currents that flow back into the equatorial region, thus completing the large gyre. Gyres of this type occur in the subtropic regions of the north and south Pacific, the north and south Atlantic, and the south Indian Oceans. The northern and southern gyres of the oceans are separated by an eastward flowing counter current. A similar gyre, although changing direction every six months, is found in the north Indian Ocean. The change in direction is due to half-yearly reversals in the atmospheric circulation pattern, called **monsoons.** Smaller and

[2] When a meteorologist refers to a west wind, he means that it blows from the west; when an oceanographer refers to a western flowing current, he means that it goes to the west.

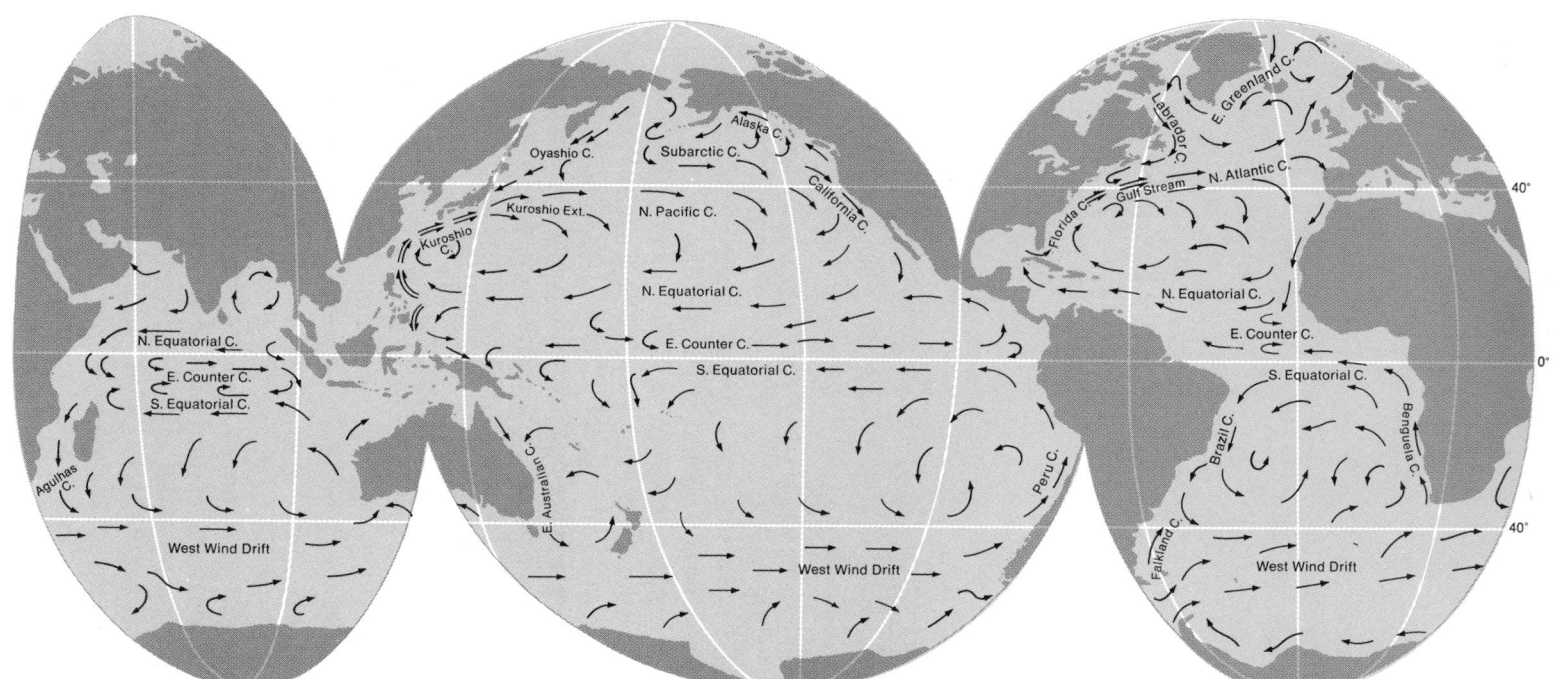

Figure 7-11   Major surface currents of the ocean. Winter conditions for the Indian Ocean. (After Sverdrup and others, 1942.)

weaker gyres are found in the northern subpolar regions of the Atlantic and Pacific Oceans. No gyres, however, occur in the southern subpolar region, probably because there are no land barriers to obstruct the flow of water and create a gyre. Therefore, the Antarctic Circumpolar or West Wind Drift flows completely around the world.

TABLE 7-1   VELOCITY AND TRANSPORT OF SOME OF THE MAJOR CURRENTS IN THE OCEAN (DATA FROM WARREN, 1966)

Current	Maximum Velocity cm/sec	Transport (m^3/sec)
Gulf Stream	200–300	100×10^6
North Equatorial Pacific	20	45×10^6
Kuroshio	>200	50×10^6
Equatorial undercurrent	100–150	40×10^6
Brazil	—	10×10^6
Antarctic Circumpolar (West Wind Drift)	—	100×10^6
Peru or Humbolt	—	20×10^6

The wind-driven circulation of the ocean is caused by differences in water pressure. These differences are the result of density variations in the sea and changes in the slope of the sea surface due to winds. The winds blowing on the water will cause the water to move and pile up in the direction that the wind is blowing (Figure 7-12a). This creates a pressure difference between the high and low areas (higher pressure where the water is piled up). The pressure difference generates a force that tends to push the surface water back towards the region of lower pressure. In other words, the water tends to go downhill or down the slope (Figure 7-12b). However, because of Coriolis force, the moving water or current will be deflected to the right in the northern hemisphere. If the pressure difference is balanced by the

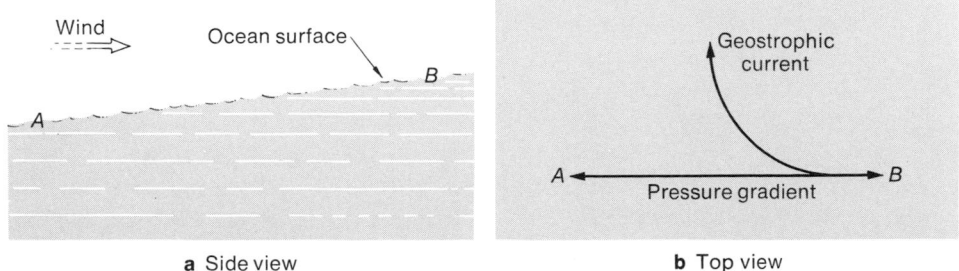

a Side view   **b** Top view

Figure 7-12   (a) Sloping sea surface produced by the wind blowing on the sea. (b) Pressure gradient and resulting geostrophic current (for northern hemisphere) produced from the situation shown in (a).

Coriolis force the current is called a **geostrophic current.** Oceanographers can calculate the geostrophic current if they know the horizontal and vertical distribution of water density. The density is determined from careful measurements of temperature and salinity. The calculated currents generally agree with the measured currents.

Most of the surface currents in the ocean are geostrophic, but some newly discovered currents may in part be nongeostrophic. These are often called°undercurrents. One of these, the Equatorial undercurrent in the Pacific, flows from west to east on the equator 100 m or more below the ocean surface. This current, also called the Cromwell current, is 300 km wide, only a few hundred meters in thickness, and has velocities as high as 3 knots (150 cm/sec). Usually the undercurrents are flowing in a direction opposite to the surface current. The origin of undercurrents and their relationships to the overlying water are not yet understood.

The action of the wind on the sea surface, besides causing horizontal movement of water, may also produce vertical motion of water. Upwelling or upward motion of water can occur when prevailing winds blow parallel to the coast. The motion of the water in many instances will be offshore (Figure 7-13a) due to Coriolis force, and submarine waters will be brought to the surface. If these subsurface waters are high in nutrient content an area of high biological productivity may result. Sinking of surface water can happen by essentially the same process, if the water flows toward the land (Figure 7-13b).

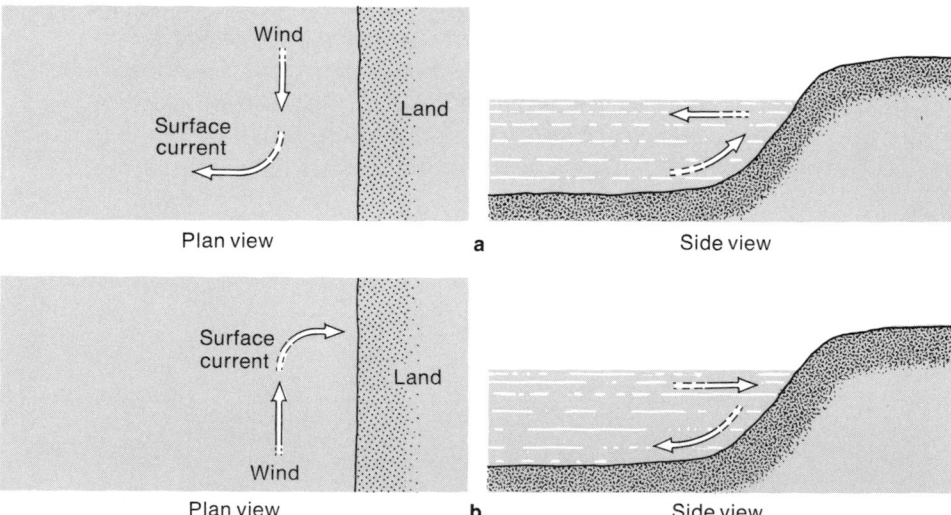

Figure 7-13 (a) Upwelling or rising of surface waters due to nearshore winds. (b) Sinking of surface waters due to nearshore winds.

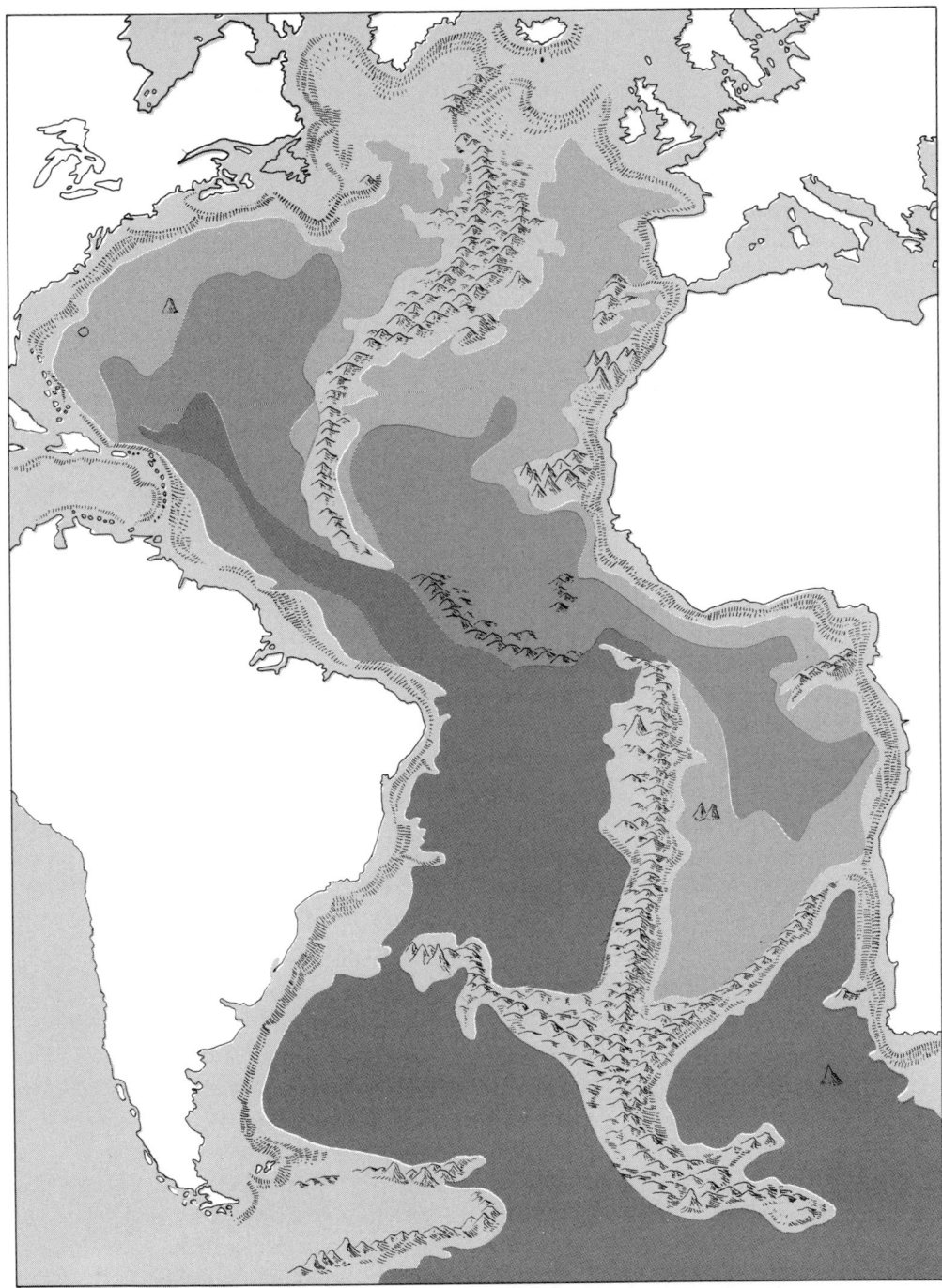

Figure 7-14   Deep circulation, at 12,000 ft, of the Antarctic Bottom Water. Lowering the sea to this level exposes the Mid-Atlantic Ridge, a mountain range which channels the flow of the bottom water to the west until it reaches a pass at the equator. The darkest tone indicates the pure bottom water before its gradual dilution. (After Stommel, 1955.)

Thermohaline Circulation

The thermohaline circulation, generally a deep-water process, is mainly caused by variations in water density. The density differences that drive this circulation generally occur at the sea-air interface. Thus the wind-driven and thermohaline circulation systems are related.

Direct observations of the deep-water thermohaline circulation are difficult to make, mainly because the circulation rate is very slow and does not affect surface vessels. Radiocarbon measurements (see p. 130) suggest current velocities of fractions of a centimeter per second for the Pacific, and somewhat higher velocities for the Atlantic. There are other data which suggest that these currents are stronger, perhaps as high as 10 to 20 cm per second. Most of the information concerning the thermohaline circulation comes from subsurface measurements of temperature, salinity, and dissolved oxygen. By measuring bottom temperature and salinity in the South Atlantic, during the Meteor Expedition, Wüst was able to deduce bottom circulation in this part of the ocean. Part of the deep circulation of the Atlantic is shown in Figure 7-14.

The thermohaline circulation is mainly a convection process whereby dense cold water formed in high latitudes sinks and slowly flows towards the equator. Apparently most of the deep water of the ocean is formed, or assumed its characteristics in two places: in the Norwegian Sea area, and in the Antarctic.

In the North Atlantic, cold heavy water sinks and moves south, near the bottom, across the equator (Figure 7-15). This water, called the North Atlantic Deep Water, is defined by its temperature and salinity, and is quite distinguishable from other water masses. In the Antarctic region an Antarctic Bottom Water and an Antarctic Inter-

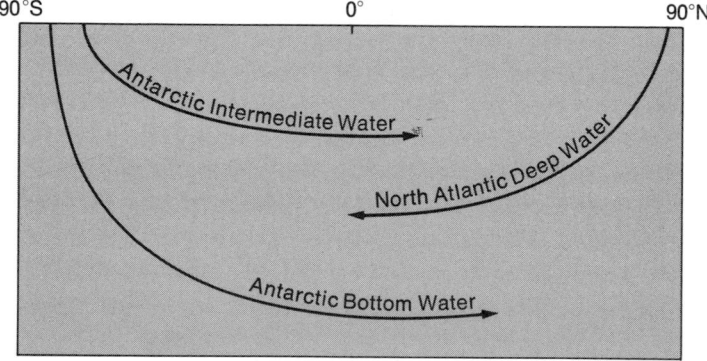

Figure 7-15 Diagrammatic section of the major subsurface water masses in the Atlantic Ocean.

mediate Water are formed. The first, one of the densest bodies of water in the ocean, travels north on the bottom across the equator. The Intermediate Water also travels north, but at a depth of about 1 km.

The bottom-flowing water masses can be influenced by the topography of the sea floor. Dense waters formed in the Arctic Ocean are prevented from reaching the Atlantic by a submarine ridge. The Mid-Atlantic Ridge can be a barrier to flow between basins of the western and eastern Atlantic (see Figure 7-14).

Even though the thermohaline circulation is very slow, the bottom waters of the ocean will again eventually come in contact with the surface.

WIND-GENERATED WAVES

Origin of Wind-Generated Waves

One effect of the wind blowing on the surface of the ocean is the formation of waves. Waves formed by the wind are only one of several types of waves found in the ocean.

Wind-generated waves are formed on the sea surface by the transfer of energy from the air to the water; the method for this transfer is not completely understood, but apparently is related to two mechanisms:

1. Wind is deflected as it blows over the wave profile, causing pressure differences that can supply energy to the waves.
2. Moving pressure fluctuations may react with water by resonance to form waves during turbulent wind conditions.

In discussing waves it is convenient to idealize the wave form (Figure 7-16). In this simplified picture the **wavelength,** L, is defined as the horizontal distance between two crests (or two other similar points on the wave form) measured parallel to the direction of travel of the wave. The period, T, is the time for the passage of successive wave crests past a fixed point. H is the wave height and is measured from the wave crest to the wave trough. The depth of water is h. The velocity of the wave, or the rate of propagation of the wave form, is the wavelength divided by the period, or $C = L/T$.

In deep water it is the wave form that is advancing; the water itself only moves forward a very small amount. Surely everyone has observed a piece of paper or a boat floating on water and going up and down with the passing waves. The wave form is moving along the surface of the water horizontally but the paper or boat is just going

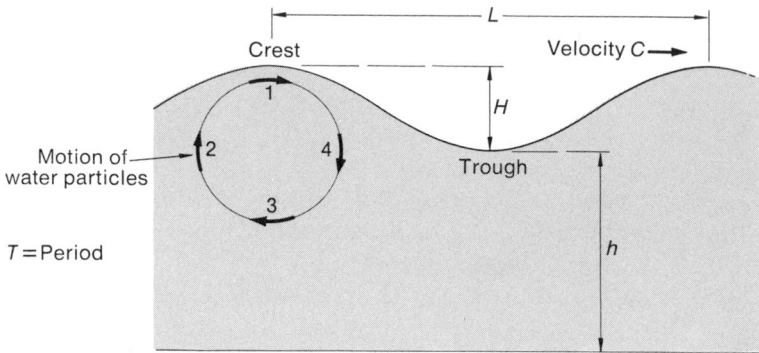

Figure 7-16 Simplified picture of important wave characteristics and the motion of water particles in a wave form.

up and down with essentially no horizontal movement (as shown by the different number position in Figure 7-16). Therefore, when talking about wave motion, a distinction must be made between the motion of the wave form and the motion of the water particles.

When the wave is in deep water the motion of the individual water particles at the surface is circular. The diameter of the circle decreases quickly with water depth; for example, at $h = L/4$ (a depth of one-quarter the wavelength), the diameter is reduced to about one-fifth its original size and the water motion is more of a back-and-forth rather than a circular motion. The velocity of the water particles also decreases rapidly with depth (Table 7-2). Waves having a period of 10 sec or less generally produce negligible motion below 100 m. Table

TABLE 7-2 VELOCITIES OF WATER PARTICLES AT DIFFERENT DEPTHS IN SURFACE WAVES OF DIFFERENT PERIODS (DATA FROM SVERDRUP, JOHNSON, AND FLEMING, 1942)

Wave Characteristics				**Velocity of Particle (cm/ sec) at Stated Depth**		
Period (sec)	Velocity (cm/sec)	Length (m)	Height (m)	0 m	20 m	1,000 m
2	312	6	.25	39	0.0	0.0
4	624	25	1.0	79	0.5	0.0
6	937	56	2.0	105	11.3	0.0
8	1,249	100	5.0	196	55.6	0.4
10	1,561	156	7.0	220	99.0	4.2
12	1,873	225	10.0	211	114.0	12.9
14	2,185	306	12.0	273	180.0	35.0
16	2,498	396	10.0	197	143.0	40.6
18	2,810	506	8.0	140	109.0	40.5
20	3,122	624	5.0	78	63.0	28.4

7-2 also shows the increasing length and velocity of longer period waves, and shows that the highest waves are not necessarily those of the longest period or length.

The height and period of wind-generated waves are functions of three factors: (1) velocity of the wind; (2) duration, or time that the wind blows; (3) **fetch,** or the distance of water over which the wind blows. The absolute effect of these factors has not been resolved but some relationships are known. Wave height and wavelength will generally increase to a definite maximum with increasing wind velocity and duration. The fetch is important in determining wavelength. Wavelengths of only a few meters are common in lakes where the fetch is relatively small, whereas wavelengths of several hundreds of meters are typical for oceanic waves because the fetch is large. In shallow waters, such as lakes, the water depth can become another important factor influencing the waves. The maximum height of wind-generated waves is not known, especially because of the difficulty of measuring wave height during storm periods. Estimates of wave height have reached about 25 m.

Different Types of Wind-Generated Waves

Wind-generated waves can be divided into three types: sea, swell, and surf (Figure 7-17a,b,c). Waves in the area directly affected by the wind are called **sea** (Figure 7-17a). Sea waves are irregular, with no systematic pattern. Sea is composed of waves of different periods and heights traveling in various directions. As these waves leave the area where they were generated and where they were under the immediate influence of the wind, the longer period waves, because of their higher velocity (see Table 7-2), will outdistance the shorter and slower waves. The waves will assume a more uniform pattern, with waves of similar dimensions tending to travel together because of their similar speed. The waves in this regular pattern are called **swell** (Figure 7-17b). As swell travels still further from the generating area, it will remain constant in length but decrease in height. A wave pattern can travel across the entire ocean. W. Munk and his associates at Scripps Institution of Oceanography have noted waves generated off the coast of New Zealand which traveled across the Pacific and eventually broke on the Alaskan coast.

The third type of wind-generated wave is **surf,** which occurs near shore when a wave shoals and breaks (Figure 7-17c). Breaking waves differ from the sea and swell waves in that the water particles are no longer traveling in an orbital motion, but now are traveling towards the beach. This results in a large amount of energy being directed toward the beach.

a

b

c

Figure 7-17 Wind-generated waves. (Photographs courtesy of Woods Hole Oceanographic Institution.) (a) Sea waves in the generating, or storm, area. (b) Swell. Note how the wave pattern has become relatively uniform. (c) Surf—breaking waves.

When waves arrive in shallow water all their characteristics, except the period, change. Wavelength and velocity decrease with decreasing depth; this change is small until the depth of water (h) equals one-half the wavelength of the wave. At this depth the wave is said to "feel" bottom, and the wave will quickly increase in height. The wave will break when the particle velocity at the crest of the wave exceeds the velocity of the wave. On a gently sloping beach this usually occurs when the ratio H/h is between 0.8 and 0.6.

If waves enter shallow water at an angle to the beach or encounter irregular changes in the nearshore bottom topography, their direction of travel will change. This change, called refraction, occurs when one part of the wave first reaches shallow water. This part will be slowed down, causing the entire wave to turn toward the shallow water. Thus the wave crests tend to parallel bottom contours (Figures 7-18 and 7-19). Refraction depends on bottom topography, wavelength, and direction of approach. On irregular coasts, refraction will cause a concentration of wave energy, or convergence, in topographically high areas, such as submerged ridges or elevated points (Figure 7-18). Wave energy will diverge over submarine canyons or in bays. Clever fishermen will moor their boats over local depressions in the bottom topography while waiting out a storm; the wave energy will diverge at these areas and the danger of the boats' capsizing is reduced.

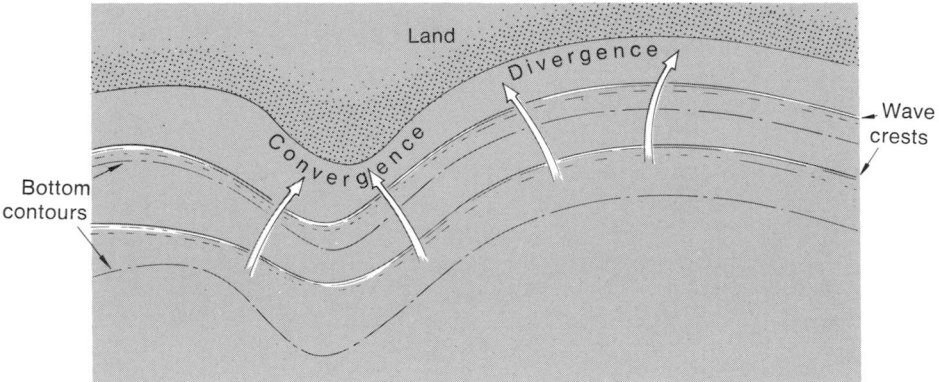

Figure 7-18 Diagrammatic illustration of wave refraction in the nearshore region.

After waves break, water is carried into the surf zone and is transported toward the barrier of the beach. Some of the water will return seaward along the bottom of the surf zone. With the usual angular approach of the waves to the beach, water will also be transported along the beach (Figure 7-20). This longshore current will increase until it can overcome the incoming waves, at which time the

Figure 7-19 Aerial photograph showing wave refraction. (Photograph courtesy of the U.S. Air Force, Cambridge Research Laboratories.)

water will flow seaward in what is called a rip current. Rip currents, because of their seaward flow, can be dangerous to swimmers.[3] The positions of rip currents are dependent on submarine topography, slope of the beach, and height and period of the waves.

The breaking of waves in the nearshore region and the subsequent transfer of energy toward the beach create an environment of quickly changing conditions. There are considerable fluctuations of velocity and direction of currents. The fluctuations of current velocity are due primarily to the grouping of similar type waves, such as a sequence of high waves followed by a sequence of low waves. Strong nearshore currents can erode and otherwise change the configuration of the beach. They make shallow water sediments coarser grained than those of more seaward areas, to which the finer particles are carried. Tidal fluctuations and storms allow breaking waves and longshore currents

[3] If caught in a rip current, let the current carry you seaward; do not try to swim against it to reach shore. As it diminishes in strength, swim parallel to the beach until the effect of the rip current disappears.

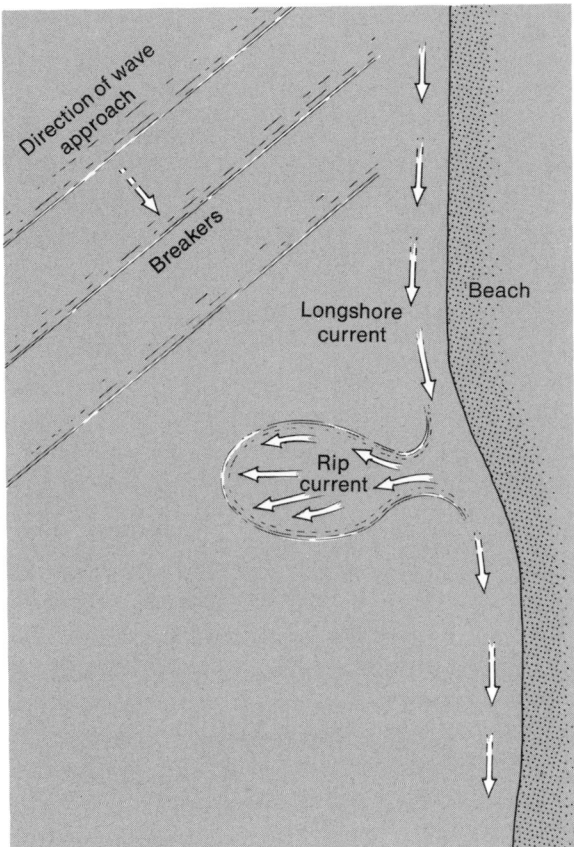

Figure 7-20   Longshore transport and rip currents in the nearshore region.

to exert their influence over a large part of the nearshore area. Animal and plant life in this region must be capable of living in a rigorous environment. Organisms must withstand not only the crushing force of the waves, but also exposure outside of the water during low tide.

INTERNAL WAVES

An internal wave, similar in many respects to a wind-generated wave, may occur where there is a vertical density gradient. Internal waves generally are not seen directly from the surface, but are usually detected by systematic and closely-spaced temperature observations. Such observations indicate that internal waves are a common phenomenon in the ocean. They usually travel more slowly than surface waves, but they may have a greater height. Internal waves have been observed to break as surface waves do. Their presence is sometimes

Figure 7-21 Sea surface expression of internal waves. The surface slicks, composed of fine-grained sediment, are related to the troughs of the internal waves. (Photograph courtesy of E. C. LaFond, U.S. Naval Undersea Center.)

Figure 7-22 Turbid water (lighter color) discharged seaward from the mouth of Cape Fear River, North Carolina. (Photograph courtesy of J. V. A. Trumbull, from Meade, 1969.)

hinted at by slow moving slicks on the ocean surface. The slicks, composed of plankton, fine-grained sediment, or surface water contamination (Figure 7-21), will form over the trough of the wave.

Any condition causing waters of different density to come in contact with each other can cause internal waves. Among these conditions are outflow of fresh water from rivers (Figure 7-22) and mixing of different water types. Tidal movements probably cause some long-period internal waves.

CATASTROPHIC WAVES

Storm Surges

Catastrophic waves are the result of unusual conditions, such as intense storms over or near the ocean or submarine slumping. Catastrophic waves often cause damage and loss of life.

Strong winds, usually associated with hurricanes, can pile water up on a coast causing an exceptionally high sea level (Figure 7-23). High-water levels or storm surges can be dangerous, especially if they coincide with times of high tides in low coastal regions. In the Gulf Coast area of the United States, storm surges have been known to raise the water level as much as 7 m. In 1900, over 6,000 people were drowned during such a storm in Galveston, Texas. Storm surges differ from other waves in having a gradual rise of the water level rather than a quick rhythmic rise and fall.

Landside Surges

The movement of large quantities of rock or ice into the ocean, due to earthquakes or glacial movements, can generate immense waves. An exceptionally large wave occurred in Lituya Bay, Alaska in 1958. It was estimated that 30,000,000 m^3 of rock fell from a height of about 1,000 m into the bay, causing a wave that rose up over 500 m onto the mountainside on the other side of the bay (Figure 7-24). Over 15,000 people were drowned by a similar wave on the Japanese island of Kyushu in 1792.

Tsunamis

Tsunamis are commonly called tidal waves but actually have nothing to do with the tides. Their origin can be traced to submarine movements caused by earthquakes, slumping, or volcanic eruptions. In deep water, tsunamis may have wavelengths as long as 180 km, travel at speeds over 350 knots, yet have wave heights, or amplitudes, of only a few centimeters. When tsunamis reach shallow water and break

Figure 7-23   Hurricane Gladys, photographed from Apollo VII in 1968. The whirlpool pattern is typical of hurricanes. This storm caused considerable damage to low-lying areas of Florida. (Photograph courtesy of the U.S. Naval Oceanographic Office.)

Figure 7-24   (a) Aerial view of Lituya Bay, Alaska, taken in 1954, before the giant wave. (b) Aerial view of Lituya Bay, Alaska, taken in 1958, showing the wave damage. (c) Aerial view of wave damage on the north shore of Lituya Bay. View is 2 miles from the entrance. Width of the zone of destruction is about 600 m at the right margin of photograph. Note trees with limbs and bark removed. (All photographs courtesy of U.S. Geological Survey.)

a

b

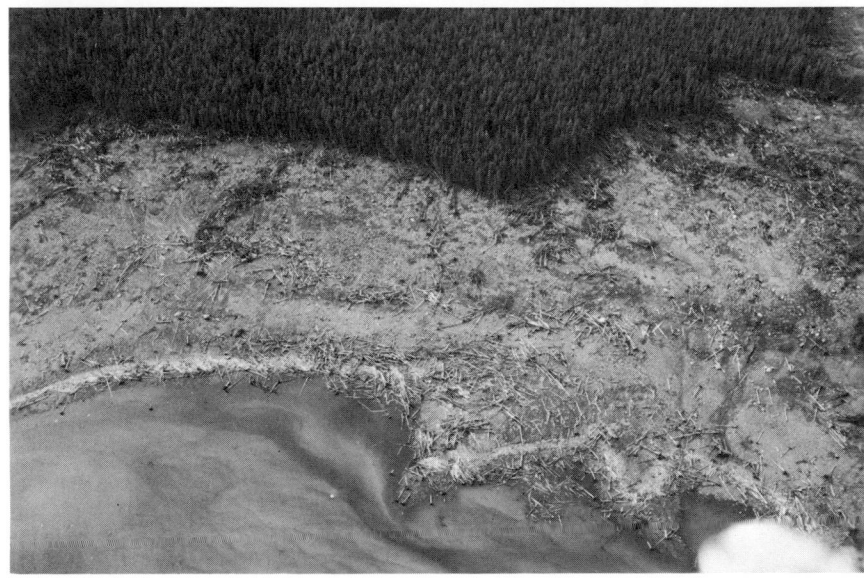

c

Figure 7-24

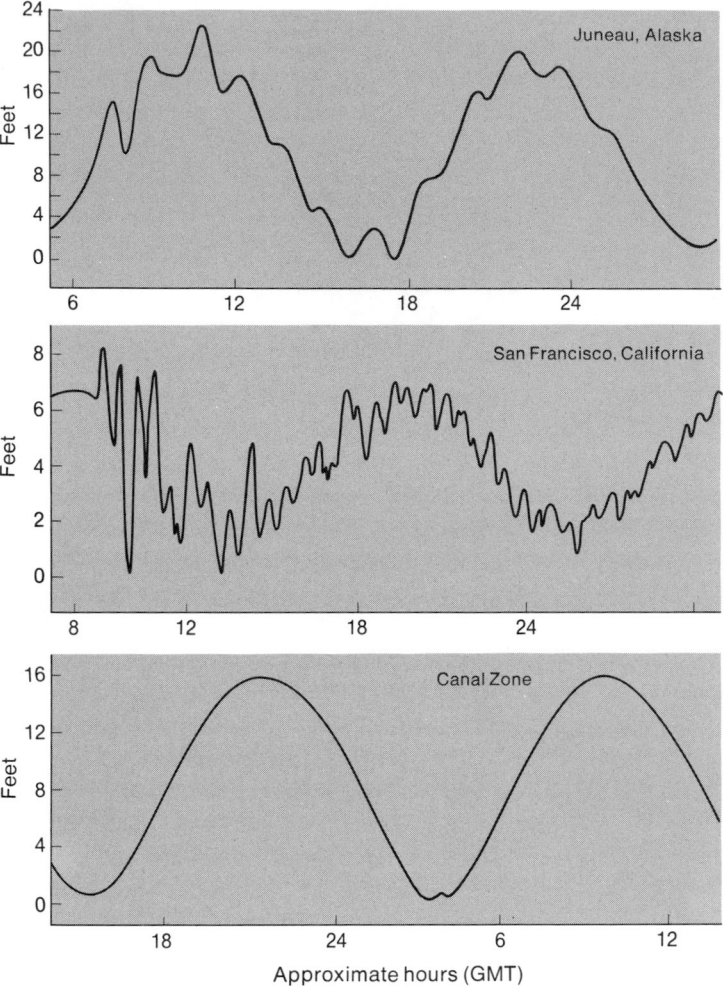

Figure 7-25 Tidal gauge records of the 1964 Alaskan tsunami, as felt in different cities. Note that the tsunami arrived later at the cities further from the earthquake center. These records do not show the individual waves, but the broad scale, up and down movement of the water. (After Spaeth and Berkman, 1967.)

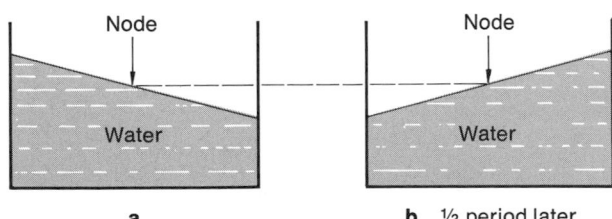

Figure 7-26 A simple stationary wave, or seiche.

against the coast, they may be higher than any wind-generated wave. The destructive effect of tsunamis is greatly controlled by submarine topography. The breaking waves generally are small near projecting points of land bordered by deep water, and are high near submarine ridges. F. P. Shepard and other scientists observed the effects of the 1946 tsunami on the island of Hawaii where wave debris was found almost 20 m above sea level and breaking waves rose 10 m above normal sea level.

Earthquakes in Chile in 1960 and in Alaska in 1964 produced large tsunamis with enormous loss of life and damage to property. A recently developed early warning system allows preventive actions to minimize the damage. Sensitive seismographs, now located at stations around the Pacific, record the shock waves from the earthquake; observers can then quickly calculate the position of the earthquake and predict the resulting tsunamis (Figure 7-25). Persons in areas that may suffer from the wave can be forewarned.

Most tsunamis in the Pacific are caused by submarine movements along the "ring of fire," an area of crustal instability that somewhat discontinuously encircles the Pacific (see p. 285). Tsunamis generated in these areas will travel outwards and reach most other areas of the Pacific. Fortunately, the west coast of the United States has received little damage from tidal waves for several reasons:

1. The west coast is relatively stable in regard to earthquakes, at least in comparison to other areas of the Pacific.
2. Tidal waves produced in the Aleutian and South American areas approach this coast diagonally, and hence are less destructive.
3. The relatively large shelf on the west coast of the United States causes the waves to lose considerable energy before reaching shore.

Stationary Waves

A wave type common to many enclosed bodies of water like bays and lakes is the stationary wave, also called **standing wave** or **seiche.** In a stationary wave, the wave form does not move forward, but the water surface moves up and down. The motion is similar to that of soup in a bowl that has been tilted, then set down on a flat surface (Figure 7-26). The water surface will remain stationary at certain locations, called nodes, while the rest of the surface moves up and down.

Stationary waves can be generated by storms, rapid changes in atmospheric conditions, or sudden disturbances to the water surface. Once generated, the lake or bay will have an oscillation that is controlled by the length and depth of the basin. Stationary waves have been responsible for considerable property damage and loss of life.

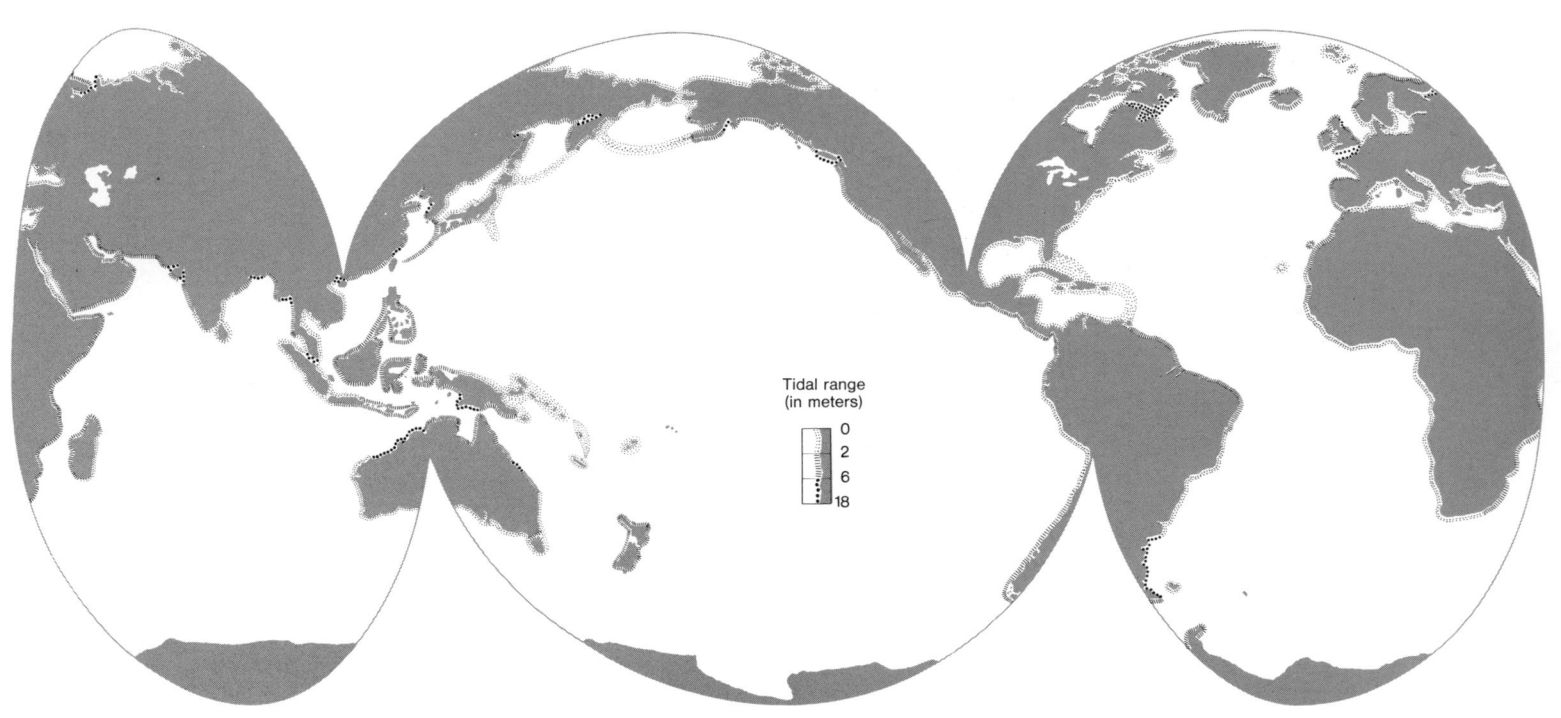

Figure 7-27 Tidal range along the coasts of the world. (After Isakov, 1953.)

TIDES

Tides are the daily or twice daily rhythmic rise and fall of sea level. Tidal movements were observed, measured, and recorded by early man, who noted their relationship to the moon. His explanation of and attempt at tidal prediction was one of man's earliest scientific ventures. Many of the theories and techniques of tidal prediction were developed in the eighteenth and nineteenth centuries. Techniques for tidal prediction have recently been improved, mainly through the use of high speed computers, but the understanding of tidal processes is still incomplete.

Tides are waves that have a period of about 12 hr and 25 min and a wavelength of about half the circumference of the earth (12,600 miles or about 23,300 km).

The tidal range (maximum height at high tide minus minimum height at low tide) averages between 1 and 3 m (Figure 7-27), but can be as high as 20 m in some areas, such as the Bay of Fundy. Exceptionally high tides are generally due to the geographic position and the geometry of the area.

Most areas have either one high and one low tide each day (diurnal tides) or, more commonly, two high and two low a day (semidiurnal tides, Figure 7-28). Individual high and low pairs of semidiurnal tides are usually of different heights. Because the time interval between high tides is about 12 hr and 25 min (half a lunar day), high tide occurs about 50 min later every day. This simple fact shows that

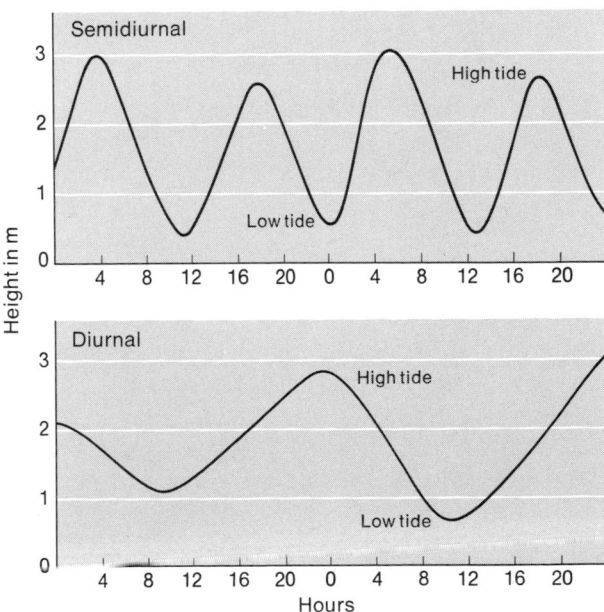

Figure 7-28   Semidiurnal and diurnal tides.

tides are primarily influenced by the moon. If they were mainly controlled by the sun, they would occur at the same time every day, the solar day being 24 hr.

Causes of the Tide

Tides are caused by the gravitational attraction of the sun and moon on the earth. This attraction affects water, solid earth, and the atmosphere, but the results on the last two cannot be observed by the unaided eye. The gravitational attraction between the earth and moon (Figure 7-29) is strongest on the side of the earth that is facing the moon. This attraction causes the water on the near side of the earth, N, to be pulled toward the moon. The gravitational attraction of the moon is at the minimum at the point farthest away, F, on the opposite side of the

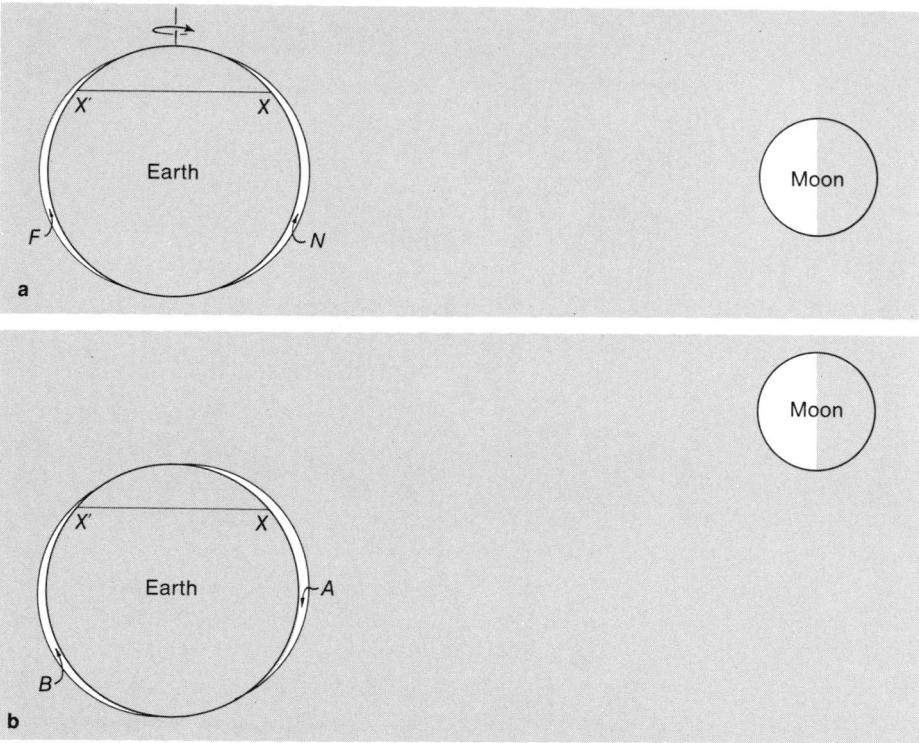

Figure 7-29 Illustration of the gravitational attraction between the earth and moon (dimensions are exaggerated). (a) The moon is parallel to the earth's equatorial plane. X and X' indicate the change in position of a point on the earth's surface after one-half a lunar day (12 hr and 25 min). This position will produce equal tides at point X or X'. (b) The moon is inclined to the earth's equatorial plane. This position will produce unequal tides at point X or X'.

earth and this, combined with **centrifugal forces,** causes the water to "bulge out." The two bulges will stay essentially aligned with the moon as the earth rotates relative to the moon. Because it takes the earth 24 hr and 50 min to rotate relative to the moon, a place on earth will experience two tidal highs and lows within this time period. The magnitude of the high tides is generally different because the moon is inclined to the earth's equatorial plane (Figure 7-29a and b).

The sun also exerts a considerable tidal influence on the ocean even though the tidal bulge produced by the sun is only 46 percent of that produced by the moon. The smaller effect of the much larger sun is due to its greater distance from the earth: gravitational forces vary inversely with the square of the distance and directly with the mass.

The effect of the sun becomes especially important when the sun and moon are lined up with the earth; the combined gravitational attraction of the two bodies produces a very strong tide, called the **spring tide.** Spring tides occur roughly every 14 days, at new and full moon (Figure 7-30). Exceptionally low tides, called **neap tides,** occur when the sun and the moon are at right angles to each other, also about every 14 days, at half moon.

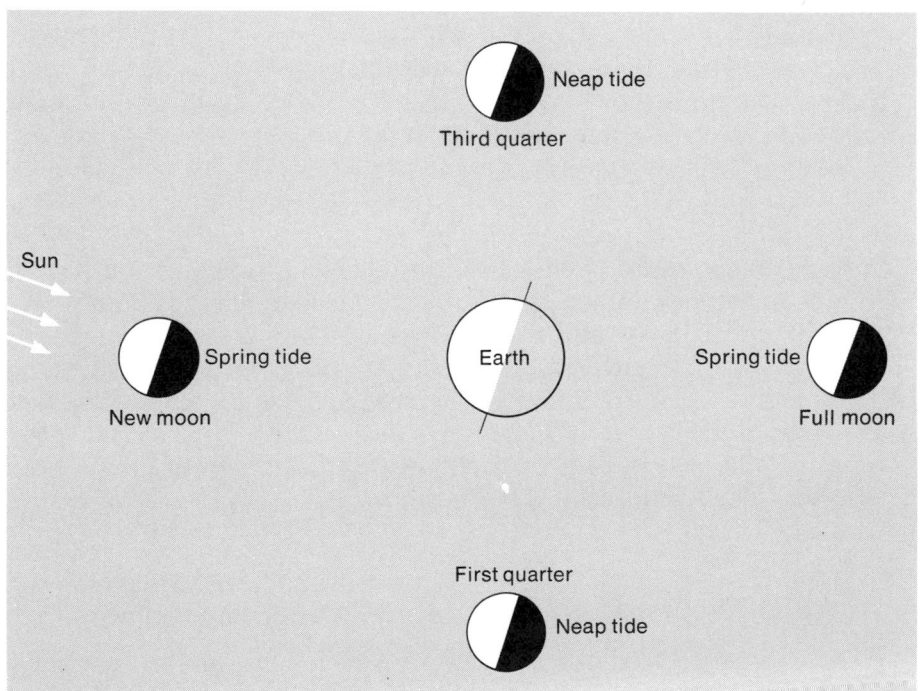

Figure 7-30 Phases of the moon and their associated spring and neap tides.

Tidal Friction

Some work has shown that the earth does not rotate smoothly under the tidal bulges, but that there is a frictional force between the earth and the water. In theory this friction should slow the earth's rotation. Calculations by K. B. Krauskopf and A. Beiser in 1966 show that this slowing rate is very small; the time between sunrise and sunset has increased by 1/1,000 of a second in the last 100 years. However small this rate, it can become significant over long periods of geological time. A decrease in the earth's rotation would also result in an increase in the speed of the moon's revolution, causing the moon to move slowly away from the earth. In the geological past, if the moon were closer to the earth the length of the day would have been shorter and the number of days in a year would have been greater. There is evidence from growth rings of ancient corals that 400 million years ago the number of days in a year was close to 400. A consequence of the moon being closer to the earth in the past is that tides would have been considerably stronger than at present. These tidal conditions could have created biological and geological conditions different from those common today. Some scientists have suggested that the increased tides, due to the proximity of the moon, may have provided the impetus for the evolution of hard-shelled organisms. Soft-shelled organisms, living in shallow water conditions, apparently would have difficulty existing in these rigorous environments. Geologically, vast inland seas, flushed once or twice daily by the high tides, would have covered many of the low-lying areas of the world.

Tidal Currents

Tidal currents in the open ocean are relatively weak. Near the land, however, they can attain speeds of several kilometers a hour. Tidal currents in shallow water and estuaries can be geologically very important. They can move large amounts of sediment which may block harbors and eventually have to be removed by dredging. In some estuaries, during times of high tide, a large wave will form and travel upstream. This wave, called a **tidal bore,** can be as high as 3 m or more and have speeds of over 15 km an hour.

TURBIDITY CURRENTS

Sediments suspended in water can produce a dense mixture that may flow down a slope on the ocean bottom. When such a flow results, it is called a **turbidity current.** If the velocity and turbulence of the current are sufficient to prevent settling of the sediment particles, the current can flow for long distances. Eventually it will stop and its sediment load will be deposited; the deposit is called a **turbidite** (see p. 306).

Turbidity currents, their origin, and their effects are one of the more controversial topics in oceanography. No direct observations of these currents have been made, although numerous searches for them have been undertaken. Considerable indirect evidence indicates that turbidity currents do exist.

The concept of turbidity currents was first suggested in 1939, but the idea was not really accepted until the laboratory experiments of P. H. Kuenen and C. I. Migliorini in 1950 showed that a mixture of sand, clay, and water could, under certain conditions, produce a current that would travel down a slope carrying its sediment load.

One of the first indications of the possible effects of turbidity currents was noted after the Grand Banks earthquake in 1929, when B. C. Heezen and M. Ewing called attention to a regular sequence in the breaking of submarine telephone cables south of the Grand Banks area: the closer the cables were to the earthquake epicenter the sooner they broke. The cable breaks may have been caused by a large turbidity current moving down the slope; this current, Heezen and Ewing suggested, had an average velocity of 50 knots in the earlier phases of the flow and an average of about 25 knots for the duration of the complete flow. Shepard in 1963, however, has questioned these velocities and argues that 15 knots may be a more accurate average velocity. Another scientist, K. Terzaghi, proposed that rather than turbidity currents, a progressive **spontaneous liquefaction** of the sediments could have broken the cables. Subsequent observations in other areas indicate that earthquakes can produce movements of large amounts of sediment possibly resulting in turbidity currents.

The best evidence for turbidity currents is provided in numerous deep-sea cores collected from the flat areas of the ocean. These cores generally contain layers of coarse-grained, sand-sized sediment between the normal deep-sea, fine-grained clay deposits. These sand layers, because of their grain size and mineral composition and their numerous shells of shallow water organisms, are deduced to be of nearshore origin. The only known mechanism that could transport and deposit them as layers is a turbidity current. The layers generally have finer grain-sized sediment overlying the coarser material at the bottom of the layer, which is what one would expect if the sediment were settling out of a current.

Many areas of the ocean, protected by trenches or distant from land, are not affected by turbidity current deposits (Figure 7-31). The topography of these areas is generally hilly and rough. Areas where turbidity current deposits are common are usually smooth due to the

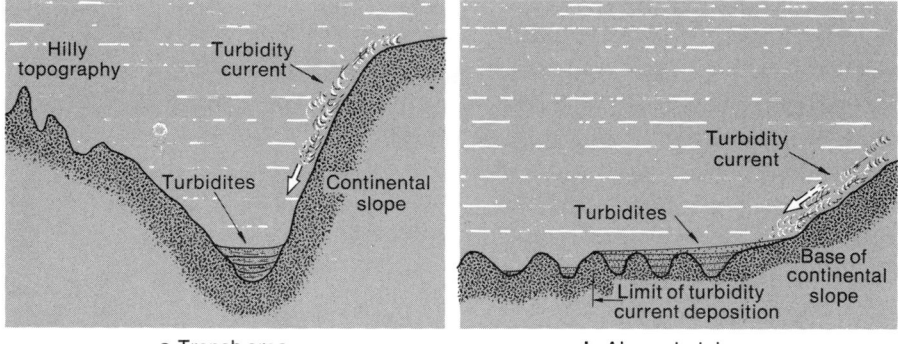

a Trench area   **b** Abyssal plain area

Figure 7-31   Turbidity current deposition in the ocean: (a) in a trench area, (b) in an abyssal plain area.

blanketing effect of the sediments; these areas are called **abyssal plains.**

The present controversy over turbidity currents involves their eroding powers, especially in conjunction with the origin of submarine canyons. Some researchers have suggested that submarine canyons were cut by turbidity currents and others suggest that erosion during times of lowered sea level cut the canyon, although they admit that the canyon may be kept free of sediment by intermittent sediment flows. Direct measurements of turbidity current velocity, perhaps by electronic devices triggered by the flow, should indicate whether turbidity currents are capable of significant erosion.

The origin of turbidity currents is also controversial. The Grand Banks evidence suggests that turbidity currents can be initiated by earthquakes that cause sediment to slump and flow. F. P. Shepard, R. F. Dill, and other workers have noted that coarse-grained sediment will accumulate in the nearshore parts of submarine canyons and then, usually after a large storm, be transported seaward by some form of mass movement. The deposits resulting from such movements are distinguished by their coarse-grained texture overlying the normal fine-grained deep-water sediments. Similar types of mass movements also occur on the continental slope, although the resulting sediment deposit would not ordinarily be called a turbidite. More likely it would be called a slump deposit. This apparently anomalous situation occurs because the finer-grained slope sediments would not produce the alternating coarse-grained and fine-grained layers typical of turbidites. Thus much of the confusion concerning the origin of turbidity currents is due to the unclear separation of the mechanism and the resulting sediment deposit. Turbidity currents should be considered a form of mass movement, where the sediment becomes suspended in the water during movement and settles according to its size and density.

UNDERWATER SOUND

Underwater sound has recently become an important tool for the oceanographer. Sound is used to measure the depths of the ocean, as well as to examine the character and thickness of the earth's crust. Biological oceanographers can use sound to detect and study organisms. Naval aspects of sound, such as submarine detection and locating and positioning objects on the sea floor, have encouraged the study of underwater sound.

Sound Velocity

The velocity of sound in the ocean depends on temperature, salinity, and pressure (depth). Sound velocity in sea water ranges from 1,400 to 1,570 m per sec; it increases with increasing salinity, temperature, and depth. The increase is 1.3 m per sec for each one thousandth part increase in salinity, about 4.5 m per sec for each degree centigrade increase in temperature, and 1.7 m per sec for each 100 m increase in depth. Although small, these changes affect estimates of water depth as determined by sound velocity. Corrections for changes in salinity, temperature, and pressure should be applied for estimates of water velocity; general correction factors have been developed for most areas of the ocean. More accurate estimates of sound velocity are possible with a sound velocimeter, a device that is lowered into the ocean to measure sound velocity directly, eliminating the need for corrections.

The vertical changes of sound velocity in the ocean can be divided into three zones (Figure 7-32):

1. The surface zone of the ocean (100 to 150 m in thickness), where the waters are well mixed and the sound velocity increases with depth due to the pressure (depth) effect
2. A zone (possibly extending down to 1,500 m) where the sound velocity decreases because of rapid temperature decreases (thermocline)
3. A zone, below 1,500 m, where the sound velocity increases with increasing pressure, the temperature being relatively constant.

Sound waves, like ocean waves, can be refracted, and hence will turn toward areas of lower sound velocity.

Refraction combined with vertical variation of sound velocity in the ocean can produce shadow zones and sound channels. A shadow zone is an area where relatively little sound will penetrate. It occurs in the upper parts of the ocean when a positive velocity gradient (increasing sound velocity) overlies a negative velocity gradient (decreas-

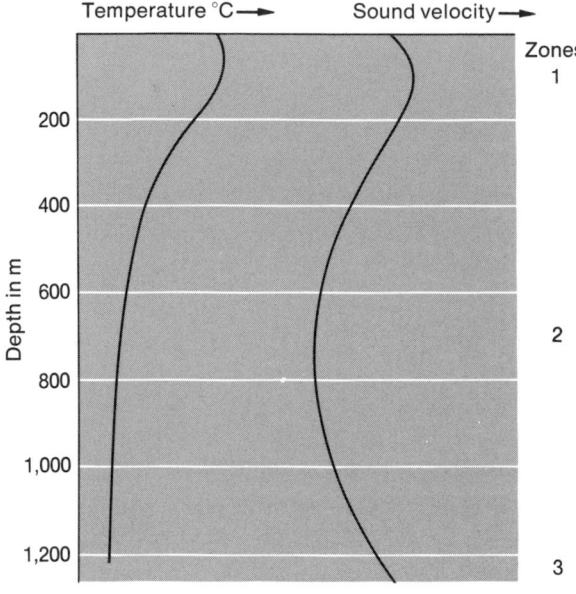

Figure 7-32 Sound velocity profiles in the ocean. Arrow indicates direction of increasing temperature or sound velocity. Different zones are discussed in the text.

ing sound velocity) and the sound is in the positive gradient (Figure 7-33). The sound will be refracted upward in the positive gradient area and downward in the negative gradient area (in both instances toward areas of lower sound velocity), producing the shadow zone. It would be very difficult to detect a submarine in a shadow zone.

A sound channel can occur in the area where the velocity of sound reaches a minimum value (see Figure 7-33). Sound traveling in this minimum value zone is refracted upward or downward to the area of lower velocity and thus back into the minimum value zone. There is little energy loss due to vertical spreading, and sound can be transmitted in this zone for thousands of kilometers. A sound velocity minimum commonly occurs at about 1,500 m depth; this area, called the SOFAR channel, has had sound transmitted through it over a distance of 25,000 km. This SOFAR channel can be used by ships in distress. An explosive charge detonated in this channel by a vessel will be detected at coastal stations and used to determine the position of the vessel by calculating the different arrival times of the sound at the different stations.

As sound travels through water it decreases in energy due to spreading, absorption, and scattering. The sound loss due to spreading is proportional to the square of the distance traveled. Sound can also be absorbed by the water and converted to heat. Absorption is proportional to the square of the sound frequency: the higher the frequency the greater the absorption. Sound can be scattered by particles, marine

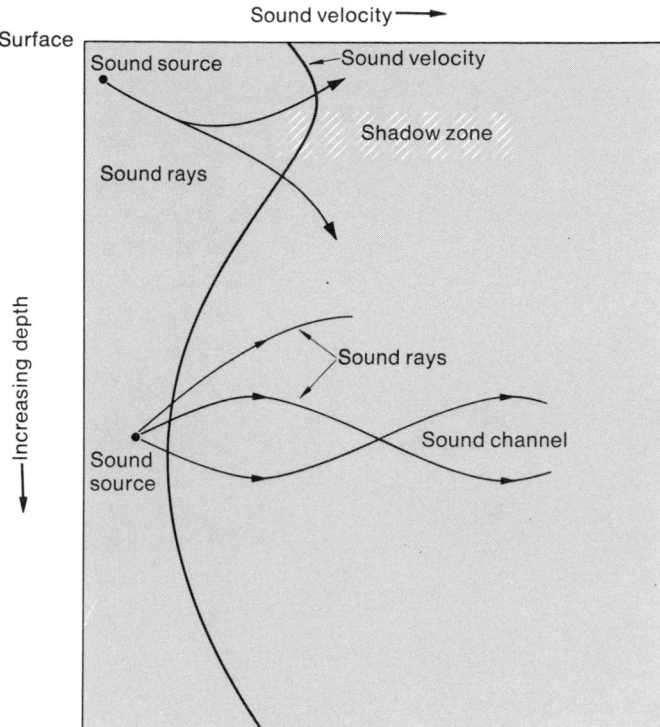

Figure 7-33 Shadow zones and a sound channel.

organisms, gas bubbles, and the ocean bottom itself (sound is also reflected from the ocean bottom). The scattering and reflecting of sound from vertically migrating marine organisms (see Figures 6-39 and 6-40) causes the phenomenon of the deep-scattering layer (discussed in Chapter 6).

LIGHT IN SEA WATER

Light from the sun and sky penetrates only the upper layers of the ocean. The transparency of sea water or the depth of penetration of the light is dependent on the amount of material that absorbs and scatters light in the water. Major absorbing and scattering materials are dissolved organic material, especially a yellow substance formed from the decomposition of organic matter, and such organic detritus as fragments of plankton.

Most of the light entering the ocean is absorbed within the first 100 m. The absorption of light varies with the different wavelengths of light. Blue light penetrates sea water more deeply than red light. This greater transparency to blue light accounts for the blue color of ocean water. If there is an abundance of scattering particles, the water may have a greenish hue.

The depth to which light penetrates determines the thickness of the photic zone where photosynthetic production of organic matter by plants takes place. Because plants are the major source of food for organisms in the ocean, the thickness of the photic zone is important. Planktonic plants generally do not grow at depths where less than about 1 percent of the available light penetrates. Thus production of planktonic food in the ocean occurs mostly in waters near the surface.

SUGGESTED FURTHER READING

Defant, A. *Physical Oceanography,* 2 Volumes. New York: Pergamon Press, 1961.

Dietrich, G. *General Oceanography, An Introduction.* Translated by Feodor Ostapoff. New York: Interscience, 1963.

Eckart, C. *Hydrodynamics of Oceans and Atmospheres.* New York: Pergamon Press, 1960.

Groen, P. *The Waters of the Sea.* London: Van Nostrand, 1967.

Hill, M. N., ed. *The Sea; Ideas and Observations on Progress in the Study of the Sea, Physical Oceanography,* Vol. 1. New York: Interscience, 1963.

Kinsman, B. *Wind Waves, Their Generation and Propagation on the Ocean Surface.* Englewood Cliffs, New Jersey: Prentice-Hall, 1965.

McLellan, H. J. *Elements of Physical Oceanography.* New York: Pergamon Press, 1965.

Neumann, G., and Pierson, W. J., Jr. *Principles of Physical Oceanography.* Englewood Cliffs, New Jersey: Prentice-Hall, 1966.

Officer, C. B. *Introduction to the Theory of Sound Transmission with Application to the Ocean.* New York: McGraw-Hill, 1958.

Pickard, G. L. *Descriptive Physical Oceanography; An Introduction.* New York: Macmillan, 1964.

Spar, J. *Earth, Sea, and Air: A Survey of the Geophysical Sciences.* Reading, Mass.: Addison-Wesley, 1962.

Stommel, H. *The Gulf Stream; A Physical and Dynamic Description.* Berkeley: University of California Press, 1958.

Sverdrup, H. U., Johnson, M. W., and Fleming, R. H. *The Oceans: Their Physics, Chemistry, and General Biology.* New York: Prentice-Hall, 1942.

von Arx, W. S. *An Introduction to Physical Oceanography.* Reading, Mass.: Addison-Wesley, 1962.

Chapter 8

MARINE GEOLOGY

AND GEOPHYSICS

INTRODUCTION

Geology includes the study of the physical history of the earth. Marine geology similarly is concerned with the physical history of that portion of the earth now covered by water. It also includes beaches, marshes, and tidal areas which, although only sometimes covered by water, are clearly influenced by the marine environment. The continental shelf, continental slope, and the deep ocean floor are also the province of the marine geologist or, as he may be called, the geological oceanographer. Objectives of marine geology are to describe and determine the origin of the topography of the sea floor, the origin of the sediments of the ocean bottom, and the origin of the structure below the floor of the ocean. The last is mainly the province of the marine geophysicist. Results of studies by marine geologists help to explain the origin of land and ocean basins and to find valuable mineral deposits. Many geological features observed on land were originally formed underwater; thus by studying the ocean we can better understand our own habitat.

History of Marine Geology and Geophysics

Dredges for sampling the animals and rocks of the sea floor were developed about 1750. By 1773, mud was dredged up from a depth of 683 fathoms in the Arctic region. The first detailed map of the sea floor was made by Maury in 1854 (see Figure 3-3). Mud that had collected in the weight at the end of sounding devices, used in making Maury's map, was studied by Bailey and Pourtales, and by 1870 they had collected more than 9,000 samples of the ocean bottom. At about the same time Charles Darwin was making studies that profoundly influenced marine geology. The Challenger Expedition (1872–1876) is usually thought to mark the beginning of a formal science of marine geology. Samples of the bottom collected on this cruise and on previous expeditions were studied by Murray and Renard in 1891; their classification of deep-sea sediments is still used today.

After the Challenger Expedition, numerous studies of the ocean floor were made, but the next major advance in marine geology did not occur until the Meteor Expedition of 1925. This expedition was the first to use echo-sounding equipment rather than to determine depths by the tedious and time-consuming method of lowering a line with heavy weights to the bottom. In the South Atlantic, the METEOR made over 70,000 depth soundings. The soundings clearly showed that the ocean bottom was not a single featureless plain, but consisted of mountains, valleys, and flat areas. Actually the ocean floor has a topography every bit as diverse as land topography. Subsequent years saw not only the development of new sampling and survey devices, but also the founding of oceanographic institutions such as Scripps and Woods Hole.

During World War II numerous studies of sea floor characteristics were initiated for naval purposes. After the war, large quantities of explosives were available for seismic refraction studies at sea. Seismic refraction techniques (see Chapter 4) were first used on land in the 1920s, and in 1937 Maurice Ewing and his co-workers had extended the technique to studies of the continental shelf. Inevitably, improved technology made use of seismic refraction possible in the deep sea. New techniques and instruments have also been developed for measuring the earth's magnetic field and the force of gravity. Measurement of gravity, which requires a stable platform, had been made previously from a ship frozen into the ice (Nansen's Polar Expedition of 1893 to 1896) and from submarines. Today the gravity measuring device, the gravimeter, is suspended so that it is not affected by the motion of the ship.

Photography of the sea floor came into use in the early 1940s and was used to detect enemy submarines in shallow water. Sophisticated devices (see Figure 4-28) can now take both black and white and color pictures in the deepest part of the ocean. In the last few years we have seen drilling programs such as JOIDES and the Deep-Sea Drilling Project, increased use of submersibles, development of continuous seismic techniques, and construction of more technologically elaborate ships and electronic equipment, all leading to better understanding of the mechanics of sound and of fluid motion in the sea.

THE CONTINENTAL MARGIN

The ocean floor can be divided into numerous parts on the basis of its depth, geography, or crustal structure. I have simply divided it into two parts: the **continental margin,** and the **ocean basin** (Figure 8-1). The continental margin includes the beaches and nearshore regions, the continental shelf, the continental slope, and the continental rise or borderland—in other words, that portion of the ocean immediately adjacent to the continents. The ocean basin is the deep-sea floor seaward of the continental margin.

The Coastal Region

The coastal region is the continental area immediately adjacent to, and obviously influenced by, the ocean. It includes the coast and shoreline, beaches, estuaries and lagoons, and marshes.

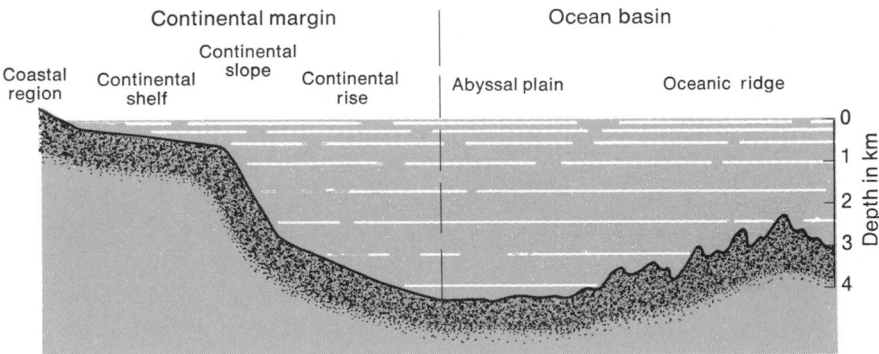

Figure 8-1 Diagrammatic profile showing the main features of the Continental Margin and the Ocean Basin.

The Coast and Shoreline

The shoreline is usually defined as the line where land and water meet, and the shore as the zone from low tide to the farthest point on land where waves transport sand (Figure 8-2). The coast is the area landward of the shore, including sea cliffs and terraces and lowlands inside the shore. These features are temporary because their position is affected by the height of sea level, which is, in turn, influenced by tides, direction of wind, and strength and height of breaking waves. Thus the shoreline is constantly changing and may move over a large area in a

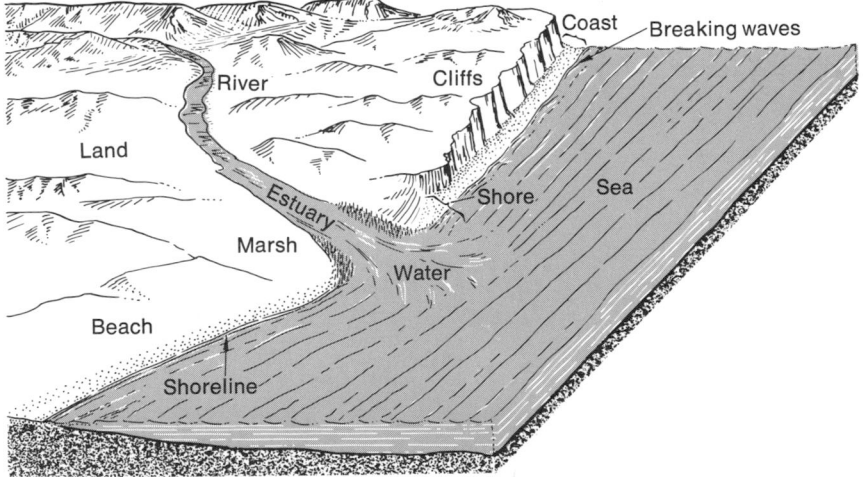

Figure 8-2 A diagrammatic view of some common features of the coastal region.

very short time. Sea level has changed considerably in the last several thousand years due to wide-spread melting of glaciers (see Figures 2-2 and 2-4), and during this time the shoreline has migrated over the breadth of most parts of the continental shelf.

There have been numerous descriptive or genetic classifications of shorelines and coasts. Clearly any classification must take into account the recent rise in sea level and its effects. Shepard in 1963 considered this and proposed a two-fold classification: (1) primary shorelines and coasts, (2) secondary shorelines and coasts.

According to this classification, primary coasts are the result of the sea meeting a land mass that has been formed mainly by terrestrial agents, including glaciers, rivers, volcanoes, deltas, or by geological movements like faulting or folding. Secondary coasts are those shaped mainly by marine or biological agents, including barrier beaches, coral reefs, and marshes. Within the concept of geological time, the character of coasts and shorelines changes quickly, and they all generally show the effect of the most recent rise in sea level from melting glaciers.

Beaches Beaches are the unconsolidated sediments (mainly sand or gravel) that cover most parts of the shore (Figure 8-3). They are usually directly under the influence of waves. Beaches are generally stable under conditions of small waves, but can be rapidly changed by large or storm waves (Figure 8-4). Beaches are also influenced daily and monthly by tidal changes. There is usually a longer seasonal effect: the higher and bigger waves typical of winter cause a net erosion of the beach, but winter erosion is generally balanced by deposition during the summer months (Figure 8-5). Beaches are also strongly influenced by the work of man. The building of jetties and other near-shore facilities usually causes one beach to expand at the expense of another (Figure 8-6). Erosion caused by man has led to increased interest in preserving beaches within the last few years.

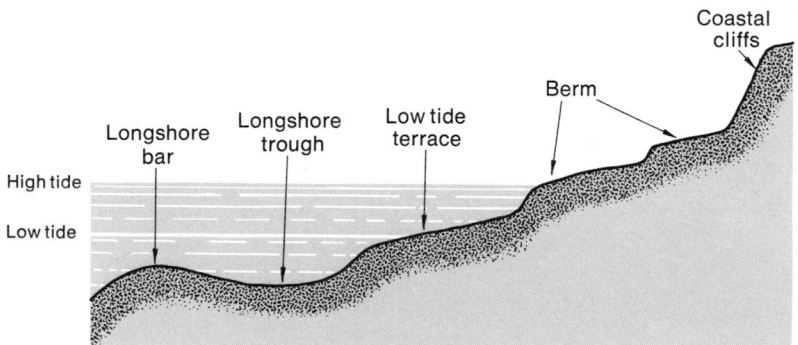

Figure 8-3   General characteristics of a beach.

a

b

Figure 8-4   (a) Picture of coastal area, Point Loma, California, taken in 1946.
(b) Picture of same area taken in 1968. Note the considerable amount of
erosion that has occurred in the 22-year period. (Photographs courtesy of
F. P. Shepard.)

a

b

Figure 8-5 (a) Gravel areas that formerly appeared every winter at La Jolla, California. (b) The same beach after sand has covered the gravel. Since 1947 the exposure of the gravel has occurred only once. (Photographs courtesy of F. P. Shepard, from *Submarine Geology*, 2nd edition, by Francis P. Shepard [Harper & Row, 1963]. Reprinted by permission of the publishers.)

254

a

b

Figure 8-6 (a) Modification of a beach by a breakwater. The breakwater has trapped sand moving along the beach (toward the foreground) and thus has built up the beach. (b) This photograph shows the area on the other side of the breakwater, where the beaches are considerably narrower because the sand that would have been carried to them has been intercepted by the breakwater. (Photographs courtesy of Jack Silver.)

255

Beaches are strongly affected by waves. If the waves are not parallel to the shore as they approach the coast, they will be refracted when they reach shallow water. Refraction causes the wave crests to turn into shallow water so that the wave crests will tend to parallel the depth contours (see Figure 7-18). Thus wave energy will converge on projecting points such as offshore bars and sea cliffs and diverge in open bay areas. Erosion by waves will therefore be stronger at points of convergence, and sediment will usually move to the quieter divergent areas (Figure 8-7).

If the waves approach the coast at an angle the discharge of water along the beach will have a longshore component, that is, there will be a net movement of water parallel to the beach. It is this longshore current, therefore, which will transport sediment along the beach. The water in the longshore current cannot accumulate; it must flow seaward as fast as the longshore current provides it (see Figure 7-20). When the rip current flows seaward, it can carry large quantities of sediment away from the beach. If this material is not returned to the beach by the incoming waves, the beach will gradually be eroded. Many beaches lose their sediment because they are situated near submarine canyons (Figure 8-8). Sand carried by longshore currents is intercepted and deposited in these submarine canyons where it is carried—probably by slumping or turbidity currents—into the deep sea after removal from the beach.

The usual direction of movement of sand is toward the beach. During times of long-period waves (generally during the summer months), sand is picked up from shallow depths and deposited on the beach.

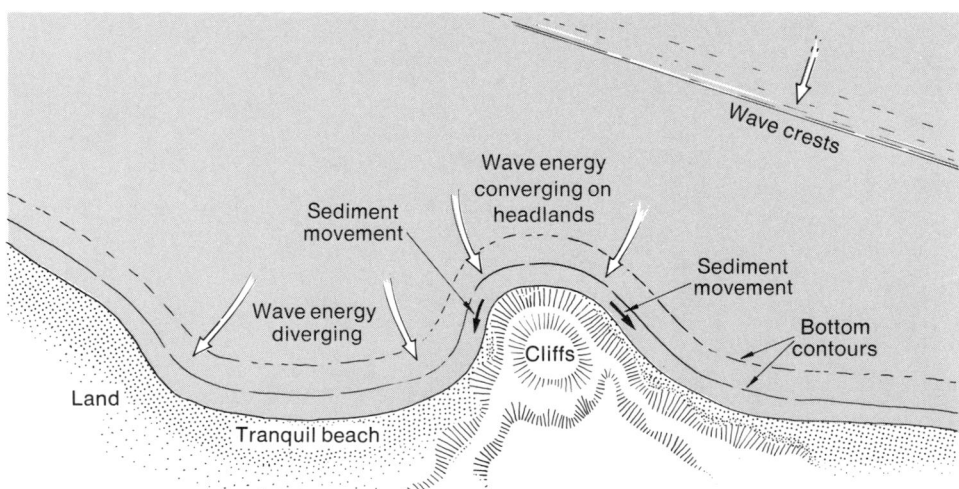

Figure 8-7   Convergence and divergence of wave energy due to the refraction of waves.

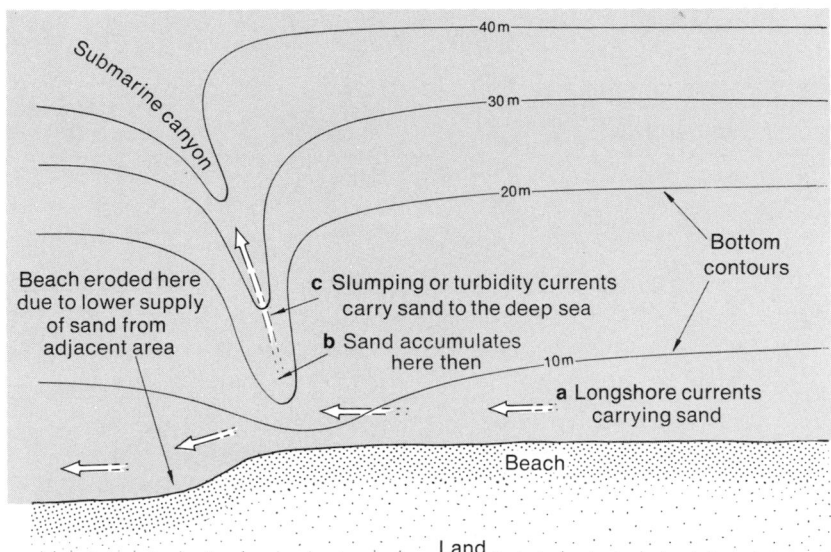

Figure 8-8   Loss of sediment from a beach due to the presence of a nearshore submarine canyon.

Sand is removed, however, by the backrush of water down the beach, is carried seaward, but then quickly settles to the bottom where it can again be carried landward to the beach by subsequent waves. The net result is deposition on the beach. During times of high waves of short period, the short period keeps the sand in suspension and prevents its settling. Therefore much of the sand washed off the beach by the backrush of water will not settle until it is carried into deeper water outside the action of subsequent waves. This situation generally occurs in winter and results in the loss of beach sand (see Figure 8-5).

Most beach sand has come from the sea floor, but its original source is the land, from which it is carried to the ocean by rivers, wind, glaciers, and cliff erosion. In most areas of the world very small quantities of sediment are presently being supplied to the ocean. This is due to the recent rise in sea level which has caused most rivers to empty directly into their estuaries, rather than into the ocean, and deposit most of their sediment into the estuary.

The slope of the beach face is related to the grain size of its sediments. As seen from Table 8-1, the coarser the grain size the steeper the beach face. Gravel beaches are common in areas of strong waves, where the sand and finer sediments have been removed by the waves, or in areas where little sand has been supplied to the beach.

On some beaches, waves will remove the sand having a relatively low density and leave behind a deposit of high-density sand composed of heavy minerals (minerals having a density greater than about

TABLE 8-1   THE RELATIONSHIP OF BEACH FACE SLOPES TO THE
DIAMETER OF THE SEDIMENT (DATA FROM SHEPARD, 1963)

Sediment Type	Diameter (mm)	Average Slope of Beach Face
Very fine sand	$\frac{1}{16}-\frac{1}{8}$	1°
Fine sand	$\frac{1}{8}-\frac{1}{4}$	3°
Medium sand	$\frac{1}{4}-\frac{1}{2}$	5°
Coarse sand	$\frac{1}{2}-1$	7°
Very coarse sand	1–2	9°
Granules	2–4	11°
Pebbles	4–64	17°
Cobbles	64–256	24°

2.9 g/cc³; the density of quartz, the most common component of beach sand, is 2.65 g/cc³). Heavy minerals are sometimes of economic importance, and they are mined in some localities. Since sea level changes have caused the shoreline to migrate over the continental shelf in recent times, many ancient beaches exist on what is now the underwater continental shelf. These ancient beaches can, if they contain heavy minerals, have important economic potential.

Estuaries and Lagoons Estuaries and lagoons are common to many coastal areas (see Figure 8-2). An **estuary,** as defined by D. W. Pritchard in 1967, is a semienclosed coastal body of water having a free connection with the open sea and within which sea water is diluted by fresh water derived from land drainage. A **lagoon** is an area of shallow water separated from the sea by low banks or bars. Due to the recent rise of sea level, most rivers of the world now flow into estuaries. K. O. Emery in 1967 noted that the distribution of estuaries and lagoons is related to the regional characteristics of the continental shelf and the coastal regions. Estuaries occur where continental shelves and coastal regions are narrow and have high relief, and lagoons occur where the shelves and coastal regions are wide and smooth. This distribution is reasonable as most estuaries are drowned river valleys or valleys (fjords) cut by glaciers, and lagoons are formed by the buildup of offshore bars in low-relief areas.

Estuaries and lagoons, like beaches and other parts of the coastal region, are temporary features. With time, both will be destroyed either by the buildup of marshes or by cutback of the coastline by marine erosion. In the former case, fresh-water marshes form at the inland areas and salt-water marshes or bars tend to close the seaward part of the estuary. Estuaries and fjords that are cut into solid rock are less likely to be affected by these processes. In many instances rivers carrying large quantities of sediment will fill in their estuary. In addition, considerable quantities of sediment can be carried into the estuary from the offshore areas. Thus if the estuary is an important navigation channel, like Chesapeake Bay, it may need almost continual dredging to keep it open.

It appears that the future of estuaries is bleak. If sea level were lowered, most estuaries would rapidly disappear, to be replaced by rivers cutting into their deposits. If sea level were to remain constant or raised a few meters, the processes of destruction would not be stopped. Only a considerable, but unlikely, rise in sea level would maintain or rejuvenate present estuaries. Thus it follows that estuaries were not common in the geological past except during periods of rising sea level or lowering of the land.

Marshes Marshes are common to many coastal regions. They usually occur in localities protected from surf, occupying a low, wet, area similar to a swamp. Generally there is a delicate balance between the marsh and the tidal channels that intersect it. Four main factors influence the development of a marsh, according to A. C. Redfield:

1. The tidal range
2. The physiology of the plants, which produce peat in relation to tidal levels
3. Processes of sedimentation on the tidal flats and within the strands of plants
4. The changing level of the sea relative to the land.

Most marshes have only a few species of life, but they are usually abundant. A plant zonation, common in most marshes, is related to exposure to the sea (Table 8-2). The plant *Zostera* (see Figure 6-11) is mostly covered by water; proceeding toward higher ground the sequence of plants usually is *Spartina, Salicornia,* and *Distichlis*.

TABLE 8-2 TYPICAL PLANT ZONATION IN A SALT WATER MARSH

Plant	Exposure
Zostera	Always submerged
Spartina	Submerged twice daily
Salicornia	Submerged once daily
Distichlis	Submerged a few times a month

If one takes a core sample from a marsh, it may be possible to determine how the marsh is forming. For example, if *Spartina* was found to be growing over *Salicornia,* it would indicate a relative rise in sea level in the marsh area, since *Spartina* will grow closer to sea level than *Salicornia*.

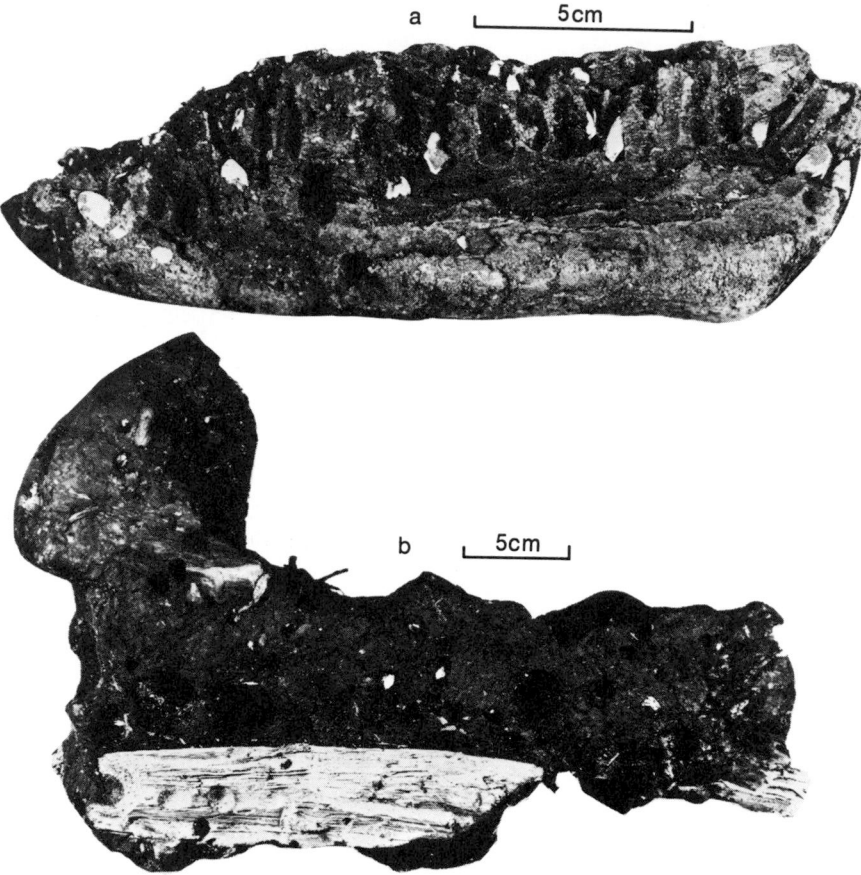

Figure 8-9   Freshwater peat collected on the continental shelf of the northeastern United States near Cape Cod. The holes in the upper part of A were bored by pelecypods. A piece of wood is enclosed in the fibrous matrix of B. (Emery and others, *Science* **158** [December, 1967]: 1304; Copyright 1967 by the American Association for the Advancement of Science.)

The accumulation of large quantities of plants such as *Salicornia* and *Spartina* in the marsh forms a deposit or soil that is called peat. Because peat forms at or near sea level, it can indicate the past position of sea level. The recent rise in sea level has resulted in many peat deposits being left on the shallow portions of the continental shelf. Studies of fresh-water peat collected from the shelf off the northeastern United States indicate that this was covered by terrestrial vegetation (Figure 8-9) about 11,000 years ago.

Continental Shelves

The **continental shelves** are the shallow part of the sea floor immediately adjacent to and surrounding the land (see Figure 8-1). They can be thought of as generally smooth platforms that terminate seaward with an abrupt change in slope, the shelf break, which leads to the continental slope.

Continental shelves cover a large area: approximately one-sixth of the world. The definition of continental shelves is important for numerous reasons. Many rights of the sea, such as free passage of ships, mineral rights, fishing rights, and military jurisdiction are determined by the position of the continental shelf. In the past, the shelf was limited to the zone inside the 100-fathom line. This is not an adequate definition because shelves rarely terminate at 100 fathoms. The present depth limit as stated by a 1957 United Nations report prepared by marine geologists is 300 fathoms.

The topography of the continental shelf is fairly well-known in some areas (Figure 8-10) and generalizations can be made. The topography is generally irregular, consisting of many small hills, valleys, and depressions. Shepard in 1963 noted the following statistics of continental shelves:

1. The average width of the shelf is 40 nautical miles.
2. The average slope of the shelf is 0°07′ (a slope undetectable by the naked eye).
3. The average depth where the greatest change of slope occurs is 72 fathoms.
4. Hills with relief of 10 fathoms or more were observed on 60 percent of the profiles he examined; depressions of 10 fathoms or more were present on 35 percent of the profiles.

Although the continental shelves of the world are quite variable, two types seem to prevail: (1) glaciated shelves and (2) unglaciated shelves. One should remember that most shelves have been recently exposed because of Pleistocene sea-level changes. When sea level started rising, about 20,000 years ago, the shoreline migrated from what is now the submerged outer edge of most continental shelves to its present position. Therefore the recent history of many shelves is very confused. An additional source of difficulty in studying shelves is that some are unstable in that they have moved up or down independent of sea-level changes. An example is seen in parts of the California coast, where recently-formed beaches are found several meters above present sea level, indicating that this area has been rising quicker than sea level.

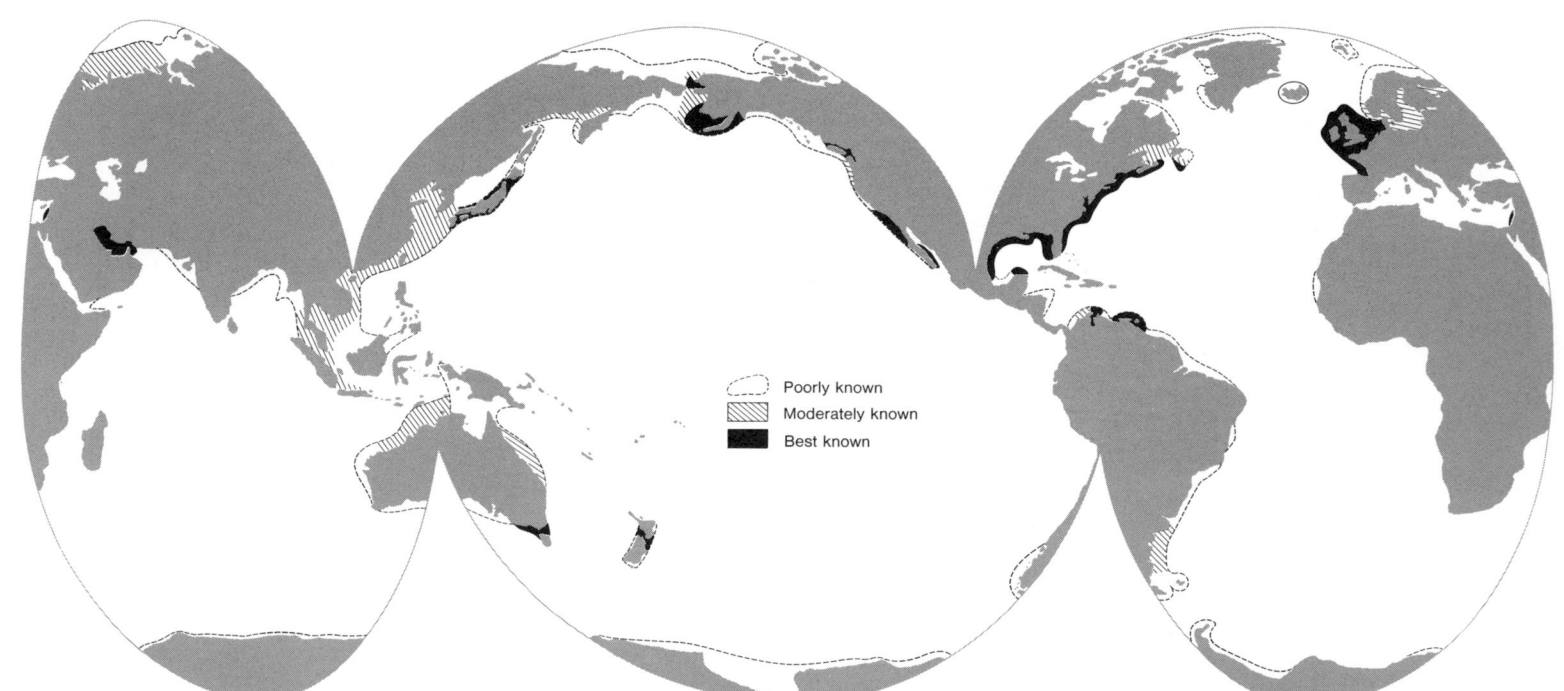

Figure 8-10   Distribution of the wider continental shelves of the world and comparative levels of geological knowledge of the shelves. For those indicated as poorly known we have little more than general topographic information; for those listed as moderately known we have additional information on sediments, on lithology, or on structure; for those indicated as best known we have information in all four fields. (After Emery, 1966.)

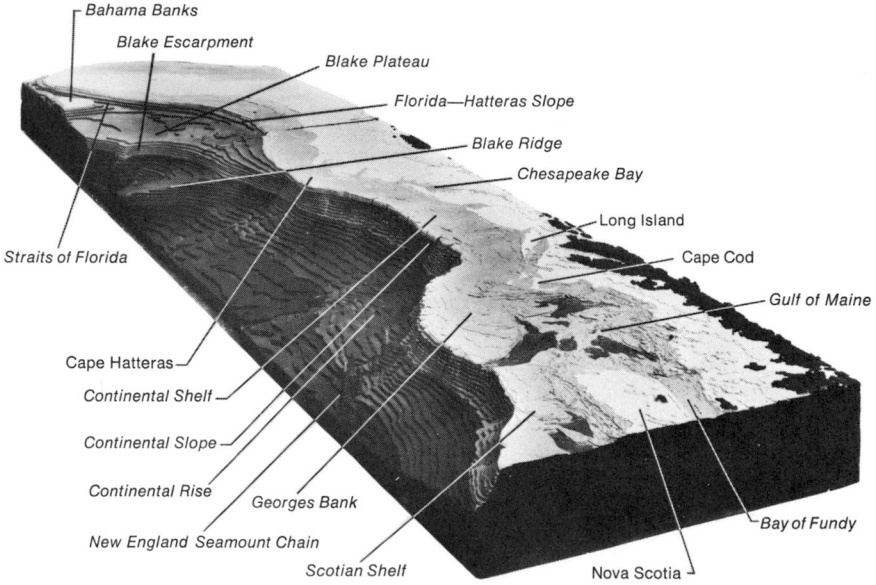

a

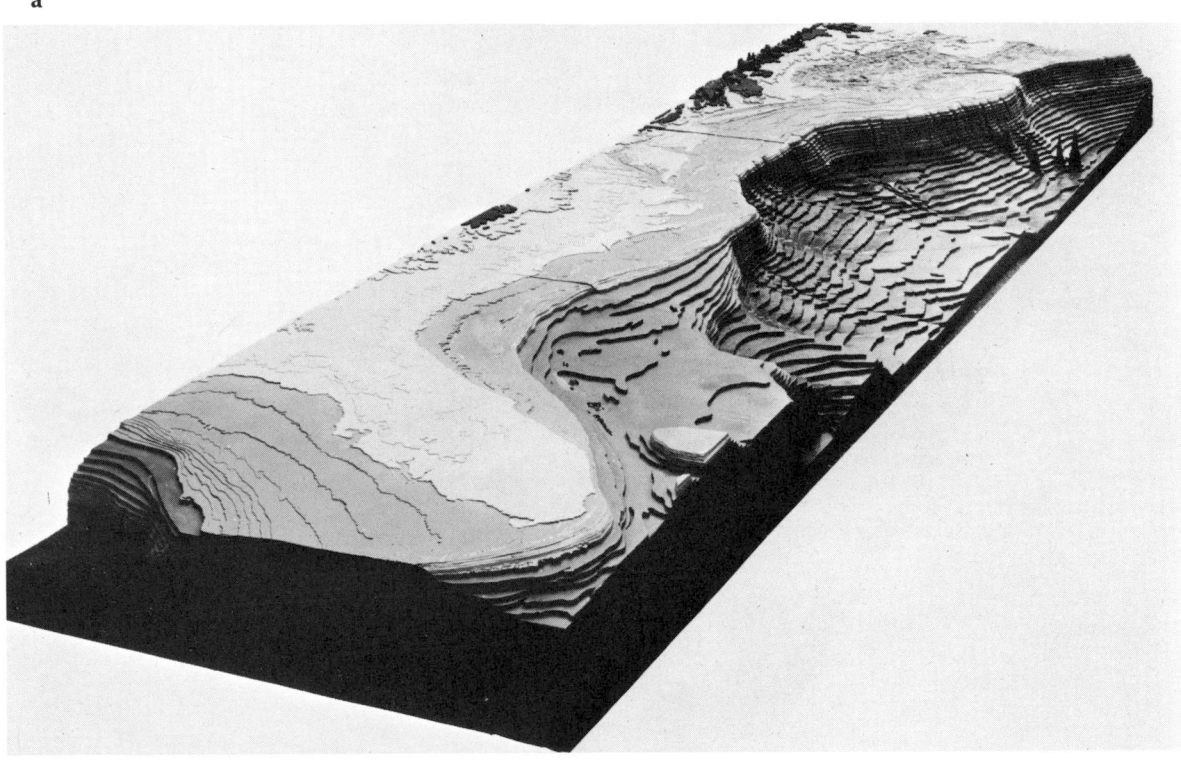

b

Figure 8-11 Topographic model of the east coast of the United States (a) looking south, (b) looking north. Color changes occur at 200 m (about the edge of the continental shelf), 2,000 m, and 4,000 m. Vertical exaggeration is 20 times. (Model constructed from Uchupi's 1965 bathymetric charts.)

Both glaciated and unglaciated shelves have been affected by the rise of sea level, but only in the first are the direct effects of the glaciers evident. An example is the northeastern coast of the United States (Figure 8-11). In the northern part the shelf has been glaciated; that is, during periods of lowered sea level, glaciers covered and eroded the shelf (Figure 8-12). The erosion is shown by the numerous banks, basins, and valleys on the shelf. The irregular topography of the Scotian shelf and the Gulf of Maine thus are indications that the glaciers may have covered part of Georges Bank, but this area is shallow and exposed to the smoothing effects of waves and tides and, therefore, little topographic evidence of this possible glaciation remains. The channel between Georges Bank and the Scotian shelf was cut by a glacier. That glaciers covered this area is also indicated by the mixture of coarse- and fine-grained sediments found in the Gulf of Maine (Figure 8-13). Sediments having such a wide range of grain size are typical of glacial deposits.

Figure 8-12   Topographic model of northern part of the east coast of the United States from Nova Scotia to south of New York. Note the irregular topography of the Gulf of Maine and the relatively smooth topography of the shelf off Long Island. Color changes occur at 200 m, 2,000 m, and 4,000 m. Vertical exaggeration is 20 times. (From charts by Uchupi, 1965.)

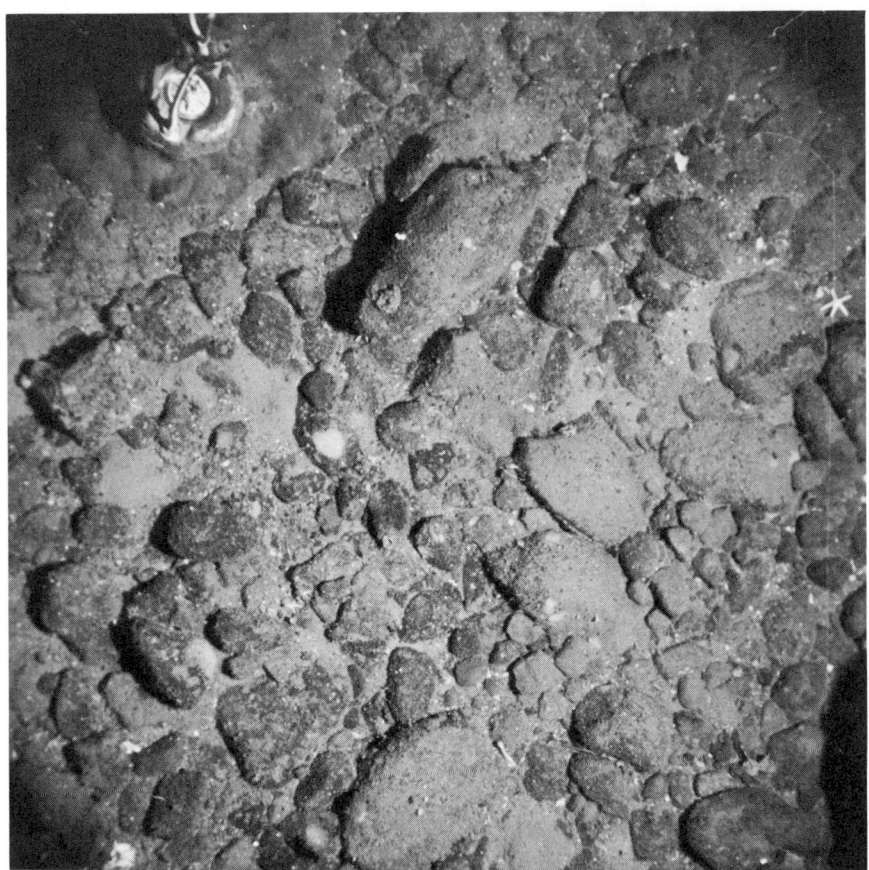

Figure 8-13 Coarse-grained sediments photographed in the Gulf of Maine Such sediments are typical of glacial deposits.

South of Cape Cod, particularly in the Long Island area (see Figure 8-12), there is an abrupt change in the character of the shelf. The deep basin, channels, and banks found to the north are absent and the topography becomes relatively smooth. This is an example of an un-glaciated shelf, which is generally smoother than the glaciated variety, although some relief may appear due to strong currents, submarine canyons, or folding and faulting (Figure 8-14).

Off coasts where there are very strong currents, the continental shelf can be narrow or almost absent. An example of this is the east coast of southern Florida (Figure 8-15) where the Gulf Stream, flowing with speeds up to 6 knots, comes close to the mainland. It is strong enough to prevent deposition of most sediment and apparently has not permitted normal development of a shelf in this area. The Gulf Stream is so strong here that, even at depths of several hundreds of

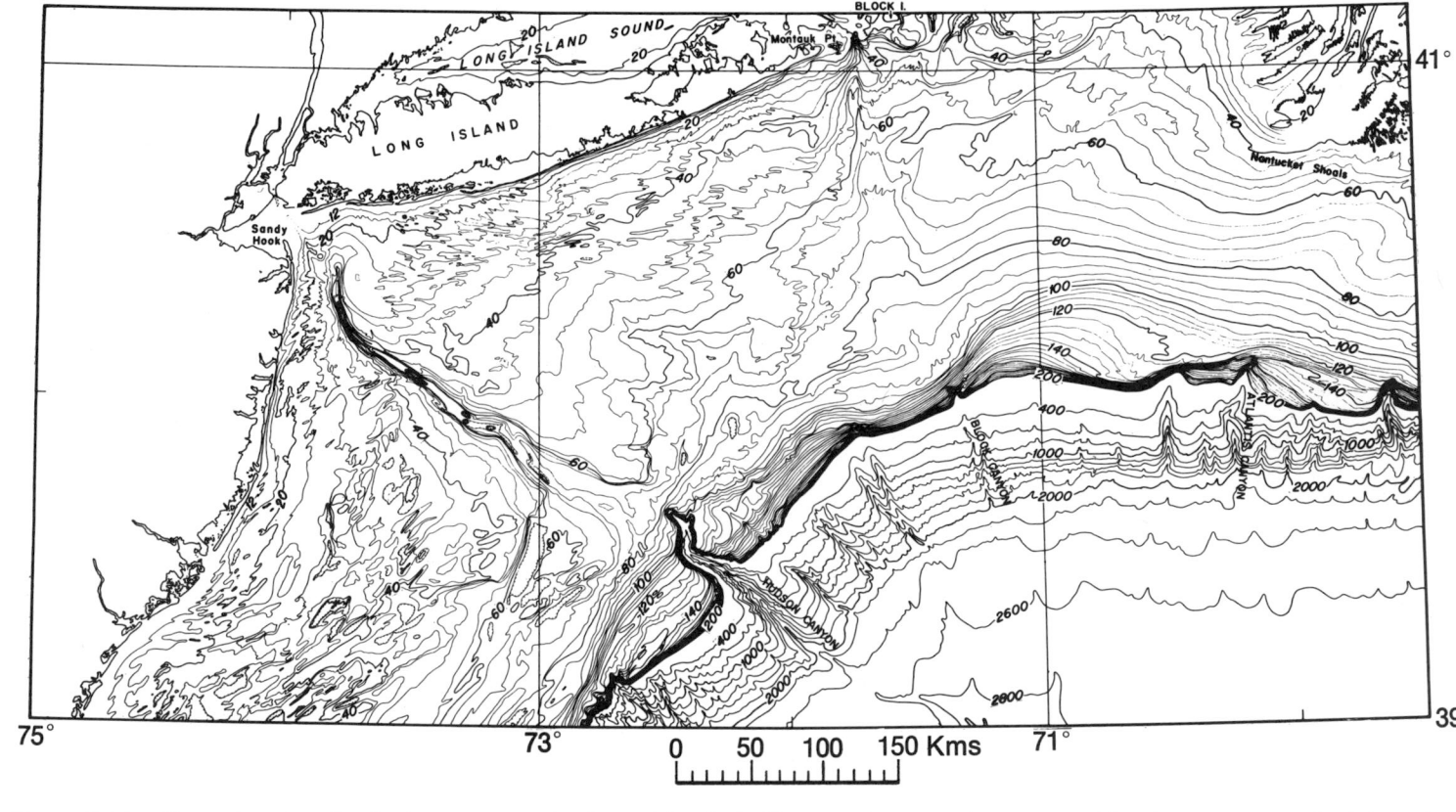

Figure 8-14   Chart showing the bathymetry on the Long Island shelf. Note the irregularity caused by the extension of Hudson Canyon and possibly Block Canyon on the shelf. Other irregularities are caused by currents that have moved the sediments, forming small ridges and valleys (contour interval in meters). (From charts by Uchupi, 1965.)

Figure 8-15 Topographic model of the continental shelf and slope off Florida. Note the absence of a shelf off the southeastern part of Florida. This absence is apparently due to the swiftly flowing Gulf Stream that comes close to the mainland of eastern Florida. Vertical exaggeration is 20 times. (From charts by Uchupi, 1965.)

fathoms on the Blake Plateau, it has scoured and removed much of the bottom sediment.

Another type of continental shelf is found near large rivers having deltas. For example, the Mississippi River has built a delta across most of its continental shelf and is now supplying sediment to the deeper parts of the Gulf of Mexico.

Most of the shelves off the west coast of the United States are unglaciated and relatively narrow. In many areas they are covered with a thin veneer of sediments. Some glaciation is evident off the coast of Washington and British Columbia.

Before development of the elaborate geophysical equipment now available to oceanographers, the usual hypothesis of the origin of continental shelves was that the shelves were created by a combination of wave cutting and wave building processes. As the waves attacked a coastline, they would cut into it, forming a terrace, and the

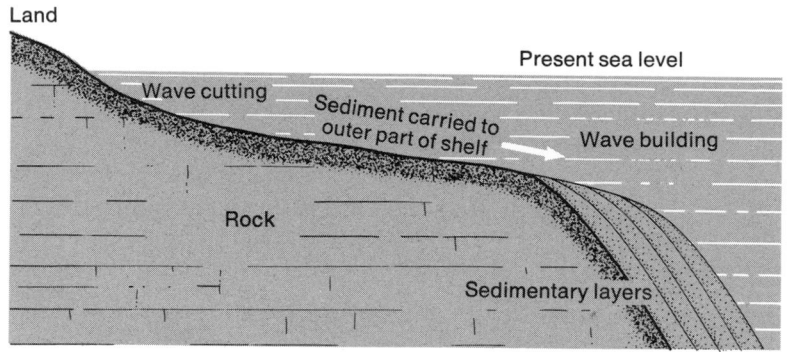

Figure 8-16 The wave cutting and building hypothesis for the origin of continental shelves.

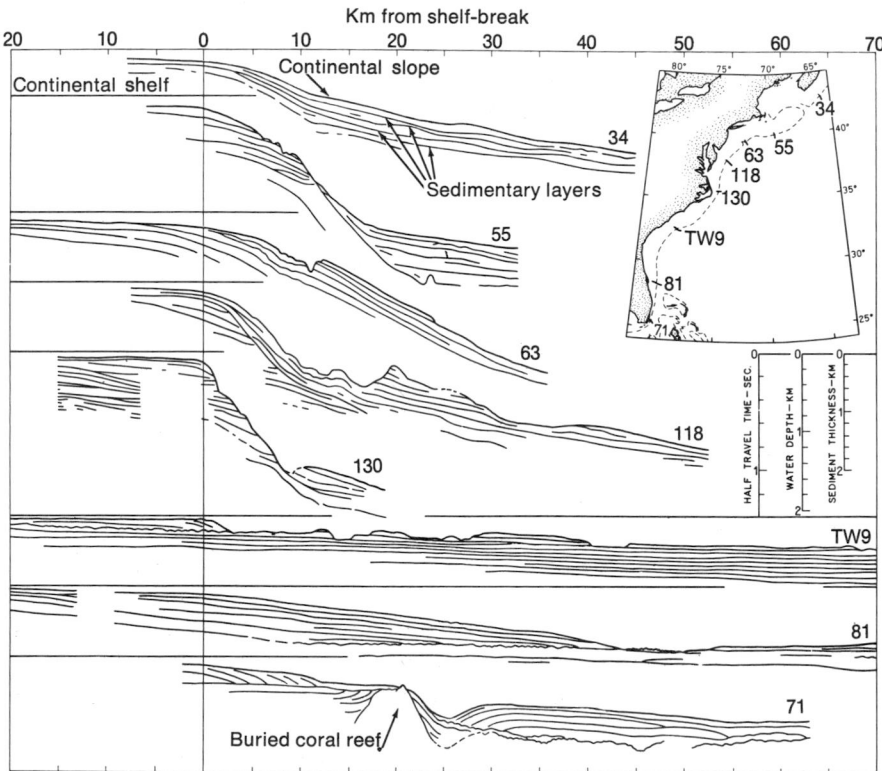

Figure 8-17 Continuous seismic profiles made off various parts of the continental shelf and slope of the United States. The lines indicate sedimentary layers. (After Emery, 1967.)

sediment removed would be carried seaward to form the outer part of the shelf (Figure 8-16). This hypothesis was found to be lacking, particularly in light of additional data revealed by continuous seismic profiling (CSP). CSP records showed that the structure of most continental shelves varies considerably and that a simple hypothesis was not adequate. CSP records from the east coast of the United States (Figure 8-17) show some of the different structures found. Profile 34 off Nova Scotia shows a thin sequence of sedimentary layers on the continental shelf, thickening toward the deeper continental slope. Profile 55 off Georges Bank and profile 130 off Cape Hatteras show an abrupt truncation of the sedimentary layers at the edge of the continental slope. Some truncation, although of a different nature, is shown in profile 118 off Delaware. Profile 63 off Long Island is intermediate in that the reflecting layers are parallel to the slope and shelf. Profiles TW 9 and 81 off South Carolina and Florida show an outbuilding of the continental shelf and slope away from the land. Profile 71 off

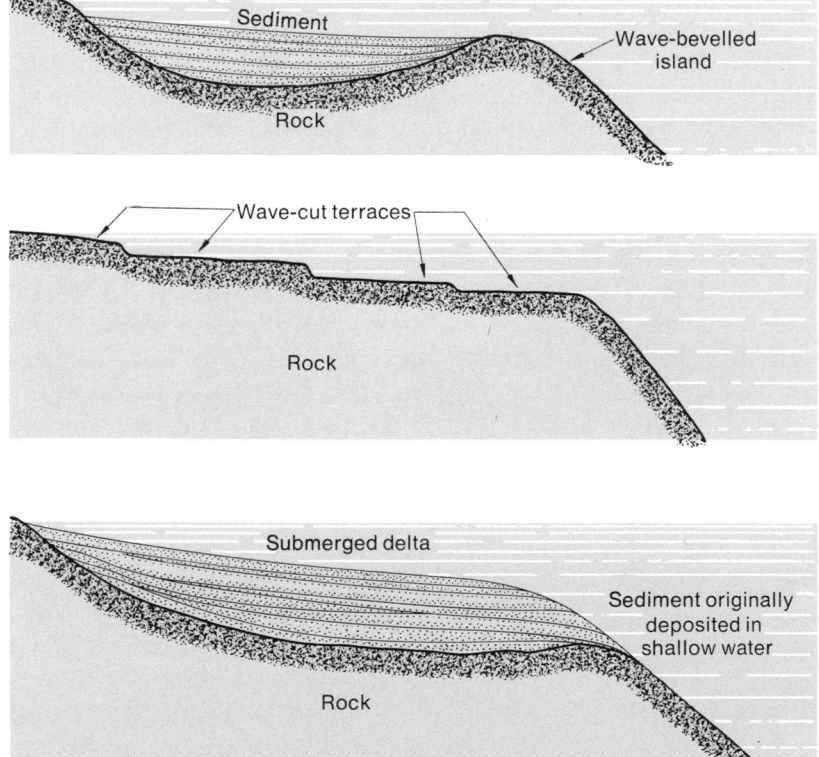

Figure 8-18   Some different methods of shelf formation. (After Shepard, 1963.)

southern Florida is complex, showing terraces covered by sediments. A buried coral reef may be present about 20 km from the **shelf break.** Profiles show that development of the continental shelf in this area has been due mainly to upbuilding by sedimentation, but that the process is complex and differs from area to area. Some other methods of shelf development are shown in Figure 8-18. From the data summarized above one must conclude that numerous methods of continental shelf formation are possible. Recent changes of sea level obviously play an important, if not dominant, role in most of these methods.

Continental Slopes

Continental slopes occur between the two major topographical features of our planet (see Figure 1-3): the land and the ocean basin. The continental slope extends downward from the outer part of the continental shelf to the deep-sea floor. In some areas its junction with the deep-sea floor is hard to define, either because of a decrease in slope or because of the presence of a deep-sea trench bordering the continental shelf. The area where the slope decreases is called the continental rise (see p. 273). Elsewhere, such as off the California coast and on the Blake Plateau off southeastern Florida, there is an intermediate area between the deep sea and the continental shelf that is called the continental borderland.

The average inclination of the continental slope is about 4° (a slope of about 70 m in 1 km or 70:1000); off the Blake Plateau and in other places the inclination may be 20° or more (see Figure 8-15). The inclination of the slope off large rivers and deltas, by contrast, can be as gentle as 1°. Shepard noted that slopes off coasts of fault origin have insignificant shelves and average about 5.6°; slopes off mountainous coasts, about 4.6°; slopes off stable coasts, about 3°; and slopes off major deltas, about 1.3°. The Pacific coast, which follows a major earthquake zone, tends to have somewhat steeper slopes than the Atlantic or Indian Ocean.

Characteristics of continental slopes vary noticeably along the Atlantic coast of the United States (see Figures 8-11, 8-12, 8-14, 8-15, and 8-17). Off the northern coast, there is a modest inclination approaching a maximum of 5° down to the continental rise. Also in many places the slope is cut by submarine canyons. South of Cape Hatteras there is an abrupt change in the slope, with one or more broad steps instead of a continuous declivity to the deep sea. A prominent terrace, called the Blake Plateau, lies at a depth of 700 to 1,100 m (Figure 8-19). The Blake Plateau is relatively smooth, due in part probably to erosion by the Gulf Stream, which flows over it.

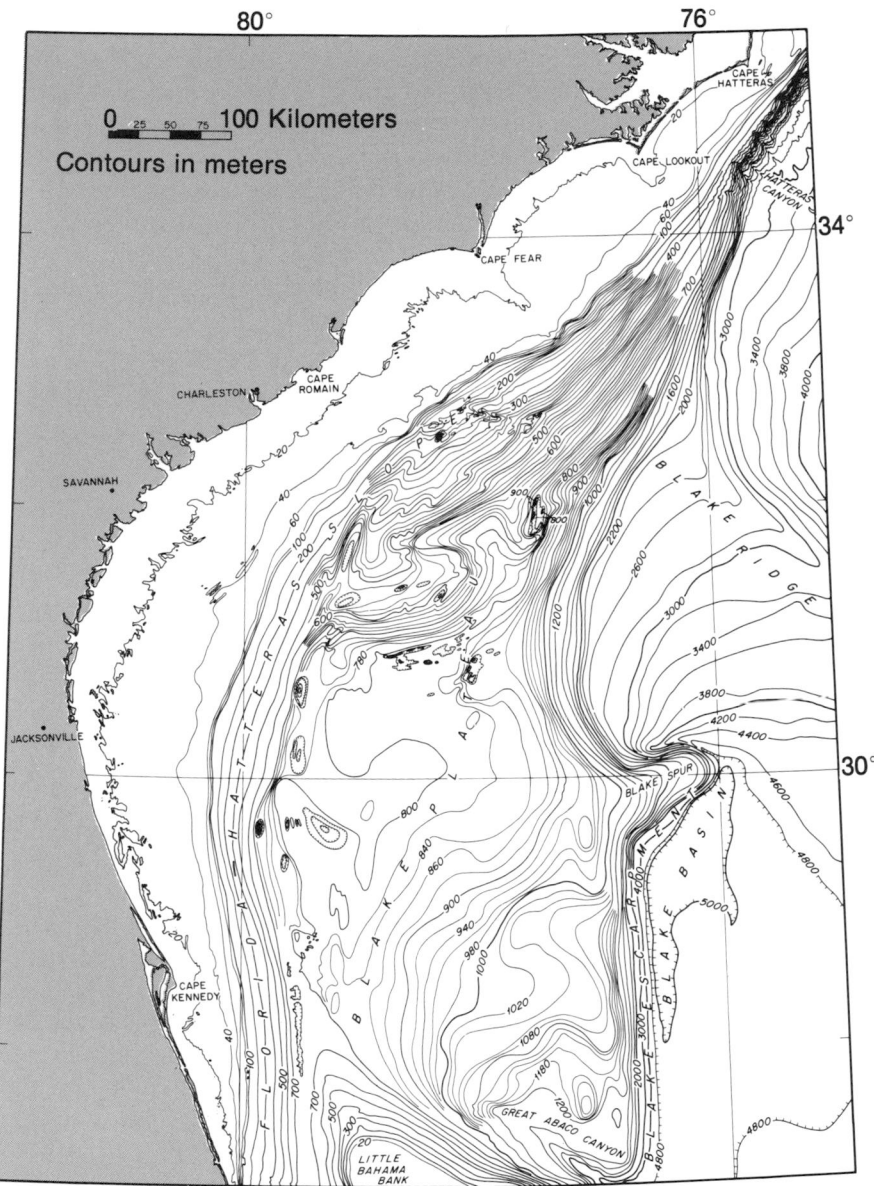

Figure 8-19 A detailed bathymetric chart of the Blake Plateau region. This broad area interrupts the continental slope dividing it into two sections. Such an intermediate area is called a continental borderland. (From Uchupi, 1967.)

The sediments of the continental slope are usually mud. Much of the mud was carried to the slope during times of lowered sea level, when erosion by rivers, wind, and other processes could have carried material directly to the continental slope. In some areas, especially those off fault or mountainous coasts, rock outcrops are common.

The sediment types of the continental shelf and slope of the east coast of the United States are shown in Figure 8-20. Sand-sized fluviatile (deposited by rivers) sediment is dominant, except for some biogenic (of biological origin) sediments on the Blake Plateau, and some authigenic sediments (minerals that formed in the place where they are found, usually the result of some chemical or biological reaction) on the continental slope. Most of the sediments of the shelf are **relict,** meaning that they do not represent the present-day environment, but are left from a previous one, in this instance before the recent rise of sea level.

The internal structure of continental slopes has been studied·by continuous seismic reflection techniques. Recent results (see Figure 8-17) show considerable variations, but most slopes show some degree of slumping or failure of the sediments. Slumping undoubtedly explains some of the rock outcrops common to many coasts. Other seismic sections show large sequences of seaward-dipped sediments. In general, the lower part of the slope is occupied by a thick wedge of sediment which constitutes the continental rise.

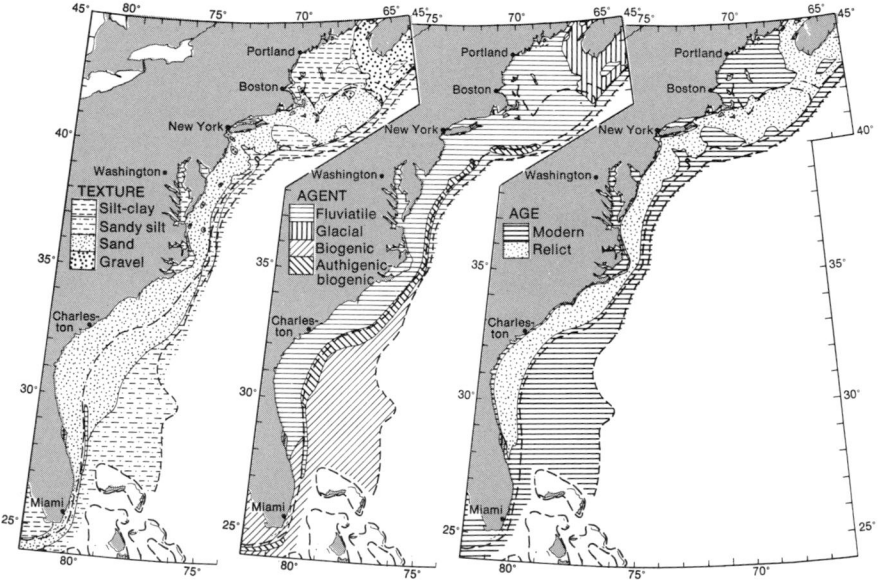

Figure 8-20 The texture, mode of deposition, and age of the surface sediments on the continental shelf and slope of the east coast of the United States. (From Emery, 1966.)

Many theories have been proposed for the origin of the continental slope; they include the wave-built theory proposed for the continental shelf, and various folding and faulting theories. The data favor a fault theory. Evidence compiled by Shepard in 1963 includes:

1. Deep trenches occur along about 50 percent of the continental slopes of the world; trenches are considered to be a very unstable part of the earth's crust.
2. Continental slopes off areas without trenches are in many aspects similar to those with trenches and also may be subject to earthquakes, indicating instability.
3. Continental slopes in some instances cut across dominant trends of land features, suggesting faulting.

The fault hypothesis doesn't necessarily suggest that most of the faulting is occurring at present, but rather that the slope is being maintained by occasional fault movements. Detailed studies indicate that although faulting may be the major cause of the slope, its effects are hidden by the deposition of undisturbed (that is, unaffected by slumping or faulting) sediments (see profile 34, Figure 8-17). Most continental slopes, however, have been modified by slides and turbidity currents, especially near submarine canyons.

Continental Rise

Many continental slopes end in a gently inclining, broad topographic feature called the **continental rise.** The continental rise usually has an inclination of less than half a degree (or less than 1:100); the average inclination of the continental slope is about 7:100. The width of the rise is usually between 100 and 1,000 km, whereas the continental slope averages about 20 km in width. Heezen and his co-workers have noted that some continental rises can be divided into an upper and lower part (Figure 8-21). Each part can be divided into three sections, an upper and lower steep section and a flatter middle section. The relief of most rises is very low, generally being interrupted only by submarine canyons or seamounts.

Geophysical observations of most continental rises show a wedge-like sequence of sediments, sometimes as much as 10 km thick. Detailed studies, using continuous seismic reflection techniques, show that much of the sediment may have accumulated by slumping down from the steeper continental slope (Figure 8-22). The continental rise may also represent that part of the continental margin that was once closer to sea level but has been downfaulted to its present depth.

The thick sequence of sediments in the continental rise has been compared to that found in many mountain ranges, suggesting that the

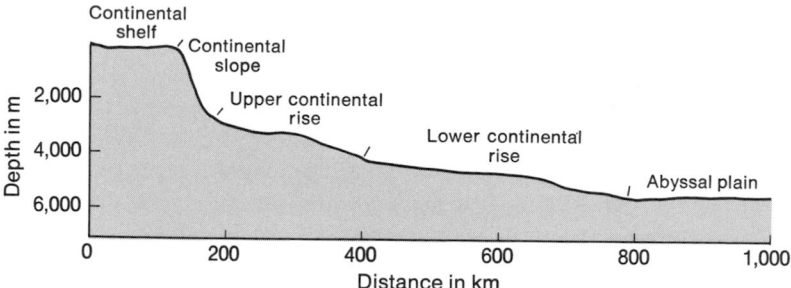

Figure 8-21 The divisions of the continental rise. This profile is representative of the area from Georges Bank to Cape Hatteras. (After Heezen and others, 1959.)

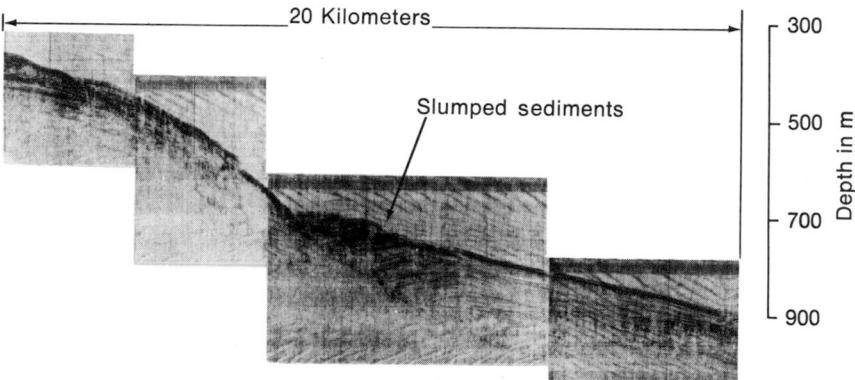

Figure 8-22 Continuous seismic profile showing evidence of sediments that have slumped down onto the continental rise. The record was obtained from the continental slope and rise southeast of Long Island. (After Uchupi, 1967.)

continental rise may, after considerable time, be uplifted above sea level and eventually form a mountain range. The long linear trend of most continental rises and their parallel position to the edge of the continent are similar to the position and form of many mountain ranges, such as the Appalachian and Sierra Nevada before they were uplifted. This suggests that continents may grow at their borders by the accretion of sediments on continental rises or in nearshore trenches.

Submarine Canyons

Many areas of the continental shelf and slope are cut by submarine canyons. These canyons may even cross the continental rise and extend into the deep ocean basins. Although canyons or valleys of glacial origin (see Northeast Channel on Figure 8-12) and of obvious fault

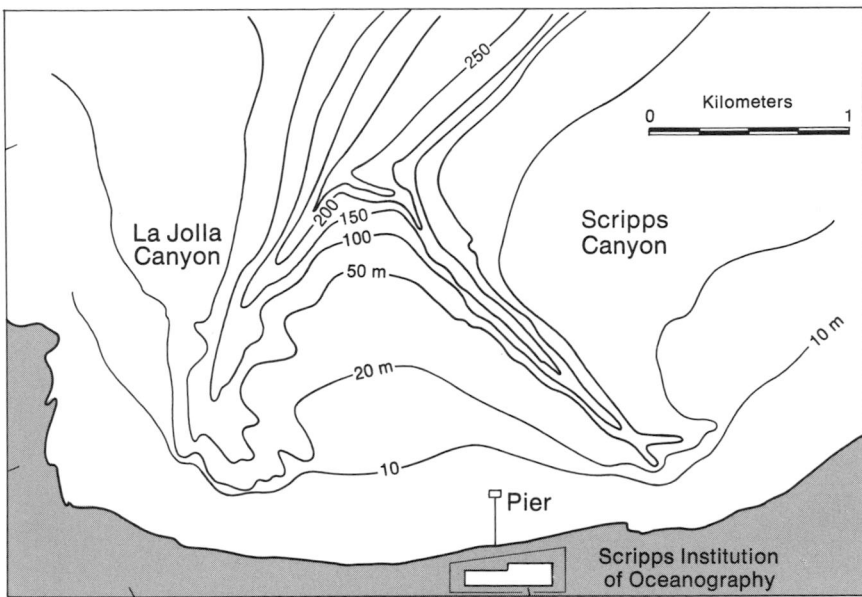

Figure 8-23   The Scripps and La Jolla Submarine Canyons, located near the Scripps Institution of Oceanography. (After Shepard and others, 1964.)

origin have been observed, the term submarine canyon is generally applied only to those canyons having winding, rock-walled, V-shaped profiles and tributary canyons that extend down the continental slope. The dimensions of some canyons are impressive: Monterey Canyon off southern California has a greater relief than the Grand Canyon; Hudson Canyon off the Hudson River extends seaward 150 miles. It then continues for another 150 miles as a leveed channel across the continental rise.

The best known canyons are off the coast of southern California, especially two that are within a mile of Scripps Institution of Oceanography (Figure 8-23)—La Jolla and Scripps Canyons. Scripps Canyon, which is a tributary of La Jolla Canyon, lies about 200 m offshore of a land canyon. Sediment accumulates in the head or nearshore parts of the submarine canyon, and during certain times of the year moves out of the canyon into deep water because of slumping or other types of movement. This sediment movement has enlarged and scoured Scripps Canyon. Such movements may result in the turbidity currents mentioned in Chapter 7. La Jolla and Scripps Canyons continue as steep-walled features to a depth of about 300 m, about 1 mile from land, where they join. A little farther out the relief of the steep precipitous walls is reduced and the canyon becomes more of a small channel cut into the underlying sediments. The channel continues seaward until it ends in a thick sedimentary deposit or fan. Large quantities of

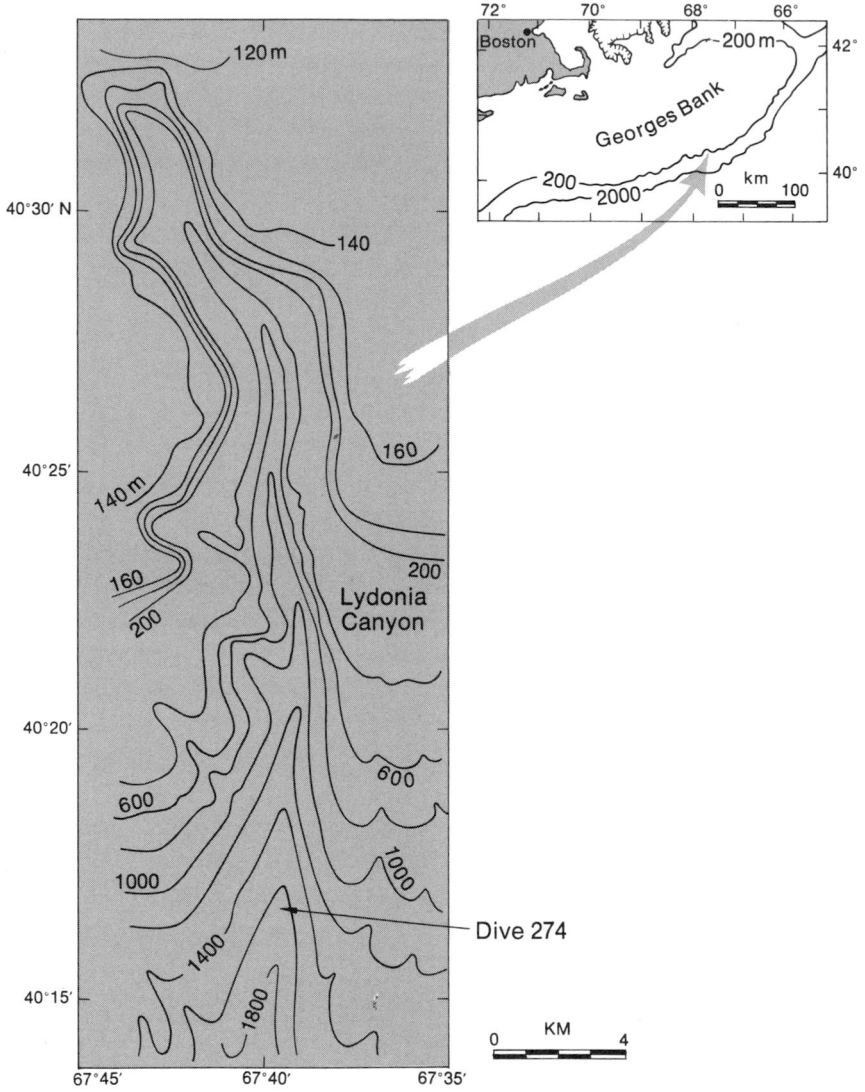

Figure 8-24   Lydonia Canyon, situated on the seaward side of Georges Bank. Note the generally straight trend of the canyon. The arrow points to the location of a dive the author made with ALVIN into the axis of the canyon (see Figure 8-26).

Figure 8-25   Pictures taken in Corsair Canyon, another canyon on the seaward side of Georges Bank. This canyon is northeast of Lydonia Canyon (see Figure 8-24). The pictures were taken from the submersible ALVIN; note the mechanical arm and instruments of the submersible in the figures. (a) Shows ripple marks on the ocean bottom sediments in the axis of the canyon at a depth of 1,604 m. (b) Shows a rock outcrop that has been undercut. The **ripple marks and the undercutting are both probably due to strong currents.** (After Ross, 1968.)

stratified coarse sand similar to that found near the head or beginning of the canyon constitute the fan, suggesting that a turbidity current or similar mechanism has carried the sediment to this area, a distance of about 20 miles.

Submarine canyons found along the northeast coast of the United States (see Figure 8-12) generally do not have tributaries and usually extend straight down the continental slope (Figure 8-24) rather than crossing it at an angle as do most of the California canyons. Atlantic coast canyons also have a V-shaped profile and contain rock outcrops.

Figure 8-25

Questions about the origin of submarine canyons are not completely resolved. Numerous indications of erosion by strong currents, presumably turbidity currents, have been observed by divers and from submersibles (Figure 8-25). The large accumulation of terrestrial sediment, of land origin, at the seaward end of most canyons also argues for the existence of turbidity currents. Some scientists have noted the similarity of submarine canyons to those canyons on land that were cut by streams and have suggested that perhaps the submarine canyons were cut during times of lowered sea level, when rivers would have crossed and cut into most continental shelves and parts of some continental slopes. Proponents of this theory have difficulty reconciling the fact that many canyons exist below the depths of even the most extreme suggested limits of lowered sea level. On the other hand, it is hard to imagine how turbidity currents could cut a winding canyon or how the currents could be strong enough to erode the hard rock into which some canyons are cut. Perhaps both hypotheses are partially correct: the canyons could have been cut during times of lowered sea level and are subsequently maintained and enlarged by turbidity currents.

Figure 8-26 Diagrammatic representation of the structure in the axis of Lydonia Canyon (see Figure 8-24) at a depth of about 1,600 m. It is most reasonable to assume that this structure arose by slumping.

Other hypotheses of submarine canyon formation include submarine springs and slumping (Figure 8-26). The increased use of submersibles in canyons should help provide definitive answers concerning the origin of submarine canyons.

THE OCEAN BASIN

To best describe the characteristics of the deep ocean basin I have chosen to first discuss the major features of the Atlantic, Pacific, Indian, and Arctic Oceans and of one marginal sea, the Red Sea. I will then discuss deep-sea sediments and some of the various hypotheses proposed to account for the features of the deep sea.

The Atlantic Ocean

The Atlantic Ocean is the second largest ocean, and probably the most explored one. (A bathymetric chart of the North Atlantic was made over a century ago, see Figure 3-3.) The most obvious feature of the Atlantic is its shape. It has an elongated, sinuous basin that extends more than 11,000 km in the north-south direction and about 32,000 km in the east-west direction. Early studies showed that its bathymetry is dominated by the Mid-Atlantic Ridge, a continuous ridge that extends down the central part of the ocean. The symmetrical shape of the ocean on either side of this ridge (Figure 8-27) and the outline of the adjacent continents, which would fit together like pieces of a jigsaw puzzle if the ocean were removed, have long fascinated scientists and lead to the hypothesis of continental drift and, more recently, to that of sea-floor spreading.

The bathymetry of the Mid-Atlantic Ridge has been studied by Heezen and his co-workers (Figure 8-28). They have suggested that the ridge is part of a continuous feature that can be traced more than 55,000 km through the Atlantic, Indian, Antarctic, and Pacific Oceans. In the Atlantic Ocean the ridge occupies the middle third of the ocean. It is highly fractured, consisting of numerous mountains and hills. The most rugged topography occurs in the central area of the ridge; a large central rift or crack, which may be continuous over most of the ridge system, strikingly appears on most profiles. The central rift can be as much as 2,000 m below the peaks of the surrounding mountains. These mountains generally rise to within 2,000 m of sea level (the average depth of the ocean is 3,729 m). In some instances the mountains protrude through the surface of the ocean forming islands, such as the Azores and Tristan da Cunha in the South Atlantic.

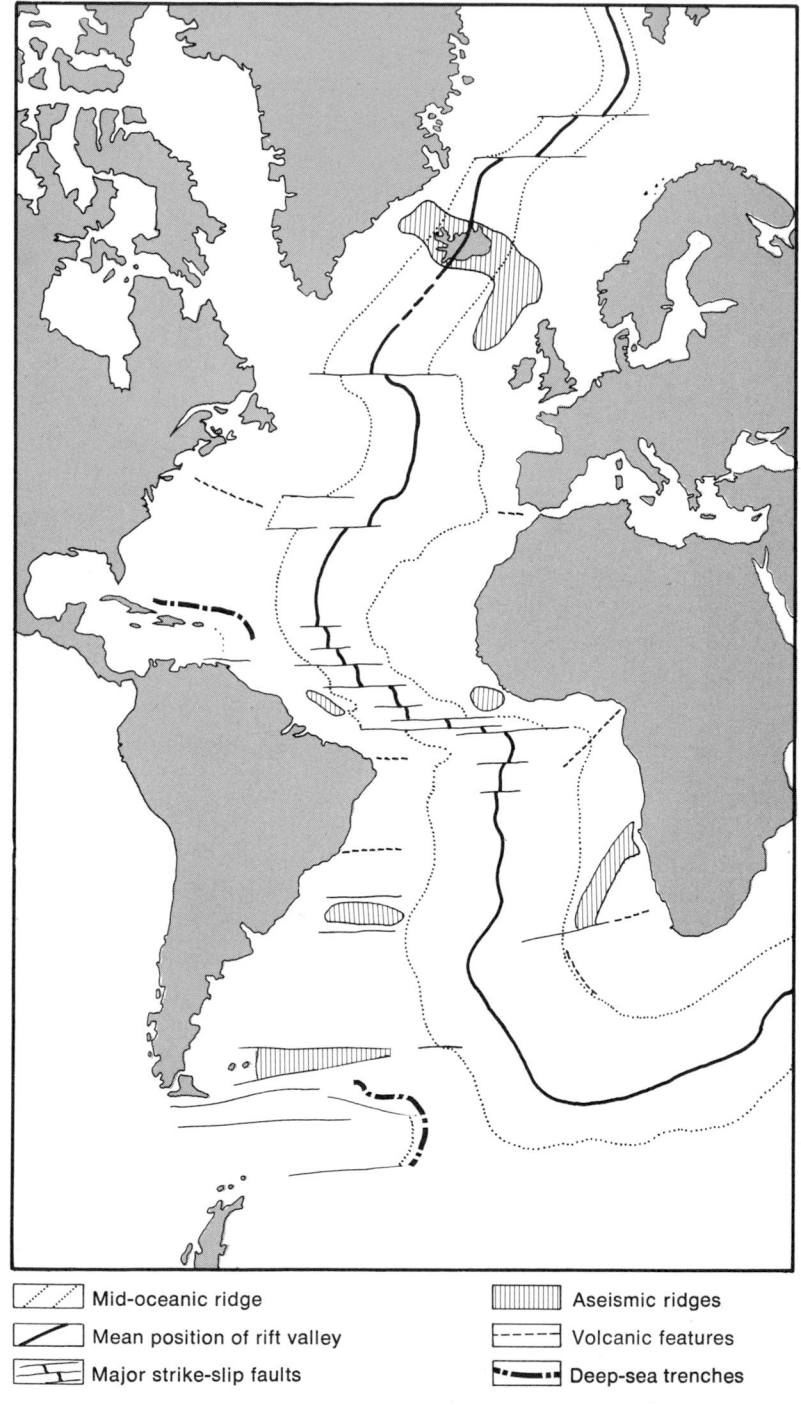

	Mid-oceanic ridge		Aseismic ridges
	Mean position of rift valley		Volcanic features
	Major strike-slip faults		Deep-sea trenches

Figure 8-27   General topographic features of the Atlantic Ocean.

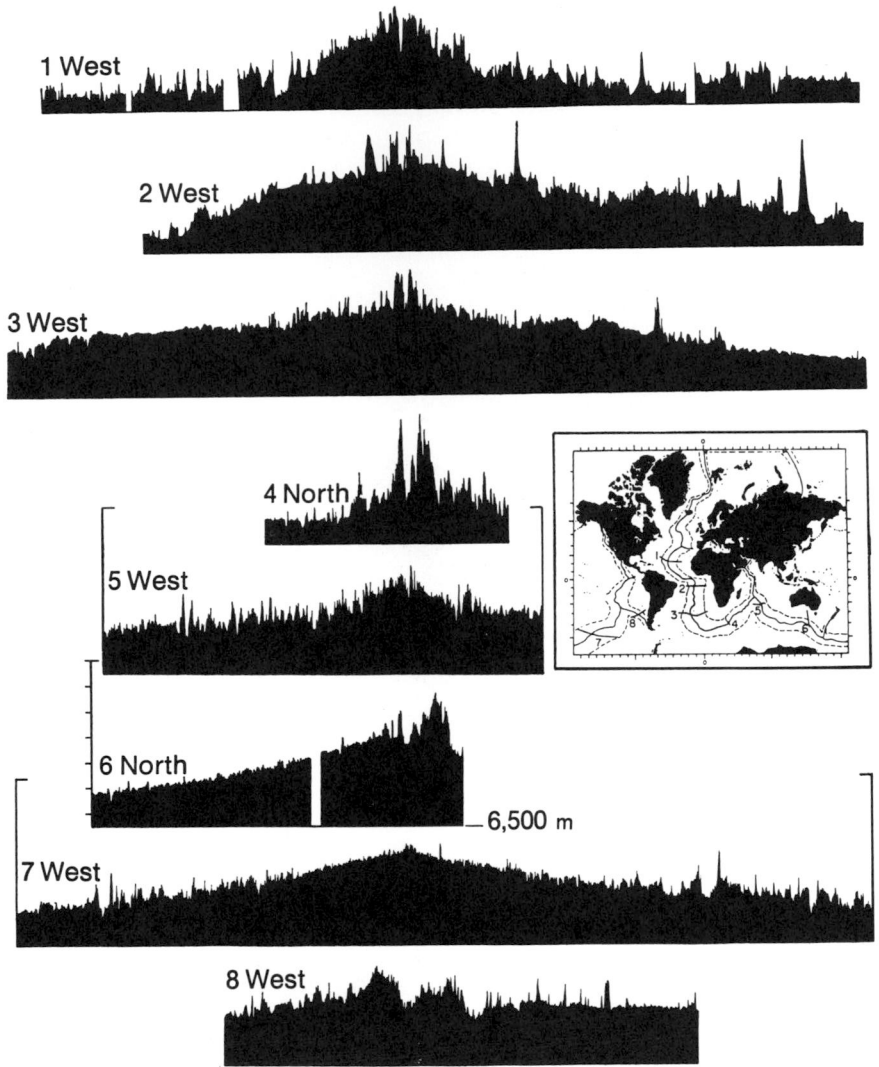

Figure 8-28 Profiles across the Mid-Atlantic Ridge, Indian Ocean Ridge, and East Pacific Rise. Base-line is 6,500m for all profiles. (From Heezen and Ewing, 1963.)

The Mid-Atlantic Ridge is seismically active, and apparently many earthquakes that occur along the ridge are centered under the central rift area. Measurements of the rate of heat being discharged from the Mid-Atlantic Ridge show relatively high values on the crest of the ridge that may be explained by the intrusion of volcanic rocks along the crest of the ridge.

Igneous rocks dredged from the ridge are basaltic, as are most rocks from other parts of the ocean (granites are the typical igneous rocks on the continents). Sediments on the ridge are generally young in age and not too abundant (usually less than 100 m thick). Except for the crest area, little sediment is present.

Heezen has shown that in many places the ridge has an east-west offset due to **fracture zones** that cross it. In the equatorial region the offset, as judged by topographic discontinuities in the position of the axis of the ridge, is over 3,000 km.

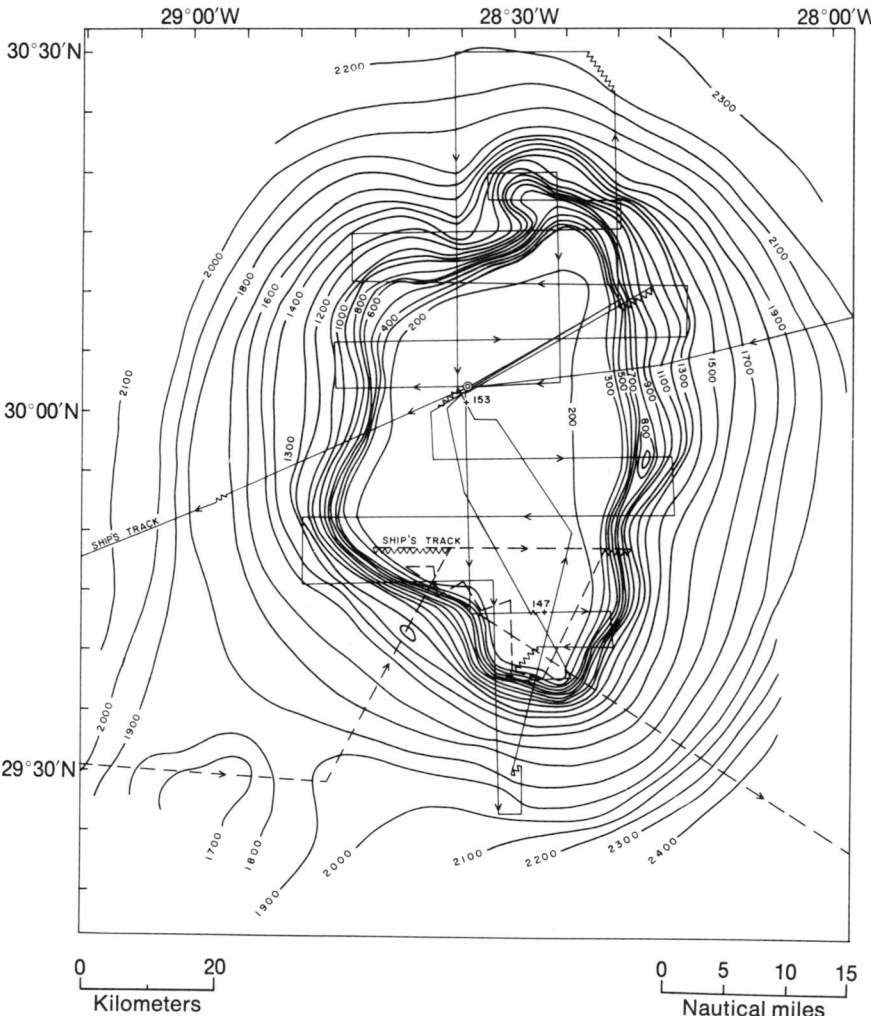

Figure 8-29 Bathymetric survey of Great Meteor Seamount. Depth in fathoms, contour interval 100 fathoms. The wide flat top of the seamount is about 30 km wide and 55 km long. (From Pratt, *Deep Sea Research*, 1963, Pergamon Press.)

On either side of the ridge are large, flat basin areas, the abyssal plains (see Figure 8-27) common to many parts of the deep sea. The flatness of abyssal plains has been ascribed to the effects of turbidity currents. These sediment-laden currents, originating from the shallower continental shelf and slope, cover and smooth out most previously existing topographic irregularities as they deposit their sediments. There is considerable evidence that such a process occurs; sediment cores taken from the abyssal plains commonly have sand layers containing shells of shallow-water organisms. Continuous seismic profiles taken across abyssal plains clearly indicate that an irregular topography has been buried by sediments.

Three deep-sea trenches are found in the Atlantic: the Puerto Rico Trench in the Caribbean region, the Romanche Trench in the equatorial region, and the Sandwich Trench off the southern part of South America. The largest is the Puerto Rico Trench, which is about 1,500 km long with a maximum depth of about 8,300 m. Impressive as that may seem, the trenches of the Atlantic are small when compared to their more numerous counterparts in the Pacific Ocean.

A difference between the Atlantic and Pacific Oceans is the relative absence of seamounts and coral atolls in the Atlantic. **Seamounts** (Figure 8-29) are isolated submarine hills often standing more than 1,000 m above the surrounding sea floor; they have steep sides terminating in a summit. Seamounts can be very large, even in the Atlantic. One of the largest is the Great Meteor Seamount in the northeastern Atlantic, which has a diameter of 110 km at its base and reaches an elevation of over 4,000 m above the sea floor. The area of its summit is about the size of Rhode Island.

The basaltic rocks usually dredged from seamounts suggest a volcanic origin. Seamounts also have typical volcano shapes. When seamounts have flattened tops, they are called **guyots.** The flattening apparently resulted when the seamount was near sea level and was subjected to wave erosion. If the seamount is located in the equatorial area and the right oceanographic conditions prevail, a coral atoll may develop (see p. 174).

The Pacific Ocean

The Pacific, the largest of the world's oceans, has a nearly circular shape leading some scientists to suggest that the moon was pulled from the earth and that the resulting water-filled hole is the Pacific Ocean.

The topography and structure of the Pacific are quite different from those of the other oceans. Its most striking topographic feature is the almost continuous series of trenches along the outer edge

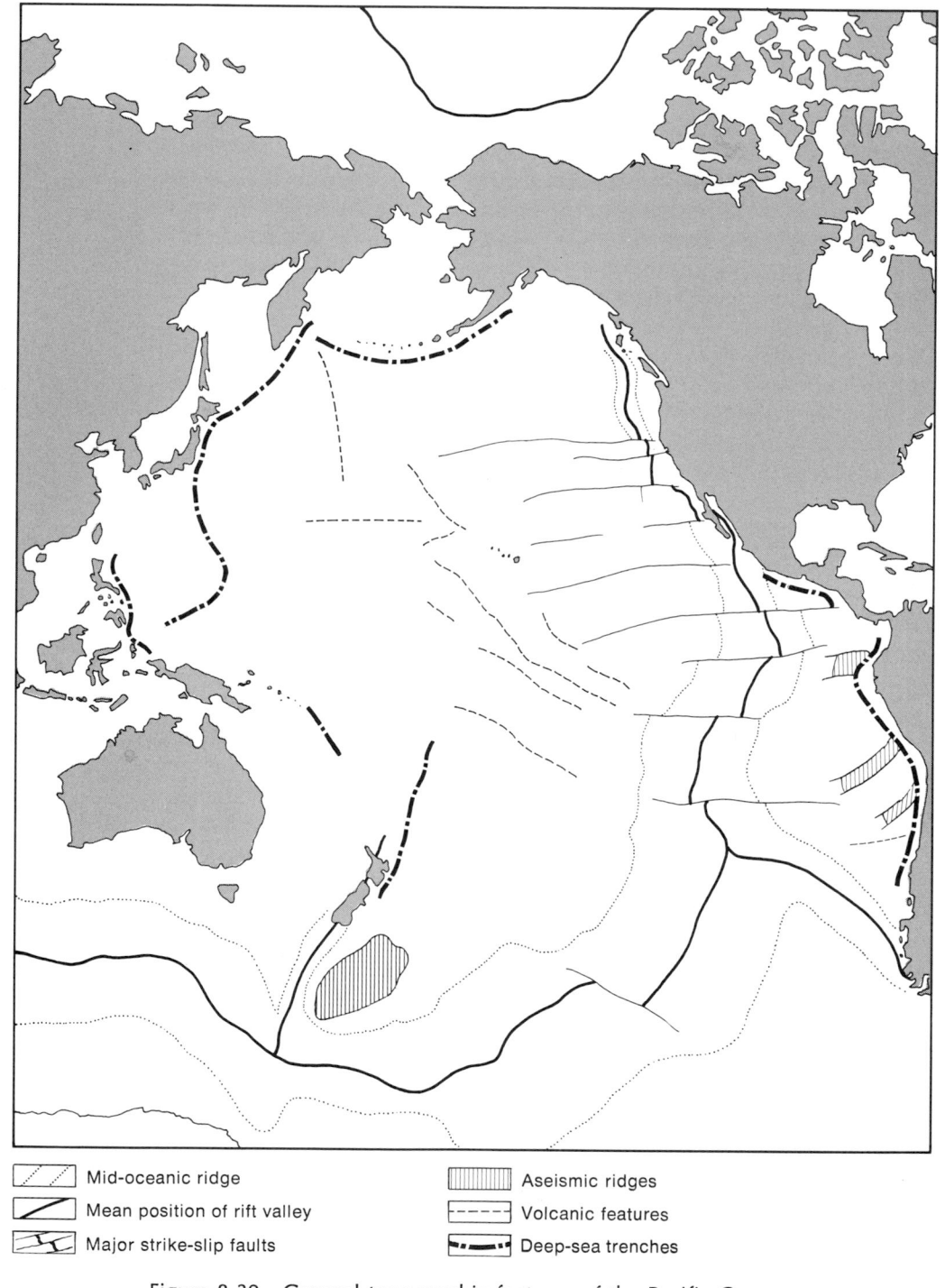

Mid-oceanic ridge		Aseismic ridges	
Mean position of rift valley		Volcanic features	
Major strike-slip faults		Deep-sea trenches	

Figure 8-30 General topographic features of the Pacific Ocean.

(Figure 8-30). On the continent side of these trenches are folded mountain ranges or a ridge (or ridges) formed by a series of islands. Trenches are seismically active and many earthquakes occur in or near the trench axis. The circular area around the Pacific has been called the ring or girdle of fire because of the many earthquakes that occur there and the many volcanoes associated with those earthquakes. There is a gap in the ring along the west coast of the United States and Canada where no trench is found, and fortunately the earthquake incidence is also low.

The deepest trench and area of the ocean is the Marianas Trench (Table 8-3), where the bathyscape TRIESTE made its famous descent in 1960 to the depth of 10,910 m near the Challenger Deep.

TABLE 8-3 SOME DIMENSIONS OF SOME TRENCHES (DATA FROM FISHER AND HESS, 1963; AND FAIRBRIDGE, 1966)

Trench	Depth (m)	Length (km)
Marianas	11,022	2,550
Tonga	10,882	1,400
Kuril-Kamchatka	10,542	2,200
Philippine	10,497	1,400
Puerto Rico	8,385	1,550
Peru-Chile	8,055	5,900
Romanche	7,856	300
Java	7,450	4,500
Middle America	6,662	2,800

Trenches tend to be V-shaped with a narrow and sometimes flat floor. The flatness of the floor may be due to turbidity or slump deposits from shallower areas. The width of the trench floor usually does not exceed a few kilometers, with a constant depth along this extent. Trenches near land usually have wider floors because of a higher inflow of sediments; good examples of this are the Peru-Chile Trench and the Middle America Trench.

A feature common to many trenches is the presence of a bench or basin perched part way up the slope (Figure 8-31). In some instances these basins can act as sediment traps and prevent material from reaching deeper parts of the trench. The slopes of most trench walls are generally between 8 and 16° (usually steeper near the bottom), but a maximum slope of about 45° is thought by some to exist in the Tonga Trench.

It has been previously mentioned that trenches are in seismically active zones. The **focus** is the point in the earth where the earthquake disturbance has occurred. It is generally near the surface in the vicinity of the trench, but can occur at greater depths in the continental direction. Some geophysicists believe that these foci indicate a fault zone that may extend as much as 700 km below the earth's surface, thus

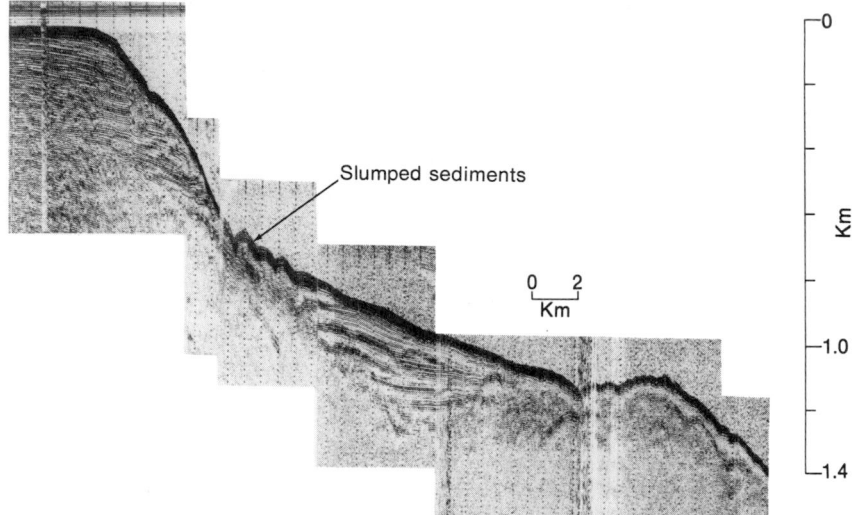

Slumped sediments

Figure 8-31 Perched basin observed on the flank of the Middle America Trench. Sediments from the continental shelf (to the left) that slump are prevented from reaching the deep sea (to the right) by this type of basin which will trap the sediments. (From Ross and Shor, 1965.)

dipping below the continents. Seismic refraction studies show another interesting feature of trenches. The Mohorovičić discontinuity (the interface between the earth's crust and the underlying mantle) considerably deepens under trenches (Figure 8-32). Thus trenches in many instances seem to mark the boundary between oceanic crust (about 5 km thick) and the continental crust (about 30 km thick).

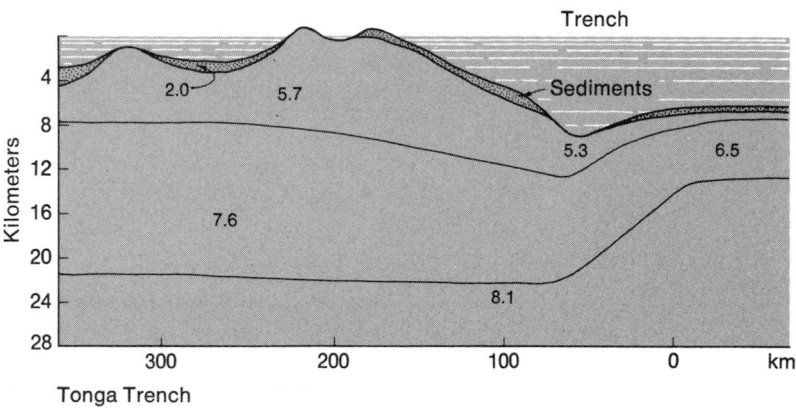

Figure 8-32 Cross section across the Tonga Trench in the western part of the Pacific. The numbers refer to the velocity of sound in the different layers (in km/sec). Note the abrupt change in depth to the Mohorovičić discontinuity (velocity about 8 km/sec) in the trench area. (After Raitt and others, 1955.)

Gravity measurements over trenches have produced some surprising results, generally showing low values of gravity centered somewhat shoreward of the axis of the trench. This low value indicates a deficiency of mass or material and suggests that the crust is being compressed or downbuckled by lateral compressional forces from the oceanic or continental side or both. This compression force is also indicated by the greater depth of the Mohorovičić discontinuity under the trench. Some scientists have, however, interpreted these data as indicating a tensional origin—or pulling apart of the crust—for trenches.

Trenches and their geological implications have long fascinated earth scientists. Many suggest that deep-seated convection currents rise to the earth's surface probably near or along the oceanic rises and sink in trench areas, which could explain the low gravity values and deepening of the Mohorovičić discontinuity in the trench area. Opponents of this idea argue that trenches are fault or tensional features. Another recent hypothesis, sea-floor spreading (see p. 312), presents some convincing support for the convection current hypothesis.

Another major feature of the Pacific is the East Pacific Rise, a continuation of the oceanic ridge system observed in the Atlantic Ocean (the Mid-Atlantic Ridge). It extends northeasterly as a broad rise from off New Zealand to the Gulf of California. This ridge differs from the Mid-Atlantic Ridge in some respects; for example, it extends across the ocean basin rather than running down the center of the basin. The topography is relatively smooth and shows no indication of a distinct central rift valley (see Figure 8-28). Its crest rises 2,000 to 3,000 m above the general level of the floor of the Pacific. Like the Mid-Atlantic Ridge, however, its crest is offset in many places by fracture zones. The East Pacific Rise is also seismically active and has higher than normal heat flow.

The East Pacific Rise apparently turns in toward land near the Gulf of California (see Figure 8-30). Considerable evidence suggests that the rise extends into the Gulf and runs along the western part of the United States, returning to the sea near Cape Mendocino, California.

Fracture zones, a series of ridges and seamounts that can be traced for considerable distances, are especially common in the eastern Pacific (Figure 8-33). The Mendocino fracture zone extends as a ridge for a distance of over 3,000 km. When a fracture zone approaches the continent, a land continuation of the structure sometimes may be observed. The Mendocino fracture zone apparently is aligned with the northern end of the San Andreas Fault of California.

Studies of the magnetic field over the fracture zones off California have shown that magnetic anomalies, due to the magnetic properties of the underlying rocks, observed on one side of a fracture do not align with the anomalies on the other side of the zone, and only with

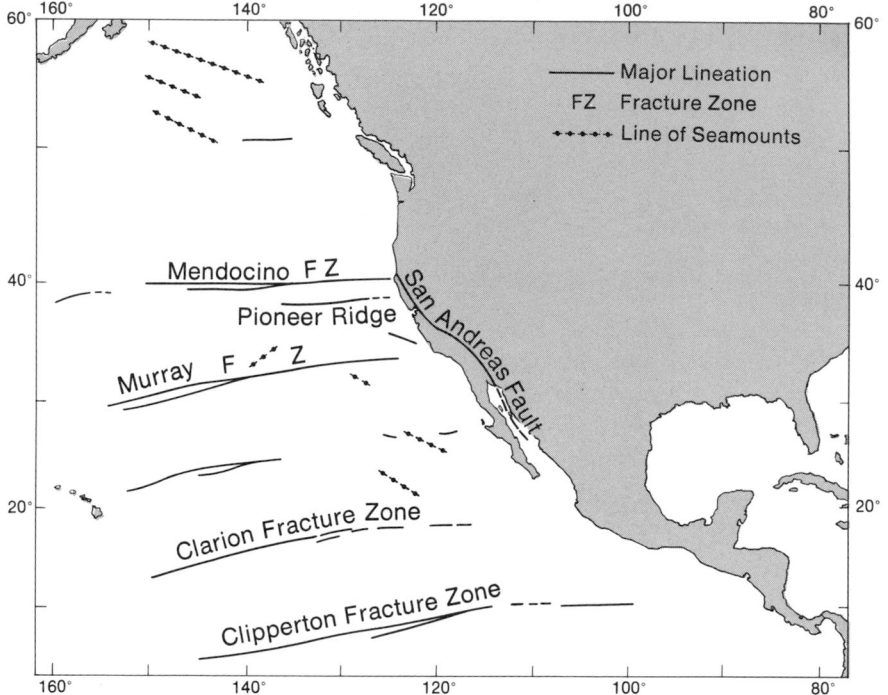

Figure 8-33 Fracture zones in the eastern Pacific. (After Menard, 1959.)

a considerable displacement could the two patterns match. The fitting together of these patterns indicates that the anomalies on one side have been displaced about 1,000 km relative to those on the other side along the Mendocino. Smaller displacements occur along the other fracture zones. Thus one side of the fracture zone may have moved a large distance relative to the other side. Bathymetric similarities on either side of the fracture zones also fit if existence of such movements is accepted. Although such extensive movements exceed what was previously thought possible by many geologists, the evidence is convincing and is now accepted by most earth scientists.

The Mendocino–San Andreas relationship (see Figure 8-33) is especially interesting; the Mendocino is being displaced to the left, but the San Andreas is being displaced to the right. So if one is correct in aligning these two features, it then appears that deep crustal material has to flow up to fill in the depression that is developing at their intersection.

Seamounts and guyots are abundant in the Pacific Ocean. H. W. Menard in 1964 listed more than 1,400, and probably many more are still unknown. Seamounts are defined as individual features, although in most instances they are concentrated in certain areas of the ocean and are called provinces or chains. This clumping together of seamounts suggests that they are related to major patterns of stress within the oceanic crust.

The volcanic origin of seamounts is well accepted now, but some questions about the sequence of events still remain. Most seamounts show evidence of some submergence, that is, they once stood higher than they do now, maybe even above sea level. In some areas a whole group of seamounts may have been submerged. Other seamounts have remained near sea level long enough for waves to have eroded and flattened their tops, forming guyots. In some instances a coral reef was established on the seamount and then grew as the seamount subsided, forming an atoll (see detailed discussion of coral atolls in Chapter 6). Drilling on Eniwetok atoll has revealed over 4,000 ft of coralline material over the basaltic rocks of the seamount (H. S. Ladd and others, 1953). The coralline material originated in shallow water and clearly shows that the seamount was submerging during deposition. During part of its history the atoll was elevated above sea level, as indicated by weathered zones of coral material obtained during the drilling.

Abyssal plains are found in some areas of the Pacific, but they are not so common as in the Atlantic for two reasons. First, abyssal plains are generally believed to be formed by turbidity current deposits covering the previous topography. The presence of an almost continuous belt of deep-sea trenches around the continents apparently serves as a sediment trap for turbidity currents (Figure 8-34) and prevents the currents from reaching the more seaward ocean basins. Secondly, a much smaller amount of sediment is carried by rivers to the Pacific than to the Atlantic (most large rivers flow into the Atlantic Ocean; see Table 8-4). It therefore follows that the incidence of turbidity currents (containing land-derived sediments) should be considerably lower in the Pacific than in the Atlantic. Turbidity currents can, however, also occur far from land where marine sediments fail and slump. The resulting deposits will also tend to cover the existing topography. This mechanism is thought to be of lesser importance than the effects of land-derived turbidity currents.

Because most of the Pacific has not been covered by thick se-

TABLE 8-4   OCEANIC AREAS AND COMPLEMENTARY LAND AREAS (IN THOUSANDS OF SQUARE KILOMETERS) DRAINING INTO THEM (DATA FROM LYMAN, 1958)

Ocean	Area	Land Area Drained	Percentage
Atlantic	98,000	67,000	68.5
Indian	65,500	17,000	26.0
Antarctic	32,000	14,000	44.0
Pacific	165,000	18,000	11.0

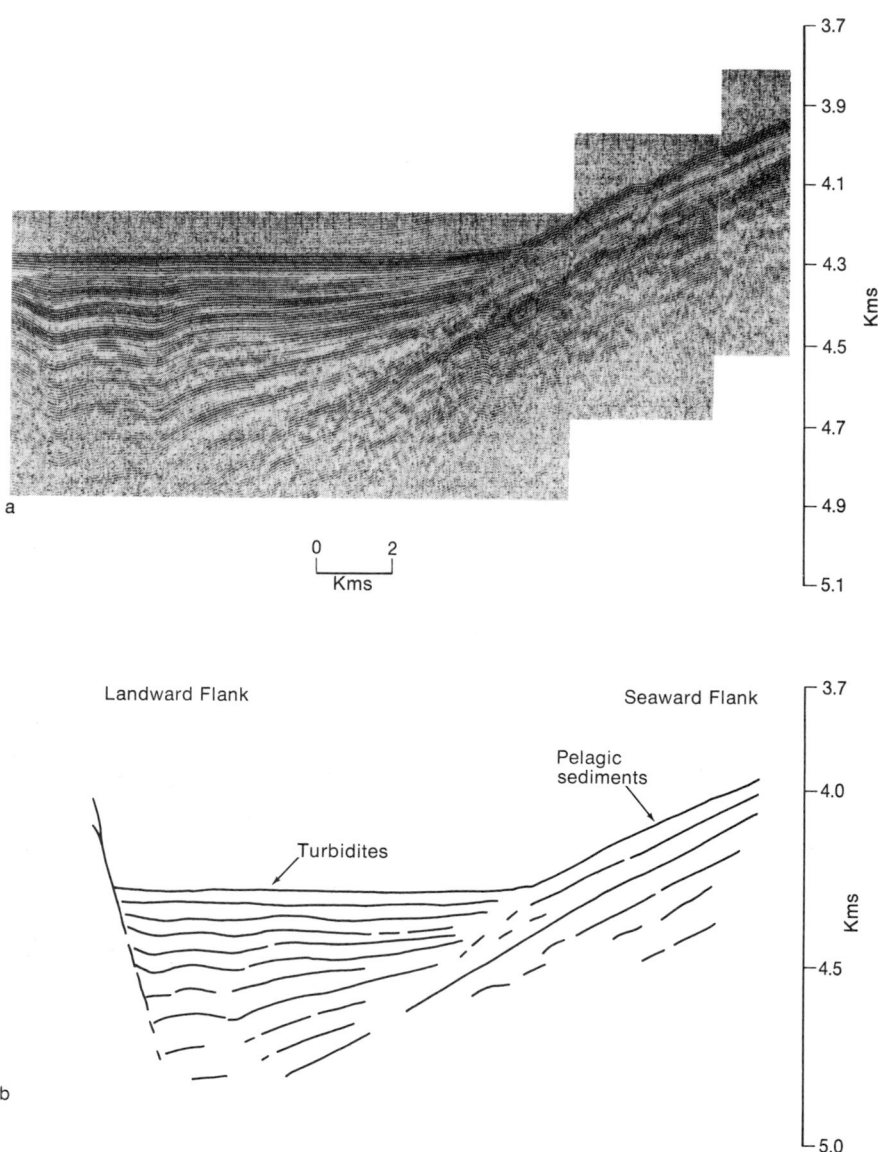

Figure 8-34 Abyssal plain area formed in the bottom of a trench. Turbidity current deposits from the upper parts of the continental slope and shelf (to the left) are prevented from reaching the deep sea (to the right) by the trench. (a) A continuous seismic profiling record; (b) the interpretation. (From Ross and Shor, 1965.)

Figure 8-35 Echo-sounding record showing the contact between an abyssal hill area (to the right) and an abyssal plain area. Depth is in fathoms; the width of the hill is about 2 miles. This is a photograph of the actual echo-sounding record and the markings on the record are shipboard notations. (Photograph courtesy of Woods Hole Oceanographic Institution.)

quences of turbidity current material, its topography has not been smoothed and much of the original topography is exposed. A prominent feature is **abyssal hills,** which are hills from 30 to 1,000 m above the sea floor and up to several miles wide (Figure 8-35). Abyssal hills may cover as much as 50 percent of the Pacific floor (Menard, 1964); this means that about 25 percent of the earth's topography is composed of these hills. In some areas abyssal hills occur at the seaward ends of abyssal plains, where they have not been completely covered by turbidites. In the north Atlantic a narrow strip of such hills parallels the Mid-Atlantic Ridge.

The study of abyssal hills is complicated by several factors. Most abyssal hills are covered with a thin veneer of sediment that makes it difficult to get a sample of the underlying rocks. The small size of these hills makes detailed surveying and the resolution of geophysical characteristics difficult. In most areas scientists cannot even be sure whether the hills occur as individual units or as part of an elongated ridge. A study of a small abyssal hill region in the Pacific showed the hills to have a linear trend (Figure 8-36).

The origin of abyssal hills is still unknown. Many scientists favor the notion of volcanic origin; they argue that the hills are similar in shape to seamounts (which are of volcanic origin), and that the hills resemble some volcanic features seen on land. Other scientists, prompted by the fact that the hills are part of the "second layer" of the crust, which may be of sedimentary origin (see Figure 8-45), have suggested a sedimentary origin for the abyssal hills. Whatever the origin, they clearly are a major and important feature of the ocean.

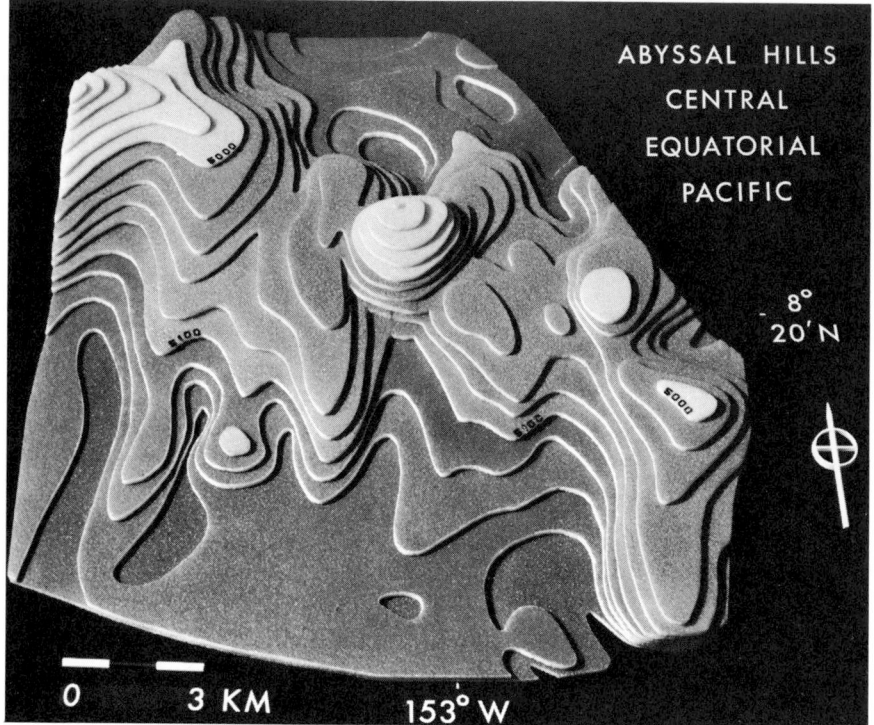

Figure 8-36   Model of the sea floor made from echo-sounding records obtained in an abyssal hill region in the central equatorial Pacific. Outer edges of the layers mark 20 m contours. The lightest color is less than 5,000 m, the intermediate shading between 5,000 and 5,100 m. Vertical exaggeration 10:1. (From Moore and Heath, 1967.)

The Indian Ocean

Relatively little is known about the Indian Ocean. The International Indian Ocean Expedition, conducted from 1960 to 1965, provided some knowledge about its topography and structure. R. W. Fairbridge and others in 1966 noted five major topographic divisions in the Indian Ocean: (1) continental margin, (2) ocean basin floor, (3) microcontinents, (4) mid-oceanic ridge, and (5) fracture zones.

The continental margins (shelf, slope, and rise) are similar to those of the other oceans. Although fewer than in the other oceans, some submarine canyons cut the slope and rise. The smaller number of canyons that have been found may only reflect the smaller amount of surveying done in the Indian Ocean. Large submarine canyons are, in fact, found off the Indus and Ganges Rivers.

The Java Trench, with a maximum depth of about 7,400 m, extends northwest from western Australia. Shallower than the Atlantic trenches, it is the major trench in the Indian Ocean (see Table 8-3).

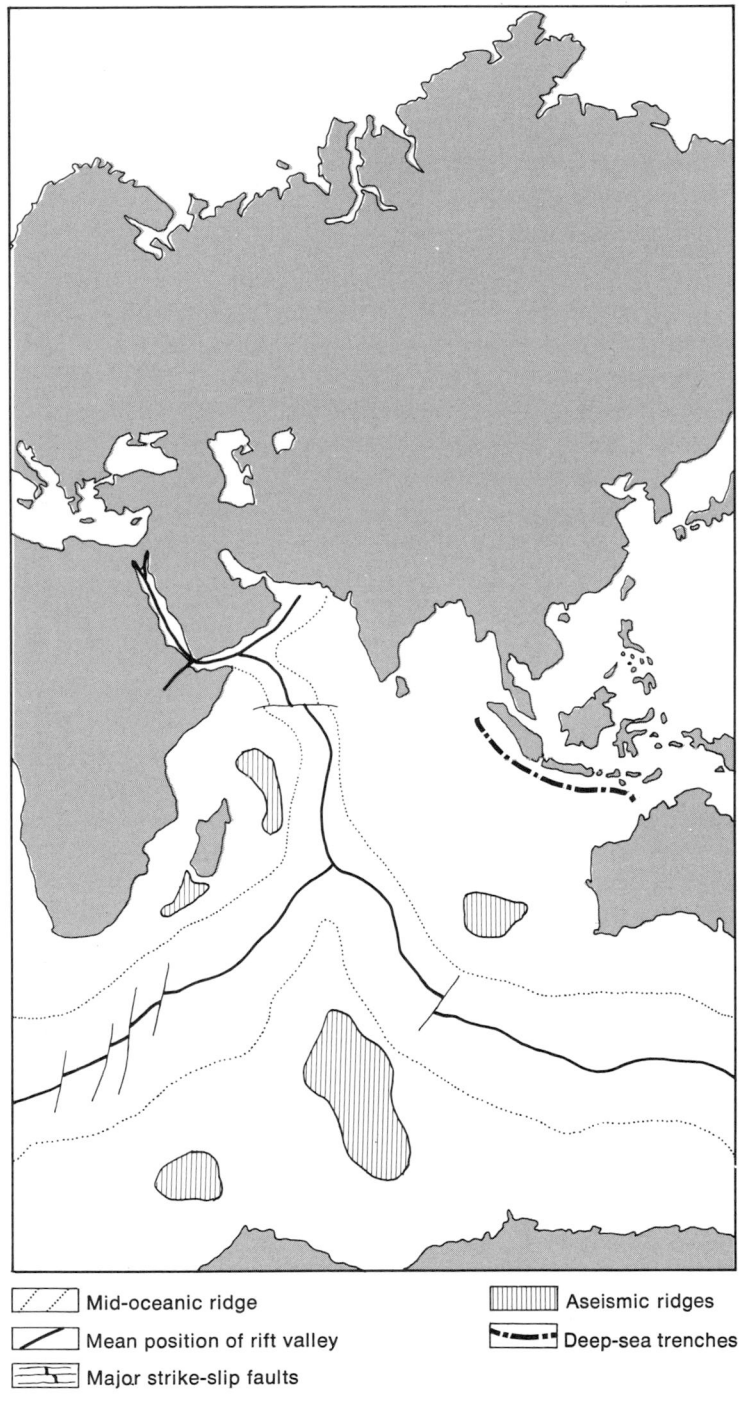

Legend:

Mid-oceanic ridge	Aseismic ridges
Mean position of rift valley	Deep-sea trenches
Major strike-slip faults	

Figure 8-37　General topographic features of the Indian Ocean.

The ocean basin floor, according to Fairbridge and his co-workers, is dominated by abyssal plains that have gradients that range from 1:1,000 to 1:7,000 and a relief usually of only a few meters. These plains are best developed in the northern and southern parts of the ocean (Figure 8-37). In some areas small channels, possibly of turbidity current origin, cut across the abyssal plains.

Microcontinents, which are seismically inactive linear ridges, are characteristic of the northern Indian Ocean. They differ from the mid-oceanic ridge in their lack of seismicity and in their general shape, being somewhat higher and more blocklike.

The major feature of the Indian Ocean is its mid-oceanic ridge, which appears to split in the center of the ocean, forming an inverted Y (see Figure 8-37). One of the split limbs goes south of Australia into the Pacific where it intersects with the East Pacific Rise. The other split limb continues south of Africa and joins with the Mid-Atlantic Ridge. The third part of the Y turns and continues to the Gulf of Aden and the Red Sea. In the Indian Ocean the ridge has characteristics similar to those of the Mid-Atlantic Ridge. It is rugged, seismically active, and may have a continuous median rift (see Figure 8-28). The Indian Ocean Ridge is also situated essentially in the central part of the ocean.

Fracture zones are very evident in the Indian Ocean, and in many places they have displaced the axis of the Indian Ocean Ridge. Some of the fracture zones contain small trenches; the Vema and Diamantina Trenches in the Indian Ocean and the Romanche Trench in the Atlantic Ocean occur in fracture zones.

The Arctic Ocean

The Arctic Ocean is the smallest of the major oceans. Most of this ocean is covered by ice, and so it has not been fully explored. Some recent observations have been made by nuclear submarines traveling under the sea ice. The Arctic Ocean is roughly circular in shape and is divided by three submarine ridges (Figure 8-38). The ridges, the Alpha, the Lomonosov (named after a Russian scientist), and a possible extension of the Mid-Atlantic Ridge, divide the ocean into a series of basins or deeps.

Between one-third and one-half of the Arctic floor consists of continental shelves, some of which extend to a depth of 300 m (for example, off the coast of Greenland). This depth may be due to a depression from the weight of the ice sheet that covers Greenland.

The basins or deeps of the Arctic Ocean are separated from the Pacific and Atlantic Oceans by shallow submarine ridges. The basin depths and general topography are similar to those of the other oceans. The extension of the Mid-Atlantic Ridge into the Arctic Ocean

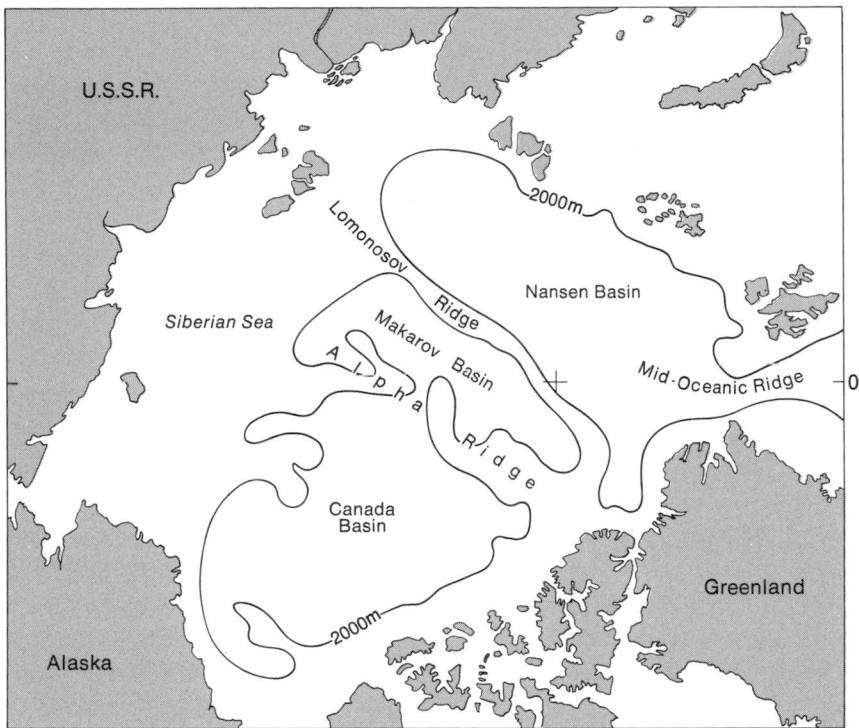

Figure 8-38   General topographic features of the Arctic Ocean.

is not completely confirmed, but is highly likely. The area has not been sufficiently surveyed to reveal where this ridge goes when it leaves the Arctic region. Perhaps it extends across the Siberian Sea into Russia.

MARGINAL SEAS

Most of the oceans have areas that can be called marginal seas. One of these, the Red Sea, will be discussed in this section. Other marginal seas are the Gulf of Mexico, the Baltic Sea, the Caribbean Sea, and the Mediterranean Sea. Most marginal seas, although partially separated from the main ocean, can influence the physical properties of the main ocean. For example, the water formed in the Mediterranean Sea can be detected at depth over a large part of the Atlantic.

The Red Sea

The Red Sea is situated along one limb of the ridge common to all the oceans. There is considerable evidence (see Figure 4-19) that Arabia on the eastern side of the Red Sea and Africa on the western side were

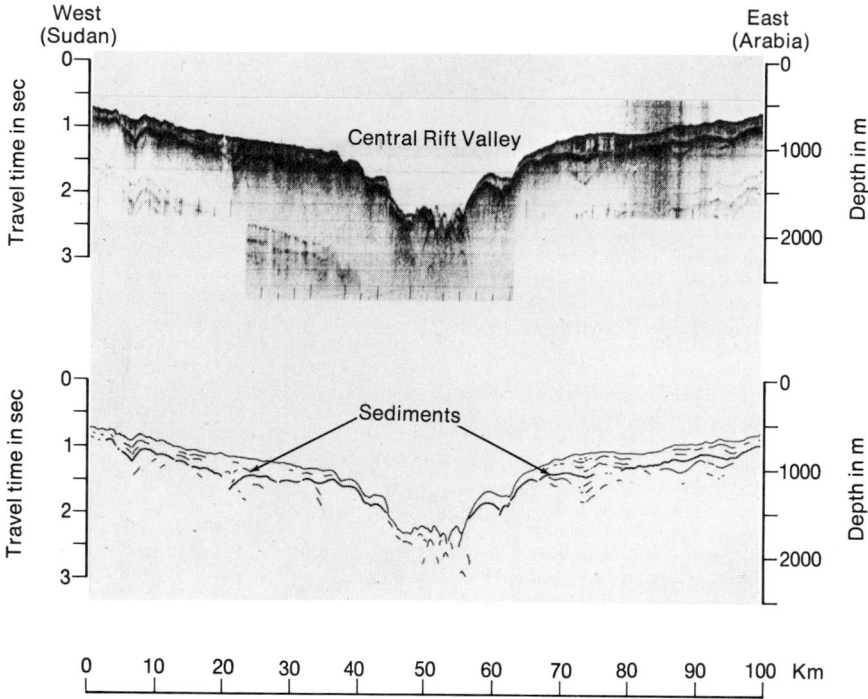

Figure 8-39   Continuous seismic profile across the Red Sea (at about 20° north latitude). Note the absence of sediment in the central rift valley. Upper figure is the actual record, lower figure is a line drawing interpretation. Travel time refers to the time it takes for the sound to travel from the ship to a particular layer.

once connected, and at some time in the geological past were rifted apart to form the Red Sea. This rifting, which may be continuing today, occurs along the median rift valley that runs up the center of the sea. Continuous seismic profiles across this area (Figure 8-39) show an intensely fractured and faulted rift valley that is generally devoid of sediment, separating a less deformed marginal area on either side. Apparently Asia and Africa have separated by tensional forces, and new crustal material (mainly basaltic rocks) has risen and filled in the resulting crack. This movement may have begun over 100 million years ago.

Evidence of this split, besides the satellite picture shown in Figure 4-19, is the similarity of geological structures and rocks on either side of the sea and the symmetry of both coasts, suggesting that they could fit together like pieces of a jig-saw puzzle.

The Red Sea is separated at its southern end from the Indian Ocean by a sill at a depth of about 125 m. It follows that during times of lowered sea level this sea was a lake, and since evaporation is high and river runoff and rainfall are very low, the lake may have almost completely evaporated at times. This situation would have a profound effect on the chemistry of the water and on the biological environment. Some of the effects can be detected by measurements of the proportions of different isotopes in the sediments and fossil shells (see Figure 5-14).

DEEP-SEA SEDIMENTS

One of the first comprehensive studies of deep-sea sediments was made by Murray and Renard in 1891. They examined more than 12,000 samples, some of which were obtained by the CHALLENGER. The two early oceanographers proposed a classification that is still valid today after hundreds of other studies have been made. Deep-sea sediments can be divided into two major groups: pelagic sediments and terrigenous sediments (Table 8-5). The distinction is based in part on the origin and in part on the method of deposition of the sediment.

TABLE 8-5   CLASSIFICATION OF DEEP-SEA DEPOSITS

Pelagic Sediments	Terrigenous Sediments
Biogenous deposits	Terrigenous muds
Inorganic deposits	Slump deposits
Authigenic deposits	Turbidites
Volcanic deposits	Glacial deposits

Pelagic Sediments

Pelagic sediments are found in the deep part of the ocean far from land; they have settled down through the water in the absence of strong currents. The deposits are usually the skeletal material of plants or animals or are fine-grained clays. The clays can be land-derived and carried to their deposition site by wind (Figure 8-40), water or currents, or both. Other sources of the fine-grained clays are volcanoes and fragments from meteorites.

Biogenous Deposits Biogenous deposits or oozes by definition contain more than 30 percent skeletal material (fragments or shells of different plants or animals). Biogenous deposits may contain sediments of in-

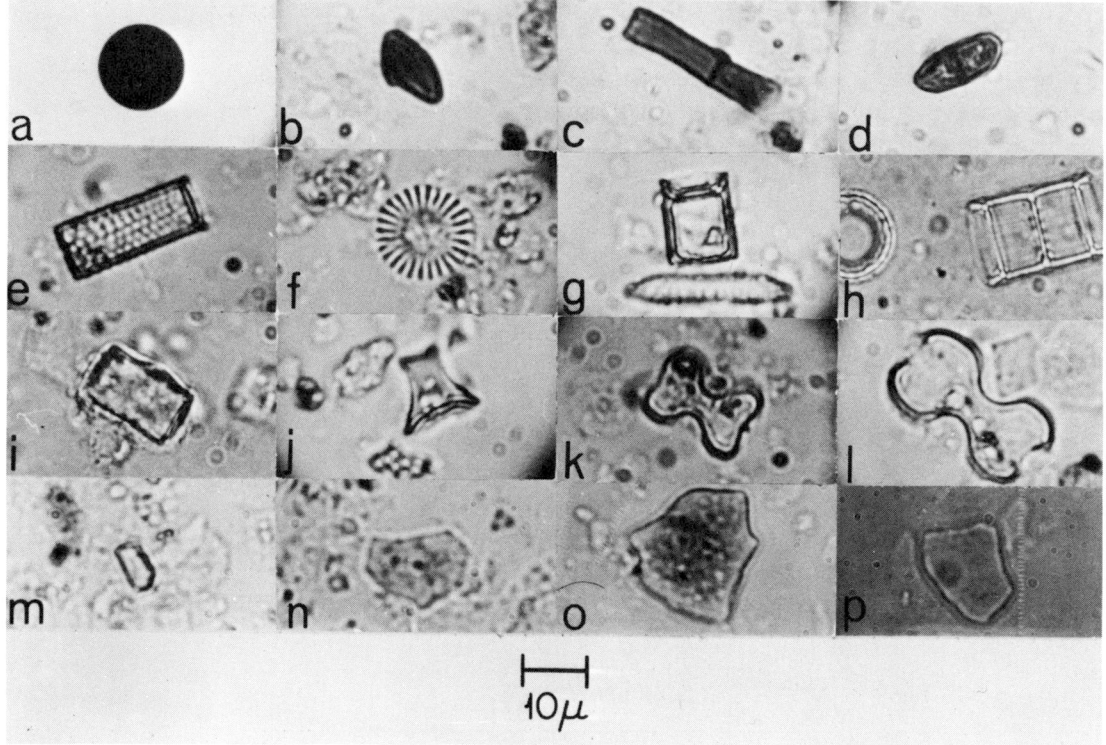

Figure 8-40 Some typical land-derived material that has been carried by wind and found in the surface water and air over the North Atlantic. a is an opaque spherule, probably of industrial origin; b through d are fungus spores; e through h are fresh water diatoms; i through l are opal particles precipitated by plants; and m through p are mineral grains. The scale line is 10 μ (one-hundredth of a millimeter). (Photograph courtesy of D. W. Folger.)

organic origin, such as brown clay. The oozes are named after the organism that is most prevalent in the deposits; common types of oozes are foraminiferal, coccolith, pteropod, radiolarian, and diatomaceous oozes (Figure 8-41). All the organisms are planktonic; diatoms and coccoliths are plants (phytoplankton) and the others are animals (zooplankton). Radiolaria and diatoms have shells made of siliceous material. The others have calcareous shells.

Most of the organisms live in the surface waters of the ocean, and when they die their shells settle to the ocean floor and form a sedimentary deposit. Occurrence of these sediments on the ocean bottom (Figure 8-42) generally reflects the conditions of the surface waters, indicating that the settling speed of the shells to the deep-sea floor is sufficiently fast to prevent the shells from being moved far in a hori-

Planktonic Foraminifera

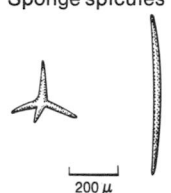

1 mm

Diatoms

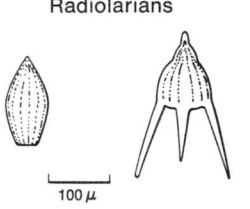

50 μ

Figure 8-41 (a) Drawings of some typical organisms that constitute different oozes found on the sea floor. (b) Electron micrograph of some coccoliths, enlarged 11,000 times. (Photograph courtesy of J. C. Hathaway.)

Sponge spicules

200 μ

Radiolarians

100 μ

a

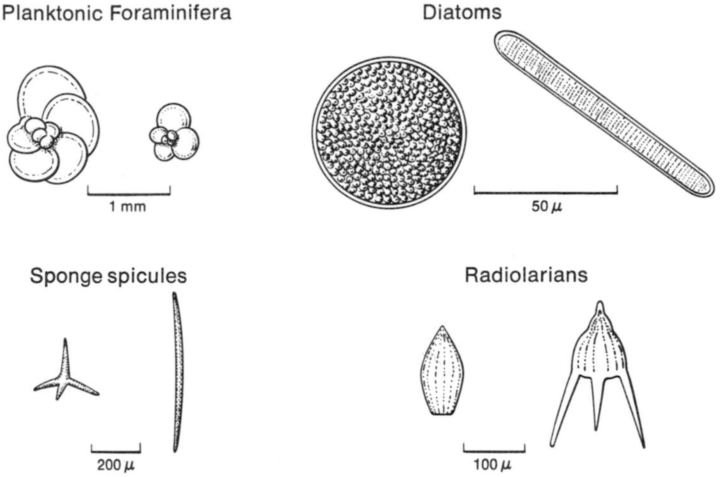

b

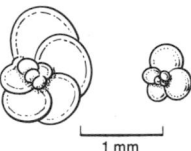

zontal direction from below the waters where the organisms lived. Calcareous oozes are usually found at shallower depths than siliceous oozes because the calcareous shells are more soluble than the siliceous shells. The effect of solubility increases with depth and decreasing temperature; thus calcareous sediment is rarely found below a depth of 5,000 m. The effect is more obvious on the small and delicate coccoliths than on the robust pteropods and Foraminifera.

Biogenous sediments are common in localities of high biological productivity, such as upwelling areas, or where the other sediment types are absent or are deposited at a very slow rate. The sedimentation rate of biogenous sediments is about 1 to 5 cm per 1,000 years, which is considerably higher than the sedimentation rate of the inorganic clays.

Biogenous deposits are valuable to oceanographers because they can be used to learn something about the environment in which the organisms lived. The organisms best suited for these studies are pelagic Foraminifera, which live mainly in the subsurface water layers of the ocean. Certain species are typical of low latitude and warm water, while other species are typical of middle or high latitude and cold water. Cores of foraminiferal ooze, in most instances, show a change in the dominant species at different depths in the core. This is due to changes in the surface water conditions (Figure 8-43). Changes indicated by different species of Foraminifera can be dated using Carbon-14 for the upper and younger parts of the core and extrapolating to the deeper and older parts. Some species also show an evolutionary change that can be used as a time marker and which allows correlation from one core to another. In addition the coiling of the shells of some species of Foraminifera changes direction, apparently in response to temperature changes in the waters where these species lived. Another technique for studying the ancient environment is to measure the isotopic composition of the shells; the $^{18}O/^{16}O$ ratio can be used to determine the temperature of the water in which the organism lived. The combination of all these techniques has made possible an acceptable description of recent changes in the ocean. The general picture is that the last glacial period ended about 11,000 years ago, and that the surface waters of the ocean have been warming since that time. Prior to the last glacial period, there was a warm period (called an interglacial period) that ended about 60,000 years ago. Between 11,000 and 60,000 years ago the oceans were relatively cold. The warm period that began 60,000 years ago extended back to 100,000 years ago and was preceded by another glacial period. Results of these techniques are not absolute; in some instances they are even in conflict with each other. One reason for discrepancy is that Foraminifera may live in a different part of the water column (and

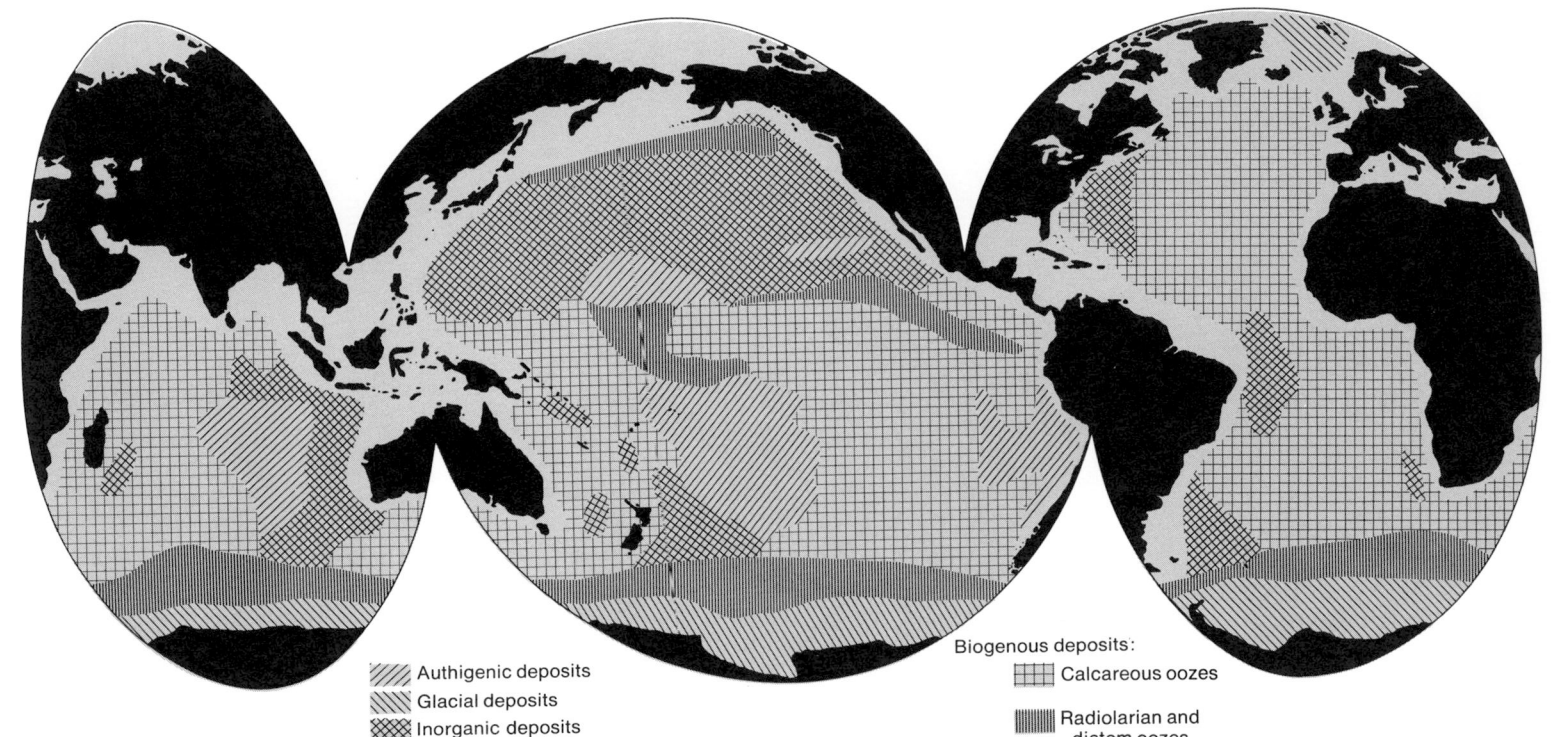

Figure 8-42   General sedimentary pattern of pelagic sediments on the ocean floor. Sediments of terrigenous origin, except for glacial deposits, are not shown. (After Arrhenius, 1963, and Shepard, 1963.)

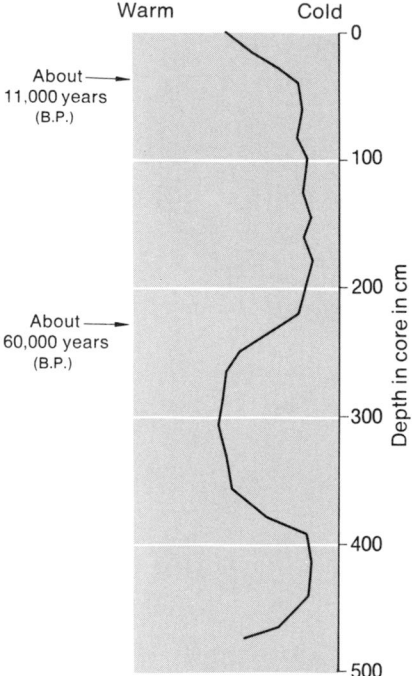

Warm   Cold

About 11,000 years (B.P.)

About 60,000 years (B.P.)

Depth in core in cm

0
100
200
300
400
500

Figure 8-43   Generalized temperature variations as observed in a deep-sea core. The ancient temperatures are estimated from the relative abundance of pelagic Foraminifera. Certain species indicate a warm temperature of the surface waters, other species cold temperature. Major changes occurred about 11,000 and 60,000 years before the present.

therefore at a different temperature) during different stages of their life history.

Another biogenous deposit is from coral reefs that have been exposed to the destructive powers of waves or other erosive forces. If the reworking by waves is especially intense, a white mud composed of fine-grained debris may result. The deposits are generally localized around the reef itself, perhaps even in the inner lagoon that is typical of most atolls.

Inorganic Deposits Inorganic deposits are the very fine-grained muds found in most of the deep ocean basins far from land. By definition they must contain less than 30 percent biogenous material. They generally have a brown color due to having been oxidized. Very little is known about the origin and source of these clays. It has been suggested that they may be derived from the Gobi Desert of Mongolia and carried to the northern Pacific by wind and ocean currents. Other possible sources are meteoric dust or volcanic ash. In some instances the clays are altered to a mineral called phillipsite and should be considered in the next group, the authigenic deposits.

The sedimentation rate of inorganic deposits is very low, usually

1 to 2 mm per 1,000 years, or 1 m per 1,000,000 years. Such a low sedimentation rate limits availability of such deposits. Obviously they will be diluted and negligible in areas where other types of sediments are forming more rapidly. Only in the very deep areas of the ocean, far from any land-derived sediments, and where solution has removed many of the calcareous shells, are inorganic deposits significant. Even under such restrictive conditions there are large portions of the ocean, notably in the Pacific, that have inorganic deposits (see Figure 8-42).

Authigenic Deposits Authigenic deposits are those that have formed in the place where they are found, before the sediment is buried. These deposits are usually precipitated directly from the ocean water. The mineral phillipsite found in large areas of the South Pacific may possibly be in this group. There is, however, some question whether it precipitated directly from sea water or if it is an alteration product of another clay mineral. Some sediments undergo chemical and physical alteration after their accumulation on the sea floor. This alteration is a different process than the formation of authigenic deposits.

Other interesting authigenic deposits include manganese nodules (see Figures 5-2 and 8-44). These deposits have been found over large

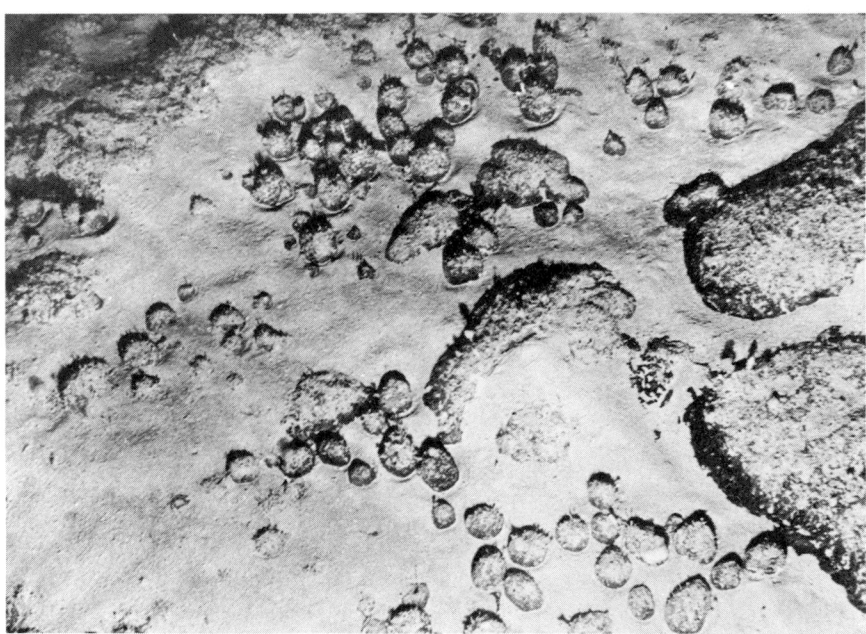

Figure 8-44   Manganese nodules photographed on the Blake Plateau. (Photograph courtesy of C. D. Hollister.)

areas of the ocean, and economically may be the most important sediment of the deep sea. They commonly occur as rounded nodules the size of a baseball and can also occur as slabs or as coatings on rocks. The nodules frequently form around small objects on the sea floor, such as a shark's tooth or the ear bone of a fish. Since the deposits form by precipitation from sea water, their deposition will stop when the nodule or rock is covered with sediment. The distribution of manganese nodules is usually restricted to areas having an otherwise low sedimentation rate, or to areas where strong currents prevent the deposition of other sediments. An example of the latter is the Blake Plateau off Florida, where the swiftly flowing Gulf Stream prevents sediment deposition.

The origin of manganese nodules has been discussed by many scientists. The following is a mechanism proposed by John Mero in 1966. The source of the manganese, iron, silica, aluminum, and other elements common to manganese nodules (Table 8-6) is sea water, which in turn is supplied to the ocean by rivers, volcanic eruptions, decomposition of submarine material, and other sources. Sea water is essentially concentrated with manganese and iron. Additional supply causes their precipitation in the form of hydrated colloidal particles. The colloidal particles, while settling through the water column, will attract other elements. On the bottom they will attach to some object. The mechanism whereby colloidal particles are transformed to nodules is not known. Other hypotheses include a bacterial or organic origin or some variation of the origin proposed by Mero.

TABLE 8-6   AVERAGE COMPOSITION OF SOME MANGANESE NODULES*
(DATA FROM MERO, 1966)

Element	Weight Percentages (Dry)	
	Pacific (54 samples)	Atlantic (4 samples)
Manganese	24.2	16.3
Iron	14.0	17.5
Silicon	9.4	11.0
Aluminum	2.9	3.1
Sodium	2.6	2.3
Magnesium	1.7	1.7
Titanium	0.67	0.8
Copper	0.53	0.20
Cobalt	0.35	0.31
Vanadium	0.05	0.07

* Only the more important elements are considered.

Regardless of the mode of formation, manganese nodules may be an important resource in the near future, not only for the manganese, but also for the rare elements such as cobalt, titanium, zirconium, and vanadium that also occur in the nodules. The manganese nodules of one area may differ in composition from those in another area (see Table 8-6). Mero, in 1962, estimated that there are about 1.6×10^{12} metric tons of nodules on the ocean bottom in the Pacific and that nodules are forming there at a rate of about 6×10^6 metric tons per year. The average rate of formation of manganese nodules is thought to be about 1 mm per 1,000 years or perhaps even less.

Another authigenic deposit of possible economic significance is phosphorite. Large deposits of this mineral are not common to the deep sea, but in general are restricted to depths of 500 m or less. This mineral apparently forms in basins that contain virtually no oxygen—an anaerobic environment. This absence of oxygen can result when large amounts of organic matter, produced in the surface waters, sink and are oxidized (consuming oxygen) in the deeper waters.

Volcanic Deposits Sediments of volcanic origin, such as volcanic dust, are common in some areas of the deep sea. One can argue that perhaps they are not of true pelagic origin because the volcano may be on land, but many of these volcanoes are submarine. In either case, the particles settle away from the influence of land and a pelagic classification seems justified.

In some areas of the ocean, volcanic dust settled at such a high rate that a distinct ash layer covers a large portion of the eastern Pacific. Some layers can be related to historical volcanic eruptions, thus serving as a convenient time horizon with which to relate to other deposits.

Recent volcanic exposions, such as the one of Krakatoa in 1883, formed a dust cloud that covered much of the world. The heavier material, of course, settled and accumulated near the eruption area. Pumice, which can float, traveled until it became water-saturated and sank. The ash layers near the eruption site generally are composed of shards of volcanic material and smaller fragments of volcanic rock. Further away, finer-grained volcanic minerals, often highly altered, are found.

Terrigenous Sediments

Terrigenous sediments are obviously derived from land and, as one would think, they tend to be found near the margin of the ocean basins close to land. They are of various grain sizes and usually have a small quantity of biogenous material, because the relatively high rate of deposition of the terrigenous sediments will dilute the more slowly deposited biogenous material. In some instances terrigenous sediments may be deposited in a catastrophic manner, such as by submarine slumping or by turbidity currents.

Terrigenous Muds Terrigenous muds are generally variable in color. The variation is caused by the difference in source, or the depositional environment. For example, black muds are common in areas where there is a large supply of organic matter but insufficient oxygen to oxidize it; red muds are typical of oxygenated areas.

Terrigenous muds may contain quartz, feldspar, and micaceous minerals typical of land rocks. The transportation of the minerals to the deep sea is mainly by ocean currents and, to a lesser extent, by wind. The rate of deposition is variable depending on nearness to the source. The deposition rates are, however, several times higher than those of pelagic sediments. Near large rivers a rate of 100 cm per 1,000 years is common.

Slump Deposits Slump deposits are those sediments that by some mechanism have moved or slumped down from a topographically higher area. They may be difficult to distinguish by coring techniques but can be recognized from seismic reflection profiles (see Figure 8-22). Such profiles, especially those made across the continental rise, frequently show large blocks of sediment that have slumped down from the higher continental slope, and have been somewhat deformed.

Under some conditions, slumped material may form a turbidity current, and the sediment does not then move as a large mass but as individual particles.

Turbidites The coarse-grained sand and silt layers found interbedded with the typical fine-grained muds of the deep sea are generally attributed to turbidity currents. These deposits are called turbidites and are common to many areas of the deep sea. Turbidites range in thickness from a few centimeters to several meters, generally showing an increase in grain size with respect to depth, with coarser material at the bottom of the layer and finer material above.

Turbidites commonly contain material such as wood fragments, shells of organisms that live in shallow water, and other materials that indicate a shallow-water origin for the sediment. In many instances, especially off large submarine canyons, large parts of the deep sea are blanketed with these sediments forming flat abyssal plains.

Considerable debate has occurred concerning the erosive and carrying powers of turbidity currents (see discussion in Chapter 7, p.

238). These currents, although never observed, have been used to explain the origin of submarine canyons and other features on the sea floor. The evidence that some form of current can exist and occur at a particular time is very compelling; the main questions are how fast does it move and can it cause significant erosion.

The sedimentation rate of turbidites is very fast. Once a turbidity current has sufficiently slowed, the sediment can quickly settle out under the force of gravity. Turbidites, besides being common in abyssal plain areas and in some deep-sea trenches, also apparently occurred in the past. They formed ancient rocks that have characteristics similar to those of their recent marine counterparts. Such rocks are commonly found in long linear basins, called **geosynclines**—areas of rapid sedimentation that were later folded and faulted to form mountain ranges such as the Appalachian Mountains.

Glacial Deposits Glacially derived sediments are common to many parts of the continental shelf (see Figure 8-13). Glacial sediments are also found in the deep sea where they can be recognized by their high sand, silt, and occasional gravel content. The sediments were initially carried by glaciers. As the glaciers melted, fragments were carried by currents over the ocean; they then dropped their debris, which fell to the sea floor and formed the deposit. Glacial deposits are especially common in the Arctic and Antarctic Oceans.

Rocks on the Sea Floor

Most rocks exposed on the sea floor are volcanic rocks that differ from the typically granitic rocks found on land. The dominant volcanic rock on the sea floor is basalt; a fine-grained rock composed mainly of the minerals feldspar and pyroxene. Basalts are found exposed on most oceanic islands, on the mid-oceanic ridges, and along some fracture zones. Their common occurrence in the ocean suggests a large uniform source, perhaps one of the subsurface crustal layers.

Other rocks found on the sea floor include manganese nodules and cemented fragments of calcareous sediments. The occurrence of cemented fragments of calcium-rich sediments is not completely understood, but in some instances may indicate that the sediment had once been either above the water or in a different environment.

Areas of Nondeposition

Apparently there are many places on the ocean floor that can be considered as areas of nondeposition, or areas where no sedimentation is presently occurring, as, for example, in shallow-water areas where strong currents on the bottom prevent the accumulation of sediments. There are places in the Atlantic and Pacific Oceans where Pleistocene sediments are absent and the uppermost sediments are of Pliocene age or older. Since these areas are in the deeper parts of the ocean, one must assume that essentially no deposition has occurred for many millions of years or, less likely, that younger deposits have been removed by erosion.

CRUSTAL STRUCTURE

After World War II the field of seismic refraction and seismic reflection advanced very rapidly (see Chapter 4, p. 93 and Figures 4-47 and 4-48). One important problem to be studied was how much sediment there was on the ocean floor. Prior to the use of seismic techniques at sea, there had been considerable speculation on this problem. Most estimates were that about 2 or 3 km of sediment should be found.

Seismic refraction and reflection studies showed that the earth's crust could be divided into three major layers on the basis of the velocity of sound within these layers (Figure 8-45). In many instances smaller units or layers could be detected within the larger layers. The first layer, which we know by sampling to be unconsolidated sediments, has a sound velocity of about 2 to 3 km/sec. This sedimentary layer is commonly about 300 m thick in the Pacific and 600 m thick in the Atlantic. The thin layer surprised most scientists, who had expected a considerably thicker accumulation. The original estimate was based on the sedimentation rate in the ocean extrapolated throughout geological time and on estimates of the quantity of material removed from the continents. Using these estimates it would have taken only about 400 million years for the sediments found in the ocean to have accumulated. This amount of time is less than 10 percent of the geological time during which the oceans are thought to have existed. There are several possible escapes from this dilemma: either the sediments have been consolidated and occur as a deeper layer within the earth's crust, or the sediments have been removed from the ocean. A third possibility is that the estimates are wrong and that the oceans are relatively recent features of the earth.

E. L. Hamilton in 1959 suggested that as sediments accumulated on the sea floor the weight of the overlying sediments would cause a compaction and consolidation of the deeper sediments, which would result in an increased sound velocity. Thus, in some areas the so-called "second layer" beneath the sediments may consist of consolidated sediments. Even if this theory were completely correct, it would not account for all the missing sediments. Perhaps the oceans have not, after all, existed from the beginning of geological time. The possibility

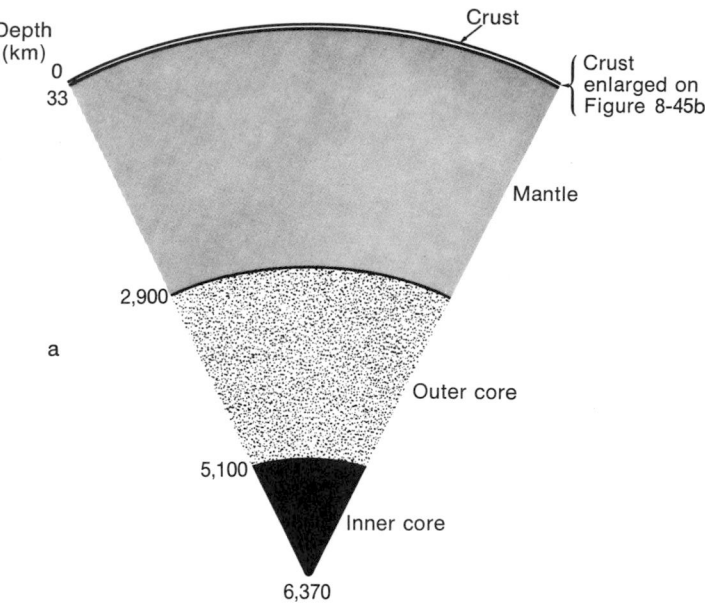

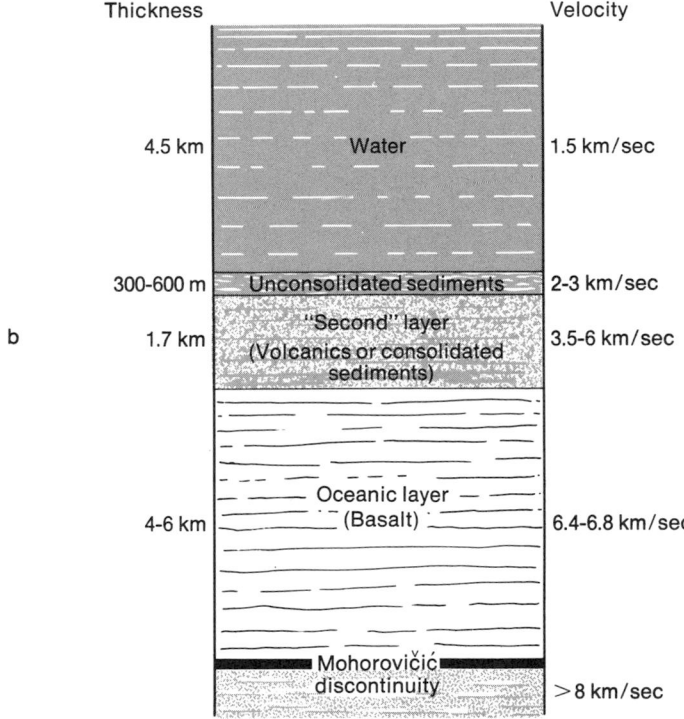

Figure 8-45 (a) The different layers of the earth drawn with no vertical exaggeration. (b) General structure of the earth's crust under the ocean as determined by seismic refraction and reflection studies. These are just the major layers. Numerous sublayers are possible within these larger ones. The scales are not exact.

that sediments have been removed from the sea floor will be discussed in the section on continental drift and sea-floor spreading (see p. 312).

The layer found underneath the sediments has a sound velocity of about 3.5 to 6.0 km/sec with an average value of about 5.0 km/sec. The thickness of this layer is about 1.7 km. These numbers can be subject to a wide variation due to differences in topography, to an uneven biased observational pattern, and to deficiencies of somewhat insensitive measuring techniques.

The sound velocities observed in the second layer are possible for a large variety of rocks, including the compacted sediments, as suggested by Hamilton. The layer could also consist of volcanic rocks in places, as evidenced by the fact that its thickness generally increases near volcanic islands. Results from deep-sea drilling will help solve the problem.

The third major layer of the ocean crust is a uniform layer, with a velocity between 6.4 and 6.7 km/sec and a thickness between 4 and 6 km. Its uniformity suggests that it is a major feature of the oceanic crust. It is called the "oceanic layer" and is assumed to be composed of basaltic rocks. This layer may come to the surface, as at the Mid-Atlantic Ridge, where basaltic rocks are dominant.

These three layers constitute the oceanic crust of the earth. There is a fundamental difference between the crust under the land and under the ocean, both in thickness and composition (Figure 8-46). The continental thickness averages about 35 km and the oceanic crust averages about 11 km deep including the overlying 4.5 km of water.

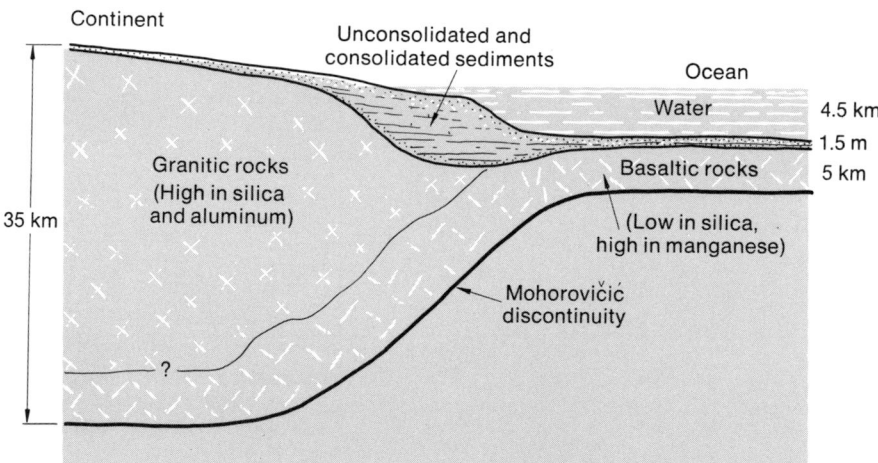

Figure 8-46 Crustal structure under the land and the ocean basin as determined by geophysical techniques. Note that the abrupt change between continent and oceanic structure occurs at the continental slope area.

The main rock type of the continents is granite, while that of the oceanic crust is basalt.

At the base of the third layer is the Mohorovičić (Moho) discontinuity where the speed of sound increases to about 8.0 km/sec. This discontinuity marks the base of the crust and the beginning of the earth's mantle. There is considerable controversy over whether this layer represents a chemical change or a phase change (like water changing to ice) due to increased pressure and temperature.

The Moho generally occurs at a depth of about 6.5 km below most of the floor of the ocean. There is, however, some variation. Under trenches and the Mid-Atlantic Ridge and East Pacific Rise, the Moho will occur somewhat deeper than under the surrounding ocean floor. In some of the marginal seas the Moho will occur at a depth intermediate to that of the oceans and the continents. (The Moho averages about 35 km under the continents.) The Moho also occurs at intermediate depths along the margins of the continents.

ORIGIN OF OCEAN BASINS

The preceding section has shown that the crustal structures of the ocean and the continents are quite different. The difference suggests that the ocean basin and the continents have remained separate for most of geological time. If part of the deep ocean basin were elevated above sea level, it would be recognizable by its sedimentary deposits. Conversely, if a continent were submerged, it should also be distinguishable by its crustal structure.

A reasonable question is why one portion of the earth should be covered with a thick crust that is essentially absent from the other parts of the earth. One theory is that the earth is expanding, and that at one time the whole earth was covered with this thick crust. The crust was split in several areas and it expanded along these zones of weakness that are now occupied by the ocean basins.

Numerous other theories have been proposed. New ones undoubtedly will be tested and old ones discarded before this book is published. The two main hypotheses are that of continental drift and, more recently, that of sea-floor speading.

Continental Drift and Sea-Floor Spreading

Early scientists noted the similar shapes of the continents on either side of the Atlantic and suggested that the crust between them had split apart some time in the past. This idea, called continental drift, was probably first advanced by von Humboldt in the early 1800s; more modern hypotheses were advanced by Suess in 1888, Taylor in 1910, and Wegener in 1912. These hypotheses assume that continents essentially float on the deeper and heavier subcrustal material. One possible moving force could be deep-seated convection currents operating within the earth's mantle (Figure 8-47). The currents are driven by the uneven heating of the earth's mantle, most of whose heat must come from decay of radioactive elements. The mantle is heated near the core and cooled near the crust; thus circulation cells develop, as in a pan of water heated at the bottom. The slow movement may drag and move parts of the lighter crust, and the continents would concentrate over the downward moving part of the convection cells. Ocean ridges, which appear to be tensional features, could form at the upward moving part of the convection cell.

Additional geological data sometimes favored continental drift, sometimes not. A geological controversy developed concerning this theory. Opponents argued that the forces needed to move continents around were immense, and that in many places the evidence for drifting was poor. If continents were moving around, a new sea floor without any sediment cover should be exposed in its wake. Another objection pointed to the completely different structure underneath the oceans and continents (see Figure 8-46), which suggests some degree of permanency to both areas. The large-scale movements (involving thousands of kilometers) also seemed unreasonable since no evidence of a similar type of massive displacement was observed on land. This objection was overcome by the magnetic work off the California coast (see Figure 8-33) that showed such displacements are possible.

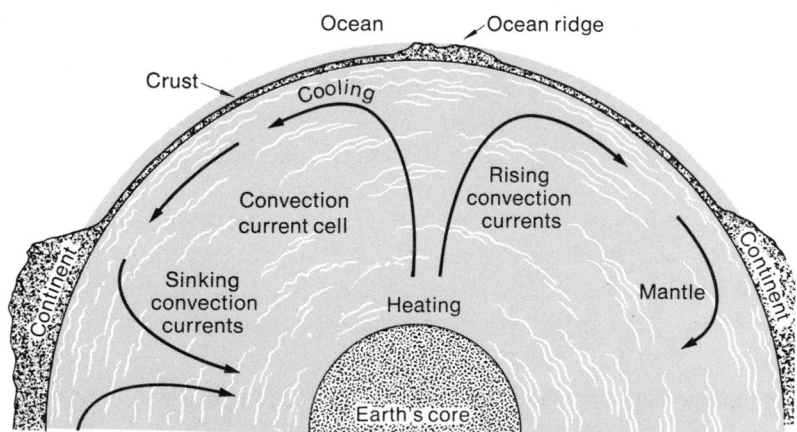

Figure 8-47   Possible model of convection current cells operating within the earth's mantle. Note that the continents are over the downward or sinking part of the convection cell and that the oceanic ridges are over the upward moving part of the cell.

Proponents of the continental drift hypothesis may differ from each other on details. They usually hold that the continents were joined in one supercontinent that split apart at some time, perhaps in the Mesozoic Era. When reconstruction of the postulated original position of the continents is made, many large-scale features can be seen to fit together and extend across several continents (Figure 8-48). There also are considerable data to suggest that the magnetic poles have migrated in the geological past. Such migration would help explain the fact that glaciers in the past covered what are now tropical areas. In other words, part of the original supercontinent may once have been situated at one of the poles. Some scientists note, however, that almost any arrangement of the continents still leaves a considerable portion of apparently glaciated land near the equator.

The main difficulty with the continental drift hypothesis is how, if the continents are light masses floating on a deeper and denser layer, a continental area can become an oceanic area.

A new hypothesis called sea-floor spreading, proposed by R. S. Dietz in 1961 and H. H. Hess in 1962, that in part incorporated older theories, has been able to overcome most of the previous objections to continental drift. The new hypothesis has considerable supporting data and can be tested (something that was difficult to do with the other hypothesis). It assumes that the sea floor itself is moving (the

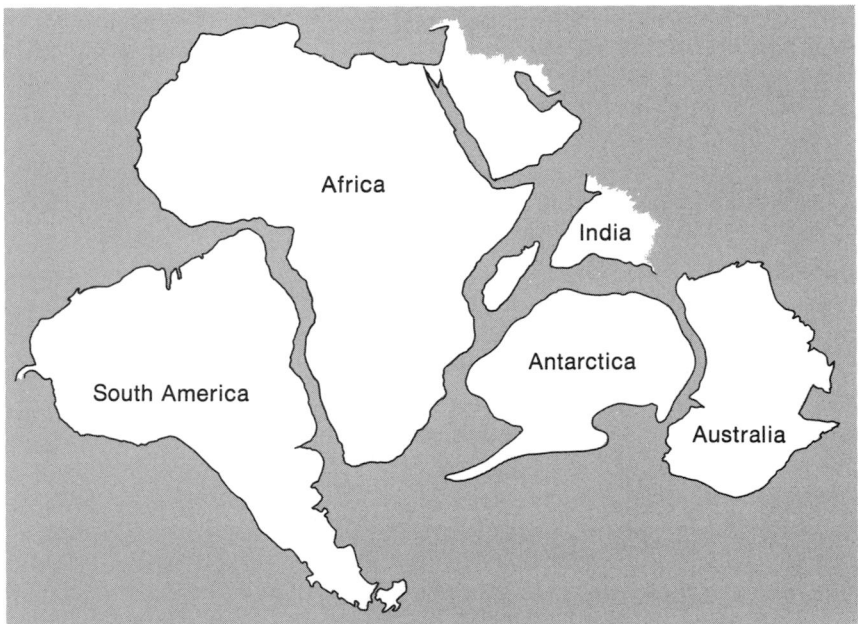

Figure 8-48   One possible reconstruction of the continents before the beginning of continental drift.

moving force being convection currents). Movement starts at the mid-ocean ridges and moves out in opposite directions from them. The resulting gap is filled with new sea floor formed from basaltic material originating in the mantle. The picture is one of a conveyor belt moving from the ridges first toward and then eventually under the continent (Figure 8-49). The ridge is therefore an area of crustal up-welling where new material is being added. The outer edges of the continents, perhaps in trenches or at the base of the continental slope, are areas of downwelling. The high heat flow and seismicity of the oceanic ridges are compatible with this hypothesis, which implies that the volcanic rocks are older as one proceeds away from the axis. Here exists a method for testing the idea of sea-floor spreading. This is one of the major problems that the Deep-Sea Drilling Project will consider: dating the age of the volcanic rocks underlying the deep-sea sediments.

The hypothesis of sea-floor spreading has been advanced considerably by magnetic observations made of the sea floor. In the early 1960s work off California showed that long linear magnetic patterns could be traced over a large part of the ocean. Observations over the ridges showed that linear magnetic patterns paralleled the ridge. These patterns have been interpreted as indicating that the underlying rock was solidified in the present earth's magnetic field, in which case it should have a positive value. If the rock had solidified in a reversed field (north and south poles are interchanged) the rock would have a negative value.

It thus appears that slow convection currents within the earth's mantle are gradually bringing volcanic (and magnetic) rock to the ridge areas. As this rock material cools it starts to solidify, at which time magnetic minerals will align themselves with the earth's field. Material cooling at the present time will be normally oriented and have a positive pattern. There have been times in the geological past

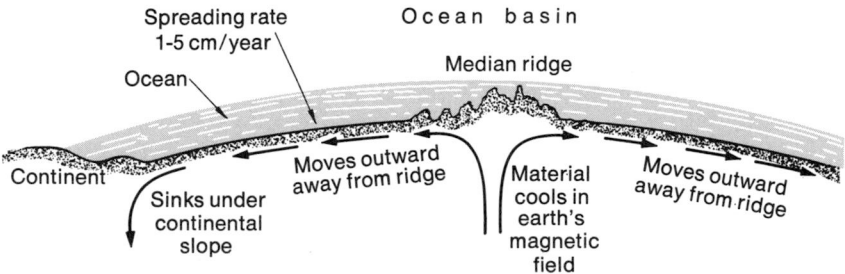

Figure 8-49 A diagram showing the basic parts of the sea-floor spreading hypothesis. As the magnetic minerals cool they are oriented along the earth's magnetic field. The resulting magnetic patterns (due to reversals of the magnetic field) can be used to estimate the rate of spreading (see Figure 8-51).

when the poles were reversed, a well documented but incompletely understood fact. Therefore rocks that solidified during such times would have a reversed pattern (Figure 8-50). Since rising basaltic material is being carried away from the ridge in a conveyor-belt fashion, measurements of the magnetic pattern of this area will show an alternating pattern of normal and reversed values. The patterns observed generally show a high degree of symmetry around the ridge area, that is, the pattern on one side is the reverse image of that on the other side (Figure 8-51). This is to be expected since the material is moving out on either side of the ridge (see Figure 8-49).

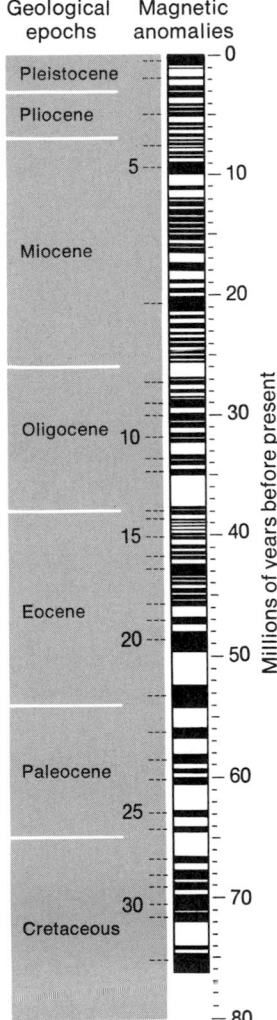

Figure 8-50 The geomagnetic time scale. This scale is determined by measuring the age of known reversals on land and extrapolating to the reversals detected in the ocean rocks (see Figure 8-51). The numbers on the left correlate with the magnetic anomaly numbers shown on Figure 8-51. The black areas indicate times when the poles were in their normal position, the blank areas when the poles were reversed. (From Heirtzler and others, *Journal of Geophysical Research* Fig. 3, **73** [1968]: 2119–2136.)

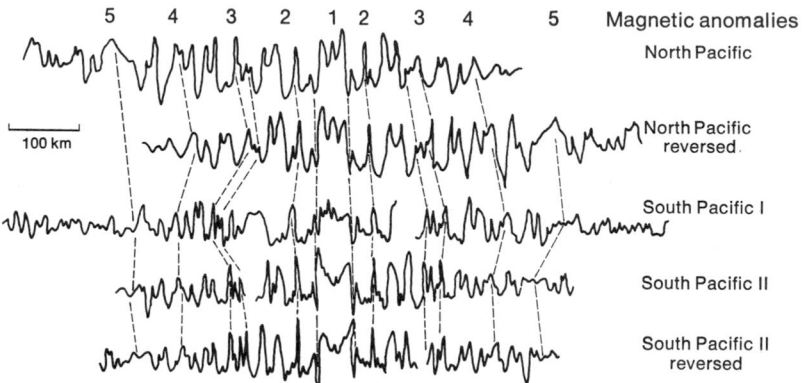

Figure 8-51 Magnetic profiles measured over various parts of the Pacific Ocean. The numbers refer to specific anomalies (see Figure 8-50), the dashed lines indicate correlation between anomalies. Anomaly number one is over the ridge axis. To show the symmetry of the patterns on either side of anomaly number one, two of the profiles are shown reversed. (From Pitman and others, *Journal of Geophysical Research* Fig. 4, **73** [1968]: 2069–2085.)

These patterns on the sea floor have been correlated with the previously mentioned land magnetic anomalies, which have, in turn, been dated by radioactive techniques. If the correlation is correct, an age can be ascribed to various parts of the pattern observed on the sea floor and an estimate can be made of the rate of spreading. This has been done for many areas, and a spreading rate of about 1 to 5 cm/year seems common (Figure 8-52). A spreading rate of 1 cm/year is equivalent to 10 km (about 6 miles) in a million years. This rate would indicate that the continents on either side of the Atlantic were joined at sometime in the Mesozoic Era, a possibility compatible with the idea of continental drift. With sea-floor spreading one need not consider the embarrassing problem of making a continental area become an oceanic one; instead, new sea floor is constantly being produced at the mid-oceanic ridges and old sea floor is disappearing at the edges of the continental blocks (see Figure 8-49). The continents can grow at their edges by the accumulation of material, while the ocean basins can also increase especially if, as many scientists believe, the earth is expanding.

The absence of large quantities of sediment on the sea floor can be explained by sea-floor spreading. The conveyor belt has carried much of the missing sediment down below the continents, and the sediment seen now is what has been deposited only within the last one or two hundred million years. Since the youngest part of the ocean basin is the ridge area, this is also the area where one would expect the smallest amount of sediments. Studies of sediment thickness by M. Ewing and J. Ewing in 1967 do indeed show that small

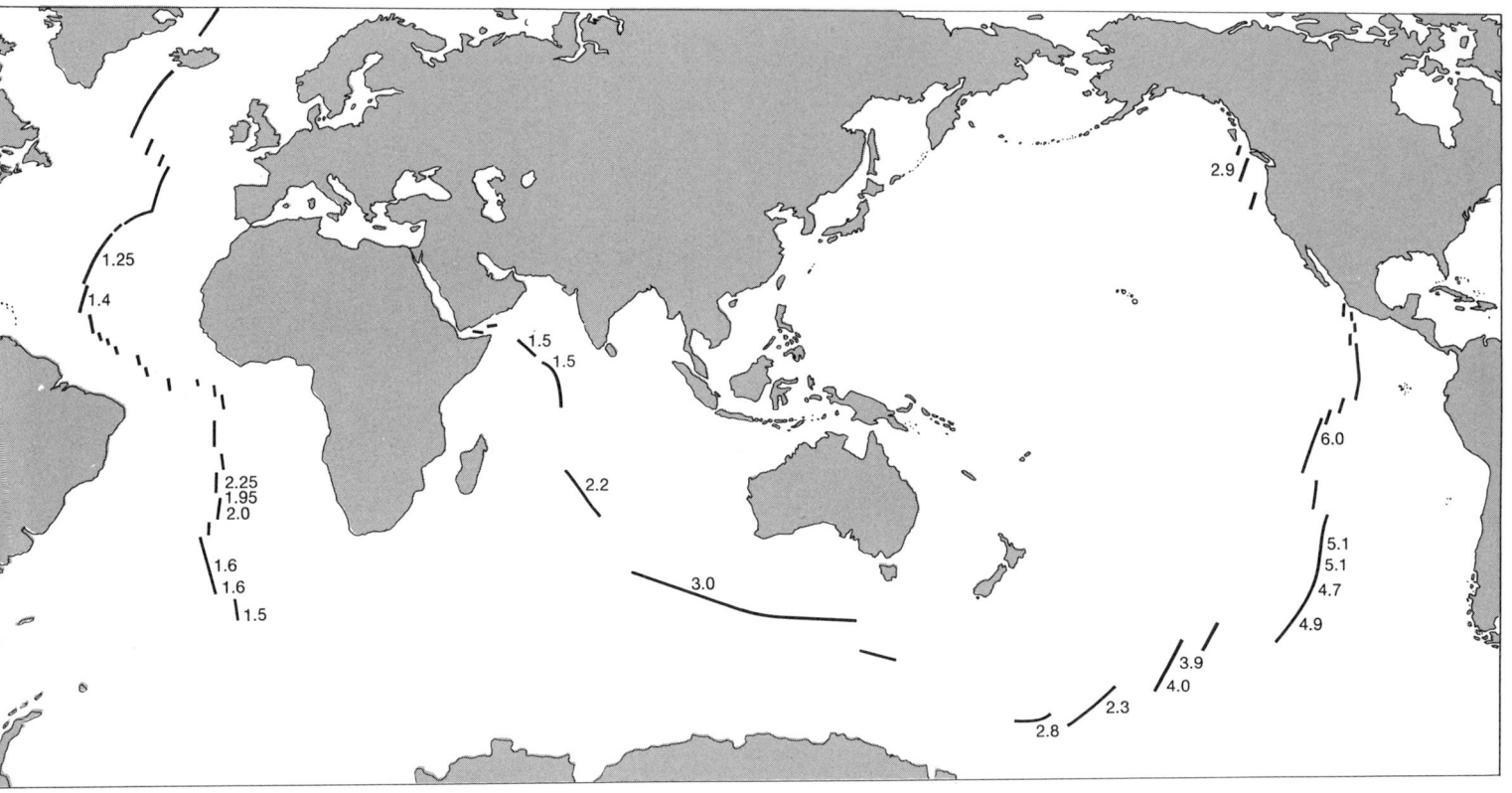

Figure 8-52 Spreading rates for different parts of the ocean. The solid line defines the mid-ocean ridge axis. The numbers near the axis give the spreading rate in centimeters per year. (After Heirtzler and others, 1968.)

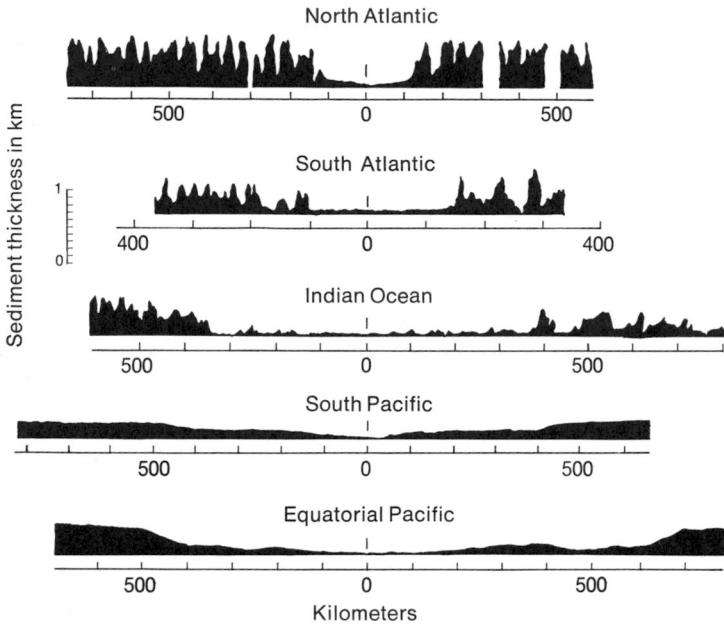

Figure 8-53 Sediment thickness observed on the mid-ocean ridge. The crest of the ridge is at 0 km. Note the general absence of sediment at the crest and the abrupt increase in sediment thickness at some distance on either side of the crest. (From Ewing and Ewing, *Science* Fig. 3, **156** [1967]: 1590–1592; Copyright 1967 by the American Association for the Advancement of Science.)

quantities of sediment are found in the ridge area and that further out from the ridge there is an abrupt increase in the sediment thickness (Figure 8-53). This has been interpreted by Ewing and Ewing as indicating a discontinuity in the spreading; they suggest that the present sea-floor spreading started about 10 million years ago, with a long period of quiescence when the sediments were deposited prior to that time. The concept of sea-floor spreading also fits nicely with the general observation that compressional features prevail on the continent and tensional features are common in the oceans. The hypothesis may also be related to the origin of continental slopes, where the ocean crust is downwelled or thrust under the continents.

More recent thoughts concerning the origin and evolution of the ocean basin are incorporated into a larger hypothesis called "New Global Tectonics." This new hypothesis covers the broader structural features of the earth and is based on earthquake studies and on the hypotheses of continental drift and sea-floor spreading. In New Global Tectonics the earth's crust is considered to be composed of about 20 large plates that move as rigid blocks (Figure 8-54). The boundaries of the plates are seismically active areas. Crustal material

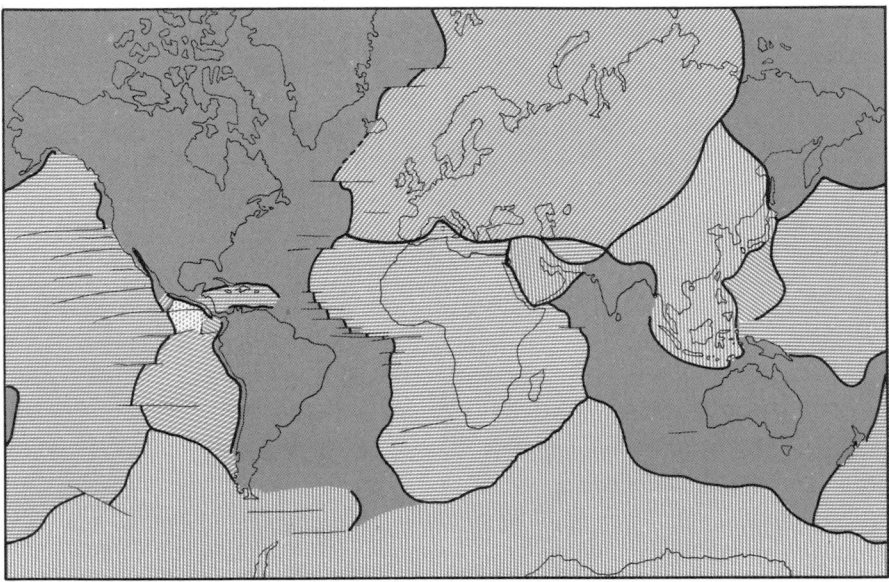

Figure 8-54 The various plates that are an important part of the New Global Tectonics hypothesis concerning the development of the earth's crust. These plates move as rigid units; their boundaries are oceanic ridges, trenches, and faults. Some boundaries are tentative and additional plates may be added as the hypothesis develops. (After Morgan, 1968.)

can be created at the ridges or destroyed at the trenches, with neither creation nor destruction occurring at the faults.

There are still some points that can be raised against all three hypotheses. For example, the forces and movements involved are large by any standard. A more perplexing problem is what happens at the margins of the continents. Here the magnetic patterns end and material is being forced under the lighter continental block. Thus one would expect the margin to be an area of intensive deformation. It occasionally is, but in some trenches (see Figure 8-34) no deformation is observed.

One of the principal advantages of these hypotheses is that they can be tested by deep drilling. Results of the Deep-Sea Drilling Project in the Atlantic indicate that the lowest, or first formed, sediments immediately above the volcanic rocks become systematically younger near the crest of the Mid-Atlantic Ridge. The systematic change in the age of the sediments (Figure 8-55) indicates a spreading rate similar to that determined from the magnetic pattern. These data strongly support the sea-floor spreading hypothesis. Perhaps when more sophisticated instruments are available, it can be tested further by measuring the actual movement across ridge areas.

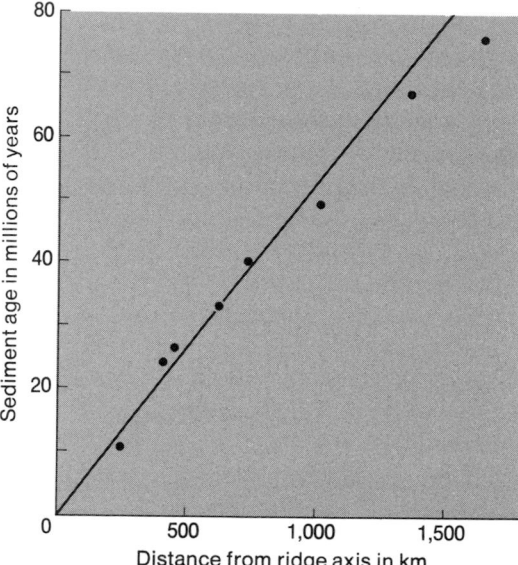

Figure 8-55 Age of the oldest sediments (from the southern Atlantic) and their distance from the ridge axis. The diagonal line indicates the sediment age and distance from the axis for a spreading rate of 2 cm/year. (After Peterson, 1969.)

Some of the large-scale features of the earth may be related to the fact that the earth wobbles somewhat on its axis. This observation was determined by taking telescopic sights on accurately located stars and noting their apparent movement. The cause of this wobbly motion has mystified scientists for many years. Recent observations, however, suggest that the motion may be related to earthquake activity. Some scientists have noted that the time when the wobbles increased generally corresponded to times when major earthquakes occurred. Actually these changes occurred several days before the large earthquakes, so that if the earth's wobble could be monitored, it would be a good means of earthquake prediction.

An American geophysicist, J. Heirtzler, suggests that the wobble causes the earthquakes rather than being a result of them. He further speculates that the wobble may influence the flow of material as visualized in the sea-floor spreading hypothesis and may even help explain reversals in the earth's magnetic field. Clearly the next few years may provide valuable information concerning the origin of the continents and the ocean basins.

SUGGESTED FURTHER READING

Clements, T., ed. *Essays in Marine Geology in Honor of K. O. Emery.* Los Angeles: University of Southern California Press, 1963.

Emery, K. O. *The Sea Off Southern California: A Modern Habitat of Petroleum.* New York: Wiley, 1960.

Ericson, D. B., and Wollin, G. *The Ever-Changing Sea.* New York: Knopf, 1967.

Kuenen, P. H. *Marine Geology.* New York: Wiley; London: Chapman and Hall, Ltd., 1950.

Menard, H. W. *Marine Geology of the Pacific.* New York: McGraw-Hill, 1964.

Miller, L., ed. *Papers in Marine Geology: Shepard Commemorative Volume.* New York: Macmillan, 1964.

Shepard, F. P. *The Earth Beneath the Sea.* Baltimore: Johns Hopkins Press, 1959.

Shepard, F. P. *Submarine Geology.* New York: Harper and Row, 1963.

Spar, J. *Earth, Sea and Air: A Survey of the Geophysical Sciences.* Reading, Mass.: Addison-Wesley, 1965.

Sverdrup, H. U., Johnson, M. W., and Fleming, R. H. *The Oceans: Their Physics, Chemistry, and General Biology.* New York: Prentice-Hall, 1942.

Chapter 9

RESOURCES

OF THE OCEAN

The preceding chapters have dealt with the various scientific divisions of oceanography. I hope that the reader has obtained a feeling for the immense size and scope of the ocean, as well as for the difficulties of working as a scientist in such an environment. In this chapter I describe the importance of the oceans to man, mainly from an economic viewpoint. One must remember that our knowledge of the ocean is constantly increasing, and perhaps even more important, our technological ability to exploit it is increasing. An example of this technological growth is shown by the progress in drilling offshore oil wells. In 1967 oil rigs were capable of drilling 15,000 ft in water depths of 135 ft if the rig was resting on the ocean bottom, or in depths of 600 ft if the rig was afloat. In late 1968 the GLOMAR CHALLENGER (Figure 9-1), a newly-built drilling vessel, drilled 2,740 ft below the ocean floor while floating 19,075 ft above the bottom. Thus we have a capability that permits almost any area of the sea floor to be reached and exploited.

The obvious point of the following discussion is that the full potential of the sea is not known, and one can only speculate on its future economic value.

Figure 9-1   The GLOMAR CHALLENGER. This vessel is 400 ft long and 65 ft wide; it was built by Global Marine, Inc. The GLOMAR CHALLENGER is designed to drill in water depths up to 20,000 ft and to obtain samples from 2,500 ft below the sea floor.

CHEMICAL RESOURCES

The chemical resources of the sea are staggeringly huge. There are about 330 million cubic miles of sea water. Each one of these cubic miles contains about 165 million tons of dissolved solids. This means that the ocean contains a total of more than 500×10^{14} tons of dissolved solids (or over 100,000,000,000,000,000,000 pounds). Another way of expressing this quantity is to consider an element in the sea that is present in just 1 part per billion parts of water; sea water would contain over 5 million tons of such an element. This storehouse of minerals is constantly being added to by the rivers flowing into the ocean.

One would think that with such a large reservoir of dissolved solids, considerable "chemical" mining of the sea would be taking place. Actually, only a few compounds are presently being recovered from the ocean in commercial quantities (Table 9-1). The cost of recovery of most elements from the ocean is very high, and in most instances the recovery is not a good economic investment. This situation could change in the future.

TABLE 9-1 COMPOUNDS RECOVERED FROM SEA WATER ON WORLD-WIDE BASIS (DATA FROM SHIGLEY, 1968)

Compounds	Tons/ Year	% Ocean Production/ Total Production
Sodium chloride	35,000,000	29
Bromine	102,000	70
Magnesium	106,000	61
Metal compounds	690,000	6
Fresh water	142,000,000	59

Salt is composed of two of the most common elements in sea water, sodium and chlorine. It has been recovered from sea water for over 5,000 years. Salt can be extracted by letting sea water evaporate. After a certain point in the evaporation process, fairly pure sodium chloride will start to crystallize out. About 5 percent of the United States' production comes from this method; the remainder comes from underground mines.

Bromine and magnesium are extracted in large quantities by several processing plants near the Gulf of Mexico. The value of these two products is about 90 million dollars per year.

Perhaps the most important product to be extracted from the sea is fresh water. In many areas of the world the main source of water is desalinated sea water. The several desalination methods include freezing, distillation, ion exchange, and osmosis techniques. Distillation is probably the most economic method, although the cost is about 1 dollar per 1,000 gallons which is about 10 times the cost of fresh water obtained from usual sources.

Today there are more than 200 desalination plants around the world, and the number is increasing rapidly. Desalination plants usually require large amounts of power, and power plants themselves always have large water demands. Combination desalination and power plants could be a possible method for reducing the cost of the fresh water produced. One such plant, using nuclear power, has been proposed for Huntington Beach near Los Angeles. When operating, it would be the world's largest, producing 150 million gallons per day at a cost of 20 cents per 1,000 gallons.

The supply of fresh water from the ocean will become more important as the cost is reduced by advances in technology. It will still be quite a few years, however, before desalinated water will be used routinely for desert irrigation.

It is probable that as man uses up his land resources he will eventually look to the ocean for his strategic materials. If the technology were available most of our national needs for such materials could be obtained from a relatively small volume of sea water. For example, 5 cubic miles of sea water contain over twenty times the United States' annual needs of bromine, chlorine, magnesium, and strontium, three times its needs of potassium and sulfur, and approximately its requirements for boron and iodine. The cost involved and technology necessary, prohibit the extraction of these materials for the present.

One method of extracting elements from sea water is through use of marine organisms. Many marine animals will concentrate trace elements from the sea water by factors of over 10,000 times the concentration of the element in the water. If these animals could be cultivated, they could provide a source of certain elements. One can't help but wonder if there is an animal in the sea that likes gold.

A new and exciting field is marine pharmacology, the science of finding substances in marine organisms that can be used as drugs to fight disease. Most of these life-saving drugs paradoxically are substances used as poisons by marine animals. Drugs that slow the heartbeat, reduce the coagulation time of blood, and reduce blood pressure have been separated from poisons secreted by different kinds of fish.

Marine animals may also be valuable in the study of cancer. Many marine organisms apparently do not suffer from cancer; some clams and oysters have chemical substances that prevent or destroy tumors, but scientists have not yet isolated these substances.

Marine pharmacology is promising. Though only a start has been made in exploiting the medical potential of the sea, the Federal Government plans to establish a National Institute of Marine Medicine and Pharmacology in the near future.

BIOLOGICAL RESOURCES

The biological resources of the sea are one of the most important aspects of oceanography. Many believe that the ocean must be used to solve the world's food problems, problems which will become so critical that only massive, long-range effort can possibly solve them. It would be very naive to think that the ocean provides an easy solution.

The food problem is such that at present 1.5 billion people, half the population of the world, suffer from a protein-deficient diet. The problem is compounded in the underdeveloped countries because their population is growing faster than their ability to produce adequate food supplies. A daily supplement of 10 to 20 g of animal protein is considered sufficient to prevent a protein diet deficiency; this is equivalent to 8 to 16 lb a year. The need is therefore for protein, a commodity present in large quantities in the ocean. As I have noted in Chapter 6, plankton comprises the largest group of organisms in the ocean. As individual organisms, most are microscopic in size. Therefore, to obtain large quantities of plankton an immense quantity of water must be filtered (as much as 1 million pounds of sea water to obtain 1 lb of plankton). There are other reasons, such as taste, why plankton are not a suitable source of protein. To find a usable source of protein one must look to a higher level of animal, such as fish.

The amount of fish caught in the world each year is constantly increasing and presently is over the 100 billion pound mark (Figure 9-2). The United States, which once was in second place in world catch, is presently in sixth place behind Peru, Japan, China (mainland), the Soviet Union, and Norway. These six countries catch over 50 percent of the total quantity of fish landed.

Why has the United States fishing industry fallen behind that of the other fishing countries? Certainly part of the answer is the lack of financial incentive to the American fishermen. In many other countries a food shortage has encouraged increased governmental support for the fishing industry. The United States, perhaps because of its wealth, doesn't seem to mind importing the fish it needs. In fact the United States presently imports over 65 percent of the fishery products it consumes each year.

There are other reasons, such as laws and customs, that have restricted the catch of American fishermen. Many American fishing

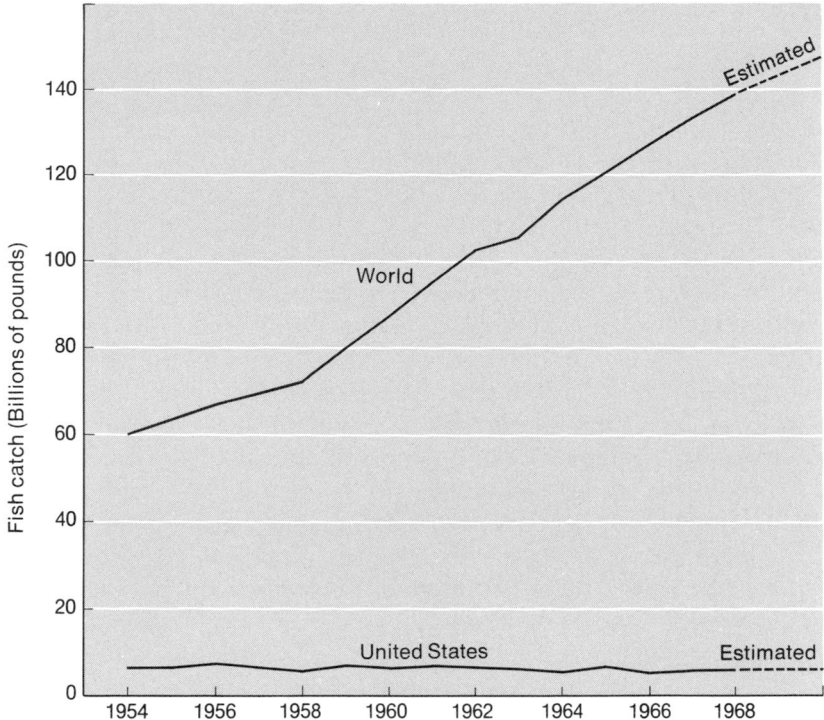

Figure 9-2   The world and United States yearly fish catch.

boats (which by law must be built in the United States) are inferior to those of other countries. Fishing regulations, although usually imposed with good intentions, can in some instances be very cumbersome and ineffective. Some regulations are necessary to prevent overfishing and depletion of a particular species of fish. In most cases these regulations should also involve other countries because many fishing areas are in international waters and the fish can migrate from one area to another.

It is not clear whether the large quantity of fish caught is in fact sufficient to feed the world's population. There is a wide diversity of opinion on the matter and several points must be considered. The total fish catch is not presently used for human consumption; large quantities are used to feed livestock (about 40 percent of the U.S. catch is used for this purpose). Fish is a difficult product to store without adequate refrigeration. The customs and religions of many countries present various sociological barriers to fish consumption. Fisheaters in most countries eat only a few species, while many other abundant fish (sometimes called "trash fish") are avoided.

There is also disagreement about the biological potential of the ocean. Some authorities believe that man already catches 50 or 75 percent of the sustainable yield of the ocean. Other, less conservative, views are that only a small percentage of the potential yield is caught. The latter view is probably closer to the truth. Using an average value of carbon production of 50 g $C/m^2/year$ for the entire ocean, man catches less than 0.04 percent of the annual production of the ocean. One must exercise a little caution here; these numbers refer to the production by phytoplankton, which are the lowest member of the food chain (see Figure 6-41). Man, however, prefers to eat organisms higher up in the food chain, like the carnivores. As one goes from one level to another in the food chain the efficiency of the conversion of the carbon into living material must be considered. The conversion, which is variable, is usually assumed to be about 10 percent of available carbon with each increase in food level. Thus if an organism two food levels above the phytoplankton is caught, it is roughly equivalent to harvesting 1 percent of the phytoplankton that this organism directly or indirectly consumed. (Only 10 percent of the carbon in the phytoplankton will be converted into organic matter in the first food chain level [herbivores] above the phytoplankton; likewise only 10 percent [or 1 percent of the original phytoplankton population] will be converted in the next level.)

This clearly shows the advantage of utilizing animals further down in the food cycle, for example herbivores such as anchovies. The anchovy constitutes a major part of the fish caught by Peru, the country that has the greatest catch from the sea.

There are several other ways that the catch from the ocean can be increased. One way is to improve fishing technology. Sophisticated methods of locating fish, such as sonar, have led to increased catches. A better understanding of how fish react with their environment would also be helpful.

Some fishermen raise organisms rather than catch them in the ocean. This process, analogous to farming on land, is called **aquaculture.** It aims at providing an environment where certain desirable species of life will grow rapidly and can be harvested. At present aquaculture is restricted to nearshore areas, like bays and estuaries, and is applied only to such animals as clams, oysters, and shrimp. It may soon be possible to extend this technique to the open ocean, as well as to other animals.

Oyster farming is potentially a very important industry. The baby oysters, called spat, float and move with the ocean currents until they encounter a shell on the bottom to which they can become attached. Oyster fishermen—actually oyster farmers is a better term—place shells on the bottom in environments suitable for oyster growth. These environments are certain bays, inlets, and other nearshore areas. The spat, after attaching to the shells, will grow until large enough to be harvested by the "farmers."

Another method (new to the United States; it has been used in Japan and Europe for decades) is to suspend shells on wires throughout the water. Thus more spat can grow in a particular area. This method, a sort of three-dimensional farming, has several other advantages: it removes the baby oysters from their natural enemies, the starfish, and places the oysters where more food is available. Bottom-living oysters can feed only on the plankton that settle to the bottom, while oysters living on suspended shells can feed on the much larger quantity of plankton that float by in the currents.

Aquaculture is not a major industry at present in the United States. If, however, we attempt to farm the sea with a vigor similar to that we apply to land farming, tremendous potential awaits us. An advantage of aquaculture is that it can be carried out in the nearshore areas of countries that most need the protein.

A new product, called fish protein concentrate (FPC), will help in a fuller utilization of the harvest from the sea. FPC is an odorless and tasteless protein concentrate powder that can be made from almost any kind of fish. It is an absolutely safe and stable product that can be stored without refrigeration. It can be easily added to the diet, perhaps even baked into bread; 10 g of FPC will provide the daily protein needs of a child at a cost of less than a penny a day. The FPC method allows the utilization of species of fish, like hake, that would not usually be consumed by humans. There is nothing wrong with these fish except that in the past they have not been culturally and socially accepted as food.

Because FPC does not spoil, most shipping and storage problems are eliminated. Several pilot plants in the United States are presently producing FPC. If this product becomes accepted in the under-nourished countries, it can solve some of the food problems of the world, at least for a few years.

THE MARINE ENVIRONMENT AND POLLUTION

Clearly the marine environment should be considered as an important resource of the ocean. For example, over 75 percent of the United States' population lives along its coastal and Great Lakes areas. It has been estimated that 30 million Americans swim in the ocean, 11 million are salt-water sport fishermen, and several million are boating enthusiasts. These activities, which in the past have been taken so casually, are threatened by the ever-increasing pollution of our near-shore waters. Estimates are that the incidence of pollution will grow seven-fold by the year 2000 unless there are definite changes in our handling of waste products.

Pollution is an emotionally-charged subject—some aspects have been blown up out of proportion, others are frighteningly dangerous. An example of the latter is air pollution. Fumes from automobile exhausts, industry, airplanes, faulty incinerators, and the like are causing damage that in the United States alone is estimated at 10 to 15 billion dollars a year, not to mention the effect on the health of the inhabitants of this country.

The effects of pollution in the marine environment are sometimes very obvious; for example, over 10 billion gallons of waste per day are discharged into Lake Erie. The result is an immense lake that is rapidly losing much of its aquatic life and that is unfit for swimming, fishing, and, certainly, drinking. Other forms of pollution are more subtle, such as the effects of pesticides, which are only now becoming known.

There are three main types of pollution that affect the marine environment:

1. Substances that directly destroy the organisms within the polluted area
2. Substances that alter the physical and chemical properties of the environment and thus favor a particular type of organism
3. Substances that are dangerous to higher forms of life, such as human beings, but are relatively harmless to lower forms of life.

Examples of pollution that can destroy large quantities of organisms are oil spills (and the detergents used to clean up the spills) and waste products from chemical industries.

One danger of offshore oil wells is the possibility of oil leakage. In 1969, one such well off Santa Barbara, California, leaked more than 250,000 gallons of oil into the Pacific Ocean before it could be plugged up. This leak produced an oil slick that covered over 800 square miles of the ocean. The oil coated and eventually killed many marine organisms, especially such birds as cormorants which dive into the water for fish. It also polluted beach areas for many miles along the coast. A similar catastrophe occurred a few years earlier when a large tanker, the TORREY CANYON, was wrecked off the coast of Southwest England. This ship was carrying over a million gallons of oil which were released into the sea, producing results like those in Santa Barbara. In this instance it was estimated that 90 percent of the animal loss was caused by the detergent used to clear up the oil.

Another serious but less well-known source of pollution comes from ships that flush their bilges at sea, thereby introducing large quantities of petroleum products into the oceans—quantities many times larger than those due to disasters like the wreck of the TORREY CANYON. Surface plankton hauls made thousands of miles from land now almost routinely yield large particles of oil.

Stronger federal and state regulations could help prevent the leaking of offshore oil wells. The federal government must balance the economic potential of the offshore oil areas against the ever-present possibility of oil pollution. One side argues that there is no safe way to extract oil from the ocean bottom, while the other side says that these disasters are isolated events caused by the peculiarities of nature. The prevention of wrecks of oil-carrying ships is one problem that does not appear to have a sure solution.

Several products have recently been developed to aid in dispersing or in chemically decomposing the oil. In some instances, unfortunately, the cure has been worse than the disease.

Alteration of the physical and chemical properties of water is a common form of pollution; included in this group are thermal pollution, sewage material, and fertilizers drained from the land.

Thermal pollution is a new problem. Many industries, especially power plants, use large quantities of water for cooling purposes. The heated water is then returned to the river or estuary where the temperature in some instances is raised to levels that are harmful or fatal to the animal and plant life.

The disposal of sewage and fertilizers is important as a source of the nutrients nitrate and phosphate. These nutrients can cause an increase in productivity, sometimes resulting in a thick growth of algae over the sea. The algae growth, besides being unattractive, can play havoc with the marine environment. After death the algae will be oxidized, and if their numbers are sufficiently high all the oxygen will be consumed, causing an anaerobic condition that is toxic to most forms of life.

The controlled growth of phytoplankton can sometimes be very useful. Phytoplankton, because they photosynthesize, can be used to fight pollution. The addition of certain phytoplankton species to sewage disposal areas will decrease pollution, because the phytoplankton will indirectly provide oxygen that aids in bacterial oxidation of certain pollutants, and will directly remove nitrogen and phosphorus compounds from the sewage.

The sea could be used to store the immense quantities of trash that are accumulating in many large cities. One problem is that many solid waste materials do not sink. One way of overcoming this is to lower the waste to such a depth that air pockets in the waste material will be compressed and replaced by water. At the same time, little is understood about the long-range effect of such disposal.

Many people feel that the ocean cannot be polluted or contaminated because of its vast size. *This is not true!* Two products by man can already be detected in the ocean: lead from the fuel used for internal combustion of engines, and radioactive isotopes from nuclear bomb blasts. The sea cannot serve as an endless reservoir for our garbage. Under the right conditions, however, material dumped into the sea *can* serve a valuable purpose. Fish, for example, will tend to concentrate around submerged objects such as sunken ships and drilling rigs. Some people have suggested forming artificial reefs on the sea floor by dumping in old cars. This may actually be beneficial to our fishing industry; however, one must be very careful where things are put since a beach landward of this artificial reef may become an accumulation area for pieces of the debris that are broken off by waves and storms.

The last type of pollution consists of substances poisonous to man, but harmless to lower forms of life. This may be the most dangerous of all. Included in this group are the radioactive substances and pesticides, which in some instances may be concentrated by the fish and plants in the ocean.

Probably the most widely known pesticide is DDT; this chemical has proved successful against typhus, malaria, and encephalitis. Its control over mosquitoes that carry malaria is estimated to have saved the lives of millions of people. It has also been important in increasing crop production—its arrest of the boll weevil helped double the United States cotton crop in the last 20 years. However, the effects of DDT last long after it has finished the job of exterminating insects. It is estimated that two-thirds of the 1.5 million tons of DDT produced may still be actively contaminating the earth and ocean. Many animals and fish are found to have high quantities of DDT—quantities that could be dangerous to man or other animals that eat these creatures. Some groups of birds, such as peregrine falcons, are becoming extinct because of high quantities of stored pesticides. One effect of pesticides on birds is in their reproduction, causing thin, easily breakable eggshells, or even a general failure to lay eggs.

How animals concentrate DDT and other pesticides (DDT is the most widely known, but not necessarily the most dangerous) is not really understood. One suggested mechanism is biological magnification (Figure 9-3). In this process DDT, which is essentially insoluble in water, enters the ocean in relatively small quantities, which are then concentrated by the zooplankton, and in turn further concentrated by the organisms that feed on the plankton. In this manner, animals at the end of the food chain receive concentrations several millions of times higher than the amount originally introduced into the water.

In response to these effects, the use of pesticides has been banned in several states, and the Federal government has curtailed the use of DDT. Little is known about how pesticides react in the environment and additional research is needed.

Most of the pollution in the ocean comes from the estuaries, which in turn are fed by the inland rivers. Estuaries often are major seaports and adjoin large industrial areas. Prior to industrial develop-

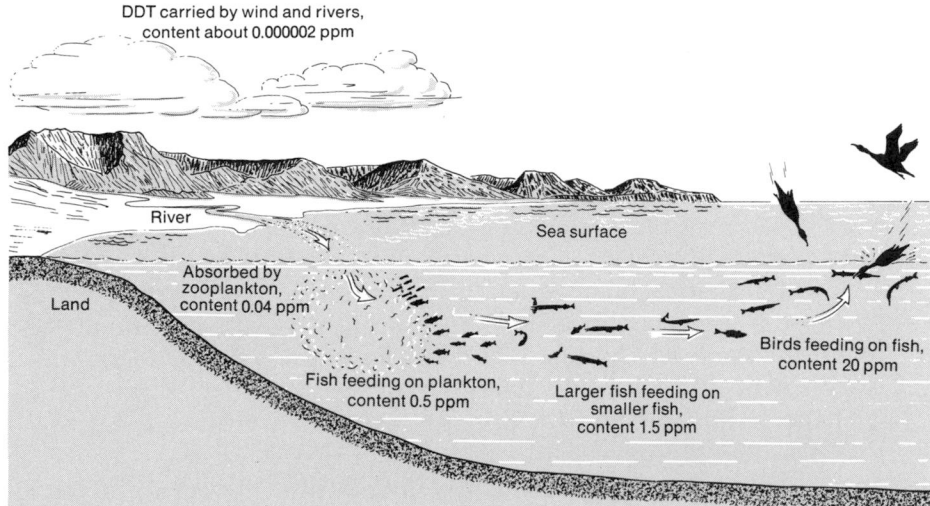

Figure 9-3 The process of biological magnification of DDT. At each level in the food chain the concentration of DDT is increased and subsequently passed on to the next level. Animals like humans and birds therefore can receive quantities of pesticides concentrated millions of times higher than the amount originally introduced into the environment.

ment, the estuaries may have been highly productive biological areas. Pollution of waters is a price paid for increased industrial development, but some balance in the amount of pollution is essential. One of the major questions of our time is to what extent can pollution be controlled. It is beyond question that the present rate of pollution can irrevocably alter the environment and life as we know it.

PHYSICAL RESOURCES

The physical resources of the ocean are perhaps not as obvious as other resources. One physical resource is the large amount of energy contained within the ocean; tidal energy has especially fascinated many scientists. Various ideas and schemes have been devised whereby the rise and fall of the tides could be used to drive electrical turbines or other devices.

The development of many of these ideas has been hampered by the vast sum of money necessary to implement them. The world's first major tidal power system, built on the Rance River in France, cost about 100 million dollars. The Soviet Union has started operation of an experimental tidal power station on the Barents Sea, 50 miles from Finland. The Soviet Union has announced its intention to build additional, larger tidal power plants in the future. Plans to build tidal power stations near the English Channel and in Passamaquoddy Bay, between the United States and Canada, have existed for years. Political influence, however, has often hindered the development of these potential sources of new power.

Actually tidal power is only one form, and a small one at that, of energy that could be harvested from the sea. The force of waves is known to anyone who lives near the sea or has seen the effects of a severe storm. At present no satisfactory method has been developed to contain and utilize wave energy. The ocean also contains vast amounts of thermal energy that could be used to warm large areas of the world—the main question is, how. Along with answering this question, one must consider that diverting warm water to some other place might well affect the delicate balance of nature in the ocean.

The ocean and the weather are very closely related (remember that over 70 percent of the earth's surface is covered by water). The association of weather and the ocean is obvious in coastal areas, but it also extends inland where storms that originate by interactions of the ocean and the atmosphere can move. To better understand the relationship between the ocean and weather, meteorologists need considerable information about conditions over the ocean. Any method that increases the ability to forecast the weather could result in vast benefits to mankind. In the future it is even possible that weather can be controlled.

The vast size of the ocean suggests that it may be a suitable place for man to live and work. The Sealab program of the United States Navy is exploring this possibility. Underwater habitats have been placed at relatively shallow depths (usually less than 600 ft) on the sea floor and men have lived there for varying lengths of time. The men, called aquanauts, are free to leave the habitat and roam and work on the sea floor.

For man the most dangerous problem in living underwater is the pressure or weight of the overlying water—this pressure increases at a rate of one-half pound per square inch with each foot that one descends into the ocean. Each 10 m of depth is equivalent to 1 atm increase in pressure. If a diver ascends too quickly from the bottom, he can be killed by gases (mostly nitrogen) that have been forced by the pressure into his tissues and are bubbling out into his blood stream as the pressure is reduced. The effect, called bends, can be avoided if the diver ascends slowly, permitting the gases to leave his blood stream without forming bubbles. The need for decompressing by slow ascent can limit the total amount of time that a diver can safely spend underwater. After a certain amount of time underwater, however, the tissues become saturated with gas and the diver can stay at the depth necessary for work or research for a long period without increased decompression time. It is this principle that has allowed some divers to stay over three weeks at a depth of 330 ft. Once man has perfected diving techniques, he can perform underwater operations, such as mining, salvaging, and perhaps even fishing, that will be beneficial to many marine industries.

GEOLOGICAL RESOURCES

The geological resources of the sea floor are generally considered to be of immense value; but in reality this is usually far from the truth. There are vast quantities of minerals in the oceans both dissolved in sea water (see the section on chemical resources) and on the sea bottom, but often the cost of recovering them is many times the value of the minerals.

The minerals of the sea floor can be divided into three groups: detrital deposits, authigenic deposits, and organic deposits. Detrital deposits are the result of erosion of pre-existing rock with the eroded material being carried to the ocean by rivers or some other mechanism. Once in the ocean the detrital material will be carried by waves and currents and eventually be deposited on the sea floor. The most abundant detrital resource is sand and gravel (broken shell fragments are included in this group). Sand and gravel are used largely as a component of building materials and as fill to replace sediment lost from beaches. The value of these deposits recovered from the sea is considerably less than that of land production (Table 9-2). It is usually simpler and cheaper to mine sand and gravel on land. But in some instances, such as when land transportation costs become high, the offshore deposits could become economically valuable.

The other type of detrital deposit is heavy mineral concentrations, that is, minerals with a density greater than 2.9 g/cm³, the upper limit for the usual components of sand. In most sandy areas, heavy minerals comprise only a small percentage of the sediment. In other areas, where there are strong currents, the lighter components of sand are carried away, leaving a residue or concentration of the heavy minerals. Some heavy minerals are found near land, close to their initial source; others are found in ancient beaches that are now submerged. The value of these detrital heavy minerals is relatively low when compared to land-derived material, which is usually easier to obtain.

Authigenic minerals are those found on the sea floor that precipitated chemically from the sea water. Two common authigenic deposits are manganese nodules and phosphorite (see Figures 5-2 and 5-3). These deposits cover vast areas of the sea floor, but are not very thick. They generally occur in areas where the sedimentation rate is low. Most commercial phosphorite is used as a fertilizer. Manganese nodules vary in composition (see Table 8-6), and some people think that

TABLE 9-2 VALUE (IN THOUSANDS OF DOLLARS) OF GEOLOGICAL RESOURCES RECOVERED FROM THE OCEAN AND FROM THE LAND (DATA FOR 1964 FROM FYE AND OTHERS, 1968)

	United States		Entire World	
	Ocean	Land	Ocean	Land
Detrital Minerals				
Sand and Gravel	35,000	860,000	100,000	2,000,000 ?
Heavy Minerals				
Titanium	9,000	11,000	33,000	37,000
Zircon	1,000	0	11,000	0
Diamonds	0	0	4,000	284,000
Tin	0	0	5,000	460,000
Monazite	0?	0?	1,500	300
Iron	0	800,000	700	5,300,000
Gold	0	50,000	0	1,310,000
Authigenic				
Phosphorite	0	160,000	0	375,000
Manganese	0	3,000	0	423,000
Organic				
Oil and gas	800,000	10,500,000	3,600,000	27,500,000
Sulfur	15,000	100,000	15,000	240,000

the minor components such as nickel, cobalt, and copper may be the most valuable part of the nodule. There is a controversy about the economic value and potential of manganese nodules, and several difficulties indicate that manganese nodules will not be recovered soon in large quantities from the sea floor. First among the difficulties is developing a technique for raising the nodules from the sea floor. There are also difficulties in refining the nodules into a usable ore.

Organic deposits result from the death of living organisms and their subsequent accumulation on the sea floor. With time, these deposits will be buried by other sediments and, according to many scientists, can be changed into oil and gas deposits. Oil and gas are the most valuable commodities to be recovered from the ocean. An example of the scale of the oil operations is that leases (not including royalties if oil is found) for offshore areas brought over 500 million dollars in 1967 for an area off Louisiana and in 1968 over 600 million dollars each for an area off California and another off Texas. Recent bidding for oil rights off Louisiana reached as high as 27,000 dollars per acre. The water depth is over 3,400 ft. In 1969 leases for areas off Alaska brought over 900 million dollars to that state; an amount several times larger than the state's yearly budget.

L. G. Weeks, a geologist, in 1968 estimated that the world's consumption of oil will triple in the next twenty years. At present the

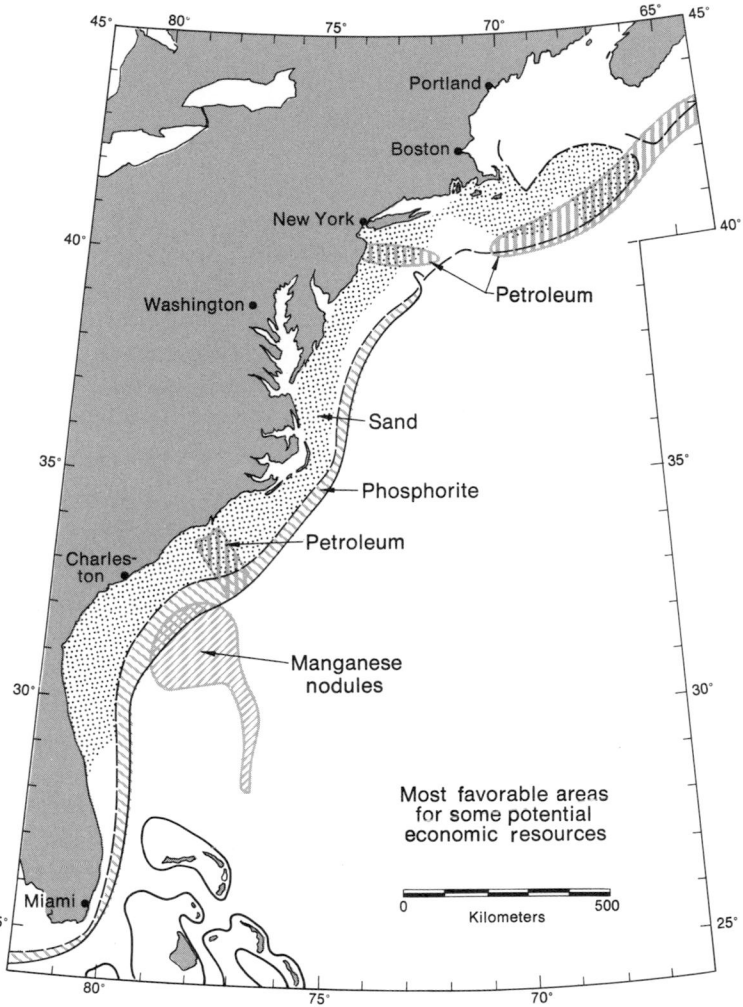

Figure 9-4   Distribution of the most favorable areas for some potential mineral deposits off the Atlantic coast of the United States. (After Emery, 1966.)

offshore reserves are about 85 billion barrels or about 20 percent of the world's supply. In the next ten years the offshore production should reach 23 million barrels per day, or 33 percent of the estimated world total of 70 million barrels per day.

The submerged part of the Atlantic Coast of the United States is one area where no oil wells have successfully been drilled, but several oil companies have recently completed preliminary exploration in this area. Apparently the general feeling is that the Atlantic Coast, especially the Georges Bank area, has excellent potential for oil (Figure 9-4).

One of the major discoveries of the Deep-Sea Drilling Project came in the second hole drilled. This hole was located in the Gulf of Mexico on what is now called the Challenger Knoll (a knoll is a small hill on the sea floor). The drilling ship, the GLOMAR CHALLENGER (see Figure 9-1), started drilling on the hill situated 11,753 ft below the ship. Samples of the drilled material were obtained at various depths. A sample obtained from 450 ft below the surface was very surprising—it showed a definite indication of gas and oil. The knoll actually is a sea-floor expression of a buried geological structure known as a salt dome and salt domes are often associated with oil deposits. The surprise was finding a salt dome with associated oil deposits at such great depth. Usually they are found at considerably shallower depths, on or near the continental shelf. The results at this site suggests that oil-forming processes may act in the deep sea, an area previously thought to have an insignificant potential for oil accumulation.

OTHER USES OF THE OCEAN

The ocean has many other uses. The seas are used for the transport of products between countries. Recent technological developments have increased the use and efficiency of ocean transport. Developments include more mechanized cargo handling, more efficient ship design, and increased size of the freighters. Cargo handling time, which accounts for much of the cost of shipping, can be reduced by the use of large containers that can easily be loaded on and off the vessel. Hydrofoils, which reach speeds of up to 60 knots, are being used in some areas as ferryboats. The hovercraft, a vehicle that rides on a cushion of air, can be used for short trips.

The oceans have always been a recreational area for man. Many ocean activities such as sailing, fishing, skin diving, surfing, and swimming are becoming increasingly popular. In many areas there is a conflict of interest between using nearshore areas for industrial development or for recreational sites.

The ocean is also used for communication; underwater telephone cables link many of the major cities of the world. In the future, direct underwater communications may be possible using lasers.

The ocean presents some very interesting engineering problems. One, corrosion, affects almost anything placed in the ocean. Sea water, because of its dissolved salts, can conduct electricity, and when a metal object is placed in the sea, electrical current is generated similar to the way it is in an automobile battery. The current will conduct particles from the metal, slowly dissolving it.

Another engineering problem concerns the building of submersibles with hulls that are cheap, light, and can withstand the pressure of depth. High-strength steels have been used for some submarines but they present welding and corrosion problems. Titanium alloys are strong and noncorrosive. Aluminum and glass are other possibilities. Glass is especially attractive, since glass spheres actually increase in strength with increased pressure, and glass is also noncorrosive.

One aspect of oceanography that has become more important in recent years is the law of the sea. If the sea floor or the fish in the sea are to be exploited, the ownership of these resources must be established. This is especially difficult with fish, which are not fenced in like animals on land and can migrate from one area to another.

Most of the questions about the law of the sea are concerned with the extent of a country's territorial waters. The territorial sea is the nearshore waters where the adjacent country has exclusive jurisdiction. The United States, like many Western countries, uses a 3-mile limit. With this limit the individual states have control over the mineral deposits and the fishing. Some countries claim wider territorial seas. The Soviet Union claims a 12-mile zone.

Many countries claim exclusive fishing zones that exceed their territorial waters. The United States recently established a 12-mile fishing limit within which only United States vessels can fish. Some countries such as Peru, Ecuador, Chile, Argentina, and Panama have established 200-mile wide zones. These zones are far beyond the continental shelf of these countries, and are therefore not recognized by all countries.

The general reason for establishing such limits is to protect the fishing industry and resources of the country concerned. If the seas were to be completely free, a country could exploit and overfish another country's resources. Many people think that the United States established a 12-mile zone because of the increased presence of Soviet fishing vessels off our coast.

An equally important problem of the law of the sea is the ownership of the minerals on and under the continental shelf. The continental shelf is an area where most of the future development and exploitation of the ocean will occur. A United Nations Convention on the Continental Shelf was held in 1958; at that time the coastal nations were given exclusive rights to the resources of the shelf out to a depth of 200 m. The Convention further stated that this exclusive right extends to a depth where the bottom can be exploited. This clause has created uncertainty as to where the shelf ends and the ocean begins. A country could claim areas far beyond a depth of 200 m simply by starting to exploit them.

In the United States the sea bottom from the end of the 3-mile limit to the end of the continental shelf belongs to the Federal Government. The government has generally followed the definition as spelled out in the Convention (that is, to a depth that can be exploited) rather than observing the geological definition of the continental shelf. Oil leases have been given by the Federal Government for areas considerably deeper than 200 m.

The consequence of this poorly-defined continental shelf clause is to discourage companies from attempting to mine the resources on or under the sea floor. Sea-floor mining projects could easily involve investment of tens of millions of dollars, and a company would hesitate to commit such a sum unless the ownership of the area was firmly established. An example of the problems in evaluating and recovering deposits from the sea floor is shown by the discovery, by Woods Hole Oceanographic Institution scientists, of a very rich deposit in the Red Sea. This deposit is comprised of zinc, copper, lead, silver, and gold, and is conservatively valued at more than 2 billion dollars. One difficulty in its recovery is the depth of the deposit—2,000 m. Another is ownership. The deposit is situated almost equidistant between Sudan and Saudi Arabia, in the central portion of the Red Sea. The Red Sea is a free and open area. Following the United Nations Convention, either Sudan or Saudi Arabia could claim it.

THE FUTURE OF OCEANOGRAPHY

The future of oceanography is promising. A recent report, "Our Nation and the Sea," by the Commission on Marine Science, Engineering and Resources recognized the widespread opportunities in the ocean and recommended an increase in our country's oceanographic budget. This report suggests that a new governmental agency, the National Oceanic and Atmospheric Agency (NOAA), be formed to coordinate and guide the government's efforts in oceanography.[1] The report calls for an increase of federal expenditures totalling 8 billion dollars over the next 10 years (this increase would be added to what is now being spent each year—about 500 million dollars). Clearly there will be an increased demand for trained oceanographers and technicians, not only for research positions, but also for industry and universities. Figure 9-5 shows how the marine science and technology dollar (actually 528 million dollars is estimated) will be spent for fiscal year 1970.

A recent report[2] of the National Council on Marine Resources

[1] In July of 1970 the President recommended that this agency be incorporated into the Department of Commerce.

[2] Marine Science Affairs—A Year of Broadened Participation. The Third Report of the President to the Congress on Marine Resources and Engineering Development, January, 1969.

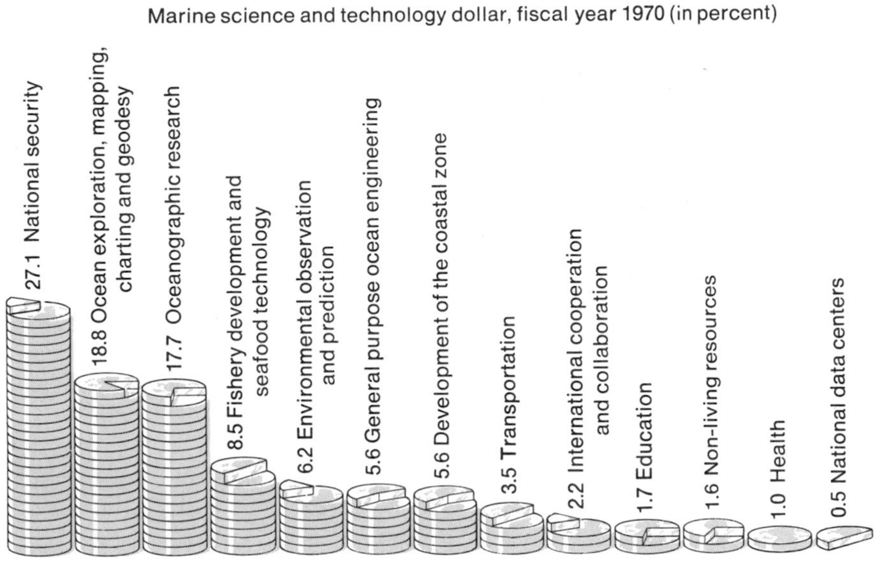

Marine science and technology dollar, fiscal year 1970 (in percent)

Figure 9-5 The distribution (in percent) of the money spent in marine science and technology for the fiscal year 1970.

and Engineering Development, whose chairman is the Vice President, has listed some of the opportunities and problems of our involvement with the ocean:

Less than 10 per cent of our continental shelf has been systematically explored, although we are confident that abundant oil and mineral resources lie in other areas of the shelf.

Protein deficiencies plague millions in a number of the developing countries located near abundant fishery resources which could provide economical sources of protein.

Only a small portion of the fishery stocks off our coasts are being fully exploited, and of the total U.S. consumption of the fish products less than one-third is provided by U.S. fishermen.

20 million children live in metropolitan areas within sight of potential water recreation areas, but are often denied their use.

Only three per cent of our ocean and Great Lakes coastline has been set aside for public use or conservation in spite of rapidly growing demands for such areas.

Pollution of our oceans and estuaries will increase many fold by the year 2000 unless there are drastic changes in waste handling; meanwhile, more than 50 million Americans engage in ocean swimming, fishing, and boating, and many millions are also directly affected by degradation of the quality of our coastal waters.

Pollutants are gradually spreading to distant reaches of the seas, as nations only slowly become concerned with maintaining the quality of ocean waters.

Only one-third of our coast has sufficiently detailed storm warnings in spite of the tens of millions of dollars of destruction annually in these areas.

Only 6 per cent of our international maritime commerce travels in U.S. flag vessels.

Unilateral acts to extend claims of national sovereignty great distances seaward threaten to erode the fundamental principle of freedom of the seas.

The next decade will be one of increased and more imaginative use of the ocean. I hope that the reader of this book has the opportunity to participate in and enjoy these developments.

SUGGESTED FURTHER READING

Emery, K. O. "Geological Methods for Locating Mineral Deposits on the Ocean Floor," *Transactions 2nd Marine Technological Society Conference, June 27–29* (1966): 24-43.

Fye, P. M., Maxwell, A. E., Emery, K. O., and Ketchum, B. H. "Ocean Science and Marine Resources." In *Uses of the Seas,* edited by Edmund A. Gullion. Englewood Cliffs, New Jersey: Prentice-Hall, 1968.

Shigley, C. M. "Seawater as Raw Material." *Ocean Industry* **3,** No. 11 (1968): 43-46.

Weeks, L. G. "The Gas, Oil and Sulfur Potentials of the Sea." *Ocean Industry* June, 1968, p. 43-51.

REFERENCES

Abdel-Gawad, M. "Geological Structures of the Red Sea Area Inferred from Satellite Pictures." In *Hot Brines and Recent Heavy Metal Deposits in the Red Sea,* edited by E. T. Degens and D. A. Ross. New York: Springer-Verlag, 1969.

Arnold, H. A. "Manned Submersibles for Research." *Science* **158** (1967): 84–95.

Arrhenius, G. "Pelagic Sediments." In *The Sea,* Vol. 3, edited by M. N. Hill. New York: Interscience, 1963.

Atkins, W. R. G. "The Phosphate Content of Sea Water in Relation to the Growth of the Algal Plankton, Part III." *Journal Marine Biological Association* **14** (1926): 447–467.

Atkins, W. R. G. "The Seasonal Variation in the Copper Content of Sea Water." *Journal Marine Biological Association* **31** (1953): 493–494.

Barth, T. F. W. *Theoretical Petrology.* New York: Wiley, 1952.

Berteaux, H. O., and Fofonoff, N. P. "Oceanographic Buoys Gather Data from Surface to Sea Floor." *Oceanology International* (July-August, 1967): 39–42.

Bigelow, H. B. *Oceanography: Its Scope, Problems, and Economic Importance.* Boston: Houghton Mifflin, 1931.

Bourne, D. W., and Heezen, B. C. "A Wandering Enteropneust from the Abyssal Pacific, and the Distribution of 'Spiral' Tracks on the Sea Floor." *Science* **150** (1965): 60–63.

Bowin, C. O., Bernstein, R., Ungar, E. D., and Madigan, J. R. "A Shipboard Oceanographic Data Processing and Control System." *Institute of Electrical and Electronic Engineers Transactions* **GE-5,** No. 2 (1967): 41–50.

Broecker, W. S. "Radio Isotopes and Large Scale Oceanic Mixing." In *The Sea,* Vol. 2, edited by M. N. Hill. New York: Interscience, 1963.

Broecker, W. S., Gerard, R. D., Ewing, M., and Heezen, B. C. "Geochemistry and Physics of Ocean Circulation." In *Oceanography,* edited by Mary Sears. American Association Advancement of Science Publication No. 67, 1961.

Brujewicz, S. W. "Tikhii Okean" (Pacific Ocean). Moscow Publishing House, 1966.

Clarke, G. L. "Dynamics of Production in a Marine Area." *Ecological Monographs* **16** (1946): 323–335.

Cox, R. A. "The Physical Properties of Sea Water." In *Chemical Oceanography,* edited by J. P. Riley and G. Skirrow. New York: Academic Press, 1965.

Cox, R. A., and Smith, N. D. "The Specific Heat of Sea Water." *Proceedings Royal Society London A.,* **252** (1959): 51–62.

Craig, H. "Isotopic Variations in Meteoric Waters." *Science* **133** (1961): 1702–1703.

Curray, J. R. "Late Quaternary Sea Level; a Discussion." *Bulletin Geological Society of America* **72** (1961): 1707–1712.

Curray, J. R. "Late Quaternary History, Continental Shelves of the United States." In *The Quaternary of the United States,* edited by H. E. Wright, Jr., and D. G. Frey. Princeton, New Jersey: Princeton University Press, 1965.

Deuser, W. G., and Degens, E. T. "$^{18}O/^{16}O$ and $^{13}C/^{12}C$ Ratios in Fossil Fora-minifera and Pteropods from the Area of the Hot-Brine Deeps of the Central Red Sea." In *Hot Brines and Recent Heavy Metal Deposits in the Red Sea,* edited by E. T. Degens and D. A. Ross. New York: Springer-Verlag, 1969.

Dietrich, G. *General Oceanography.* New York: Wiley, 1963.

Dietz, R. S., "Continent and Ocean Basin Evolution by Spreading of the Sea Floor." *Nature* **190** (1961): 854–857.

Dill, R. F. "Contemporary Submarine Erosion in Scripps Submarine Canyon." Unpublished Ph.D. Thesis, University of California, San Diego, 1964.

Du Toit, A. L. *Our Wandering Continents, and Hypothesis of Continental Drifting.* Edinburgh: Oliver and Boyd, 1937.

Effective Use of the Sea—Report of the Panel on Oceanography of the President's Science Advisory Committee, June 1966.

Emery, K. O. "Atlantic Continental Shelf and Slope of the United States, Geologic Background." *United States Geological Survey Professional Paper* 529-A (1966): 1–23.

Emery, K. O. "Geological Methods for Locating Mineral Deposits on the Ocean Floor." *Transactions 2nd Marine Technological Society Conference, June 27-29, 1966* (1966): 24–43.

Emery, K. O. "Estuaries and Lagoons in Relation to Continental Shelves." In *Estuaries,* edited by G. H. Lauff. American Association for the Advancement of Science Publication No. 83, 1967.

Emery, K. O. "The Atlantic Continental Margin of the United States During the Past 70 Million Years." *Geological Association of Canada,* Special Paper 4, Geology of the Atlantic Region (1967): 53–70.

Emery, K. O., and Ross, D. A. "Topography and Sediments of a Small Area of the Continental Slope South of Martha's Vineyard." *Deep-Sea Research* **15** (1968): 415–422.

Emery, K. O., Wigley, R. L., Bartless, A. S., Rubin, M., and Barghoorn, E. S. "Freshwater Peat on the Continental Shelf." *Science* **158** (1967): 1301–1307.

Emiliani, C. "Pleistocene Temperatures." *Journal Geology* **63** (1955): 538–578.

Emiliani, C. "Paleo-temperature Analysis of the Caribbean Cores A 254-BR-C and CP-28." *Bulletin Geological Society of America* **175** (1964): 129–144.

Epstein, S., and Mayeda, T. "Variation of ^{18}O Content of Waters from Natural Sources." *Geochemica et Cosmochemica Acta* **4** (1953): 213–224.

Fairbridge, R. W. "Trenches and Related Deep Sea Troughs." In *Encyclopedia of Oceanography,* edited by R. W. Fairbridge. New York: Reinhold, 1966.

Fairbridge, R. W., Heezen, B. C., Ichiye, T., and Tharp, M. "Indian Ocean." In *Encyclopedia of Oceanography,* edited by R. W. Fairbridge. New York: Reinhold, 1966.

Fairbridge, R. W., Reid, J. L., Jr., Olaussen, E., and Peterson, M. N. A. "Pacific Ocean." In *Encyclopedia of Oceanography,* edited by R. W. Fairbridge. New York: Reinhold, 1966.

Fisher, R. L., and Hess, H. H. "Trenches." In *The Sea,* Vol. 3, edited by M. N. Hill. New York: Interscience, 1963.

Fleming, R. H. "The Control of Diatom Population by Grazing." Conseil Perm. Internat. p. l'Explor de la Mer, *Journal du Conseil* **14,** No. 2 (1939): 210–227.

Fleming, R. H. "The Composition of Plankton and Units for Reporting Population and Production." *Proceedings Sixth Pacific Science Congress California, 1939* **3** (1940): 535–540.

Folger, D. W., and Heezen, B. C. "Trans-Atlantic Sediment Transport by Wind," (abstract). New Orleans: Annual Meeting of the Geological Society of America, 1967.

Freedman, I. "Deuterium Content of Natural Waters and Other Substances." *Geochemica et Cosmochemica Acta* **4** (1953): 89–103.

Fuglister, F. C. "Temperature and Salinity Profiles and Data from the International Geophysical Year of 1957–1958." *Atlantic Ocean Atlas,* The Woods Hole Oceanographic Institution Atlas Series **1** (1960).

Fye, P. M., Maxwell, A. E., Emery, K. O., and Ketchum, B. H. "Ocean Science and Marine Resources." In *Uses of the Seas,* edited by E. A. Gullion. Englewood Cliffs, New Jersey: Prentice-Hall, 1968.

Gaarder, T., and Gran, H. H. "Investigations of the Production of Plankton in the Oslo Fjord." Rapp. Proc. Verb. Conseil Internat. Explor de la Mer **42** (1927): 1–48.

Goldberg, E. D. "The Oceans as a Chemical System." In *The Sea,* Vol. 2, edited by M. N. Hill. New York: Interscience, 1963.

Goldberg, E. D., and Arrhenius, G. O. "Chemistry of Pacific Pelagic Sediments." *Geochemica et Cosmochemica Acta* **13** (1958): 153–212.

Gould, H. R. "Some Quantitative Aspects of Lake Meade Turbidity Currents." *Society of Economic Paleontology and Mineralogy Special Publication* No. 2 (1951): 34–52.

Graham, H. W., and Moberg, E. G. "Chemical Results of the Last Cruise of the CARNEGIE." Chemistry I, *Publications of the Carnegie Institute Washington* No. 562 (1944).

Guilcher, A., Liemen, Ph. H., Shepard, F. P., and Zenkovitch, V. R. "Scientific Considerations Relating to the Continental Shelf." *United Nations Educational Scientific and Cultural Organization, Conference on the Law of the Sea* 13/2 (1957).

Hamilton, E. L. "Thickness and Consolidation of Deep-Sea Sediments." *Bulletin Geological Society of America* **70** (1959): 1399–1424.

Harvey, H. W. "On the Production of Living Matter in the Sea off Plymouth." *Journal Marine Biological Association* **29** (1950): 97–137.

Harvey, H. W. *The Chemistry and Fertility of Sea Waters.* Cambridge, England: Cambridge University Press, 1960.

Heezen, B. C. "The Deep Sea Floor." In *Continental Drift,* International Geophysics Series, edited by S. K. Runcorn. New York: Academic Press, 1962.

Heezen, B. C., and Ewing, M. "Turbidity Currents and Submarine Slumps, and the 1929 Grand Banks Earthquake." *American Journal of Science* **250** (1952): 849–873.

Heezen, B. C., and Ewing, M. "The Mid-Oceanic Ridge." In *The Sea,* Vol. 3, edited by M. N. Hill. New York: Interscience, 1963.

Heezen, B. C., and Fox, P. J. "Mid-Oceanic Ridge." In *Encyclopedia of Oceanography,* edited by R. W. Fairbridge. New York: Reinhold, 1966.

Heezen, B. C., and Hollister, C. "Deep-Sea Current Evidence from Abyssal Sediments." *Marine Geology* **1** (1964): 141–174.

Heezen, B. C., Tharp, M., and Ewing, M. "The Floors of the Ocean, North Atlantic." *Geological Society of America* Special Paper No. 65 (1959).

Heirtzler, J. R., Dickson, G. O., Herron, E. M., Pitman, W. C. III, and Le Pichon, X. "Marine Magnetic Anomalies, Geomagnetic Field Reversals, and Motions of the Ocean Floor and Continents." *Journal of Geophysical Research* **73** (1968): 2119–2136.

Hersey, J. B., ed. *Deep-Sea Photography.* Baltimore: The Johns Hopkins Press, 1967.

Hersey, J. B., and Backus, R. H. "Sound Scattering by Marine Organisms." In *The Sea,* Vol. 1, edited by M. N. Hill. New York: Interscience, 1962.

Hess, H. H. "History of Ocean Basins." In *Petrologic Studies: A Volume to Honor A. F. Buddington.* New York: Geological Society of America, 1962

Hessler, R. R., and Sanders, H. L. "Faunal Diversity in the Deep-Sea." *Deep-Sea Research* **14** (1967): 65–78.

Holmes, A. "A Revised Geological Time Scale." *Edinburgh Geological Society,* Transaction 17, Part 3 (1960): 204.

Hood, D. W. "Chemical Oceanography." *Oceanographic and Marine Biology Annual Review* **1** (1963): 129–155.

Hood, D. W. "Seawater: Chemistry." In *Encyclopedia of Oceanography,* edited by R. W. Fairbridge. New York: Reinhold, 1966.

Hunkins, K. L. "Drifting Ice Stations." In *Encyclopedia of Oceanography,* edited by R. W. Fairbridge. New York: Reinhold, 1966.

Isaacs, J. D., and Iselin, C. O. D., eds. "Oceanographic Instruments." National Academy of Science, National Research Council Publication No. 309 (1952).

Isakov, I. S., (chief). "Ministry of the Navy of the U.S.S.R." *Morskai Atlas* **2** (1953).

Jenkins, P. M. "Oxygen Production by the Diatom *Coscinodiscus excentricus,* in Relation to Submarine Illumination in the English Channel." *Journal Marine Biological Association* **22** (1937): 301–343.

Jerlov, N. G. "Optical Studies of Ocean Waters." *Reports of the Swedish Deep Sea Expedition,* Physics and Chemistry **3,** No. 1 (1951): 1–59.

Kallie, K., and Wattenberg, H. "Uber den Kupfergehalt des Ozeanwassers." *Naturwissenschaften* **26** (1938): 630–631.

King, C. A. M. "Ocean Waves." In *Encyclopedia of Oceanography,* edited by R. W. Fairbridge. New York: Reinhold, 1966.

Krauskopf, K. B. "Factors Controlling the Concentrations of Thirteen Rare Metals in Sea Water." *Geochemica et Cosmochemica Acta* **9** (1956): 1–33.

Krauskopf, K., and Beiser, A. *Fundamentals of Physical Science.* New York: McGraw-Hill, 1966.

Ku, T. L. "Carbon 14 in Brines and Sediments." In *Hot Brines and Recent Heavy Metal Deposits in the Red Sea,* edited by E. T. Degens and D. A. Ross. New York: Springer-Verlag, 1969.

Kuenen, Ph. H., and Migliorini, C. I., "Turbidity Currents as a Cause of Graded Bedding." *Journal of Geology* **58** (1950): 91–129.

Kullenburg, B. "The Piston Core Sampler." *Sv. Hydr-Biol. Komm. skr.*, 3, ser., Hydro. Bed. 1, Göteborg, Sweden, 1947.

Ladd, H. S., Ingerson, E., Townsend, R. C., Russell, M., and Stephenson, H. K. "Drilling on Eniwetok Atoll, Marshall Islands." *Bulletin of the American Association of Petroleum Geologists* **37** (1953): 2257–2280.

Laevestu, T., and Thompson, T. G. "Soluble Iron in Coastal Waters." *Journal Marine Research* **16** (1958): 192–198.

La Fond, E. C. "Fixed Platforms." In *Encyclopedia of Oceanography*, edited by R. W. Fairbridge. New York: Reinhold, 1966.

La Fond, E. C. "Temperature Structure in the Sea." In *Encyclopedia of Oceanography*, edited by R. W. Fairbridge. New York: Reinhold, 1966.

Lamar, D. L., and Merifield, P. M. "Cambrian Fossils and the Origin of the Earth-Moon System." *Bulletin Geological Society of America* **78** (1967): 1359–1368.

Leopold, L. P., and Davis, K. S. *Water*. New York: Time Incorporated, 1966.

Lyman, J. "Chemical Considerations." *Physical and Chemical Properties of Sea Water*. National Academy of Science—National Research Council, Publication No. 600 (1958).

Madsen, F. J. "Abyssal Zone." In *Encyclopedia of Oceanography*, edited by R. W. Fairbridge. New York: Reinhold, 1966.

Mason, R. G., and Raff, A. D. "Magnetic Survey off the West Coast of North America, 32° N. Latitude to 42° N. Latitude." *Bulletin Geological Society of America* **72** (1961): 1259–1266.

Matthews, D. J. "Tables of the Velocity of Sound in Pure Water and Sea Water for Use in Echo-Sounding and Sound-Ranging." *London Hydrographic Department, Admiralty*, 2nd ed. (1939).

McCoy, F. W., Jr., Von Herzen, R. P., Owen, D. M., and Boutin, P. R. "Deep-Sea Corehead Camera Photography and Piston Coring." Woods Hole Oceanographic Institution Reference No. 69–19 (1969).

McGuinness, W. T. "Acoustics" (Underwater). In *Encyclopedia of Oceanography*, edited by R. W. Fairbridge. New York: Reinhold, 1966.

Meade, R. H. "Landward Transport of Bottom Sediments in Estuaries of the Atlantic Coastal Plain." *Journal of Sedimentary Petrology* **39** (1969): 222–234.

Menard, H. W. *Marine Geology of the Pacific*. New York: McGraw-Hill, 1964.

Menard, H. W., and Smith, S. M. "Hypsometry of Ocean Basin Provinces." *Journal of Geophysical Research* **71** (1966): 4305–4325.

Mero, J. L. "Ocean-Floor Manganese Nodules." *Economic Geology* **57** (1962): 747–767.

Mero, J. L. "Manganese Nodules (Deep-Sea)." In *Encyclopedia of Oceanography*, edited by R. W. Fairbridge. New York: Reinhold, 1966.

Miller, D. J. "Giant Waves in Lituya Bay, Alaska." *U. S. Geological Survey Professional Paper* No. 354-C (1960): 51–86.

Miller, S. L. "The Origin of Life." In *The Sea*, Vol. 3, edited by M. N. Hill. New York: Interscience, 1963.

Milliman, J. D. "Carbonate Sedimentation on Hogsty Reef, a Bahamian Atoll." *Journal of Sedimentary Petrology* **37** (1967): 658–676.

Milliman, J. D., and Emery, K. O. "Sea Levels During the Past 35,000 Years." *Science* **162** (1968): 1121–1123.

Moore, D. G. "The Free-Corer; Sampling Without Wire and Winch." *Journal of Sedimentary Petrology* **31** (1961): 672–680.

Moore, T. C., and Heath, G. R. "Abyssal Hills in the Central Equatorial Pacific: Detailed Structure of the Sea Floor and Subbottom Reflectors." *Marine Geology* **5** (1967): 161–179.

Morgan, J. W. "Rises, Trenches, Great Faults, and Crustal Blocks." *Journal Geophysical Research* **73** (1968): 1959–1982

Murray, J., and Renard, A. F. "Deep Sea Deposits, Scientific Results of the Exploration Voyage of H.M.S. CHALLENGER, 1872–1876." *CHALLENGER Reports.* London: Longsmans, 1891.

Oceanographic Vessels of the World, International Geophysical Year, World Data Center for Oceanography and the National Oceanographic Data Center, U.S. Navy Oceanographic Office, Washington, D.C., 1963.

Opdyke, N. D., Glass, B., Hays, J. D., and Foster, J. "Paleomagnetic Study of Antarctic Deep Sea Cores." *Science* **154** (1966): 349–357.

Ostenso, N. A. "Arctic Ocean." In *Encyclopedia of Oceanography,* edited by R. W. Fairbridge. New York: Reinhold, 1966.

Pattullo, J. G. "Tides." In *Encyclopedia of Oceanography,* edited by R. W. Fairbridge. New York: Reinhold, 1966.

Peterson, M. N. A. "Scientific Goals and Achievements (Deep-Sea Drilling Program)." *Ocean Industry Magazine* (May, 1969): 62–66.

Pitman, W. C. III, Herron, E. M., and Heirtzler, J. R. "Magnetic Anomalies in the Pacific and Sea Floor Spreading." *Journal of Geophysical Research* **73** (1968): 2069–2085.

Pratt, R. M. "Great Meteor Seamount." *Deep-Sea Research* **10** (1963): 17–25.

Pritchard, D. W. "Observations of Circulation in Coastal Plain Estuaries." In *Estuaries,* edited by G. H. Lauff. American Association for the Advancement of Science Publication Number 83 (1967): 37–44.

Prospero, J. M., and Koczy, F. F. "Radionuclides in Oceans and Sediments." In *Encyclopedia of Oceanography,* edited by R. W. Fairbridge. New York: Reinhold, 1966.

Prospero, J. M., and Koczy, F. F. "Radionuclides: Their Applications in Oceanography." In *Encyclopedia of Oceanography,* edited by R. W. Fairbridge. New York: Reinhold, 1966.

Raitt, R. W., Fisher, R. L., and Mason, R. G. "Tonga Trench." In *The Crust of the Earth,* Geological Society of America, Special Paper 62 (1955): 237–254.

Rakestraw, M. N., Rudd, D. P., and Dole, M. "Isotopic Composition of Oxygen in Air Dissolved in Pacific Ocean Water as a Function of Depth." *Journal of the American Chemical Society* **73** (1951): 2976.

Raymont, J. E. G. *Plankton and Productivity in the Oceans.* New York: Macmillan, 1963.

Redfield, A. C. "On the Proportions of Organic Derivatives in Sea Water and their Relation to the Composition of Plankton." *James Johnstone Memorial Volume* (1934): 177–192.

Redfield, A. C. "Ontogeny of a Salt Marsh Estuary." *Science* **147** (1965): 50–55.

Redfield, A. C., Ketchum, B. H., and Richards, F. A. "The Influence of Organisms on the Composition of Sea-Water." In *The Sea,* Vol. 2, edited by M. N. Hill. New York: Interscience, 1963.

Richards, A. F. "Chemical Oceanography, General." In *Encyclopedia of Oceanography*, edited by R. W. Fairbridge. New York: Reinhold, 1966.

Riley, G. A. "Factors Controlling Phytoplankton Populations on Georges Bank." *Journal of Marine Research* **6** (1946) 54–78.

Riley, J. P., "Historical Introduction." In *Chemical Oceanography*, edited by J. P. Riley and G. Skirrow. New York: Academic Press, 1965.

Ross, D. A. "Current Action in a Submarine Canyon." *Nature* **218** (1968): 1242–1245.

Ross, D. A., and Shor, G. G., Jr. "Reflection Profiles Across the Middle America Trench." *Journal Geophysical Research* **70** (1965): 5551–5571.

Runcorn, S. K. "Changes in the Earth's Moment of Inertia." *Nature* **204** (1964): 823–825.

Russell, F. S. "Hydrographical and Biological Conditions in the North Sea as Indicated by Plankton Organisms." *Journal du Conseil Internat. Explor. de la Mer* **14** (1939): 171–192.

Ryther, J. H., and Yentsch, C. S. "Primary Production of Continental Shelf Waters off New York." *Limnology and Oceanography* **3** (1958): 327–335.

Sachs, P. L., and Raymond, S. O. "A New Unattached Sediment Sampler." *Journal of Marine Research* **23** (1965): 44–53.

Sanders, J. E., Emery, K. O., and Uchupi, E. "Microtopography of the Continental Shelf by Side-Scanning Sonar." *Bulletin Geological Society America* **80** (1969): 561–572.

Shepard, F. P. *Submarine Geology,* 2nd ed. New York: Harper and Row, 1963.

Shepard, F. P., Curray, J. R., Inman, D. L., Murray, E. A., Winterer, E. L., and Dill, R. F. "Submarine Geology by Diving Saucer." *Science* **145** (1964): 1042–1046

Shepard, F. P., and Einsele, G. "Sedimentation in San Diego Trough and Contributing Submarine Canyons." *Sedimentology* **1,** No. 2 (1962): 81–133.

Shepard, F. P., MacDonald, G. A., and Cox, D. C. "The Tsunami of April 1, 1946." *Bulletin Scripps Institution Oceanography, University of California* **5** (1950): 391–455.

Shigley, C. M. "Seawater as Raw Material." *Ocean Industry* **3,** No. 11 (1968): 43–46.

Spaeth, M. G., and Berkman, S. C. "The Tsunami of March 28, 1964, as Recorded at Tide Stations." *Coast and Geodetic Survey Technical Bulletin* No. 33 (1967).

Spar, J. *Earth, Sea, and Air; A Survey of the Geophysical Sciences.* Reading, Mass.: Addison-Wesley, 1965.

Spiess, F. N., Mudie, J. D., and Lowenstein, C. D. "Deeply Towed Marine Geophysical Observational System." *Transactions American Geophysical Union* **48** (1967): 133.

Stevenson, R. A., Jr. "Underwater Television." *Oceanology International* (Nov Dec., 1967): 30–35.

Stommel, H. "The Anatomy of the Atlantic." *Scientific American,* Jan. 1955.

Stommel, H. "A Survey of Ocean Current Theory." *Deep-Sea Research* **4** (1957): 149–184.

Sverdrup, H. U., Johnson, M. W., and Fleming, R. H. *The Oceans: Their Physics, Chemistry, and General Biology.* New York: Prentice-Hall, 1942.

Terzaghi, K. "Varieties of Submarine Slope Failures." *Proceedings 8th Texas Conference on Soil Mechanics and Foundation Engineering Special Publication 29*. Austin, Texas: Bureau of Engineering Research, University of Texas, 1956.

Thompson, T. G. "The Physical Properties of Sea Water." *Physics of the Earth*, Oceanography National Research Council, Bulletin 85 **5** (1932): 63–94.

Tucker, M. J. "Sideways Looking Sonar for Marine Geology." *Geo-Marine Technology* **5** (1966): 332–338.

Uchupi, E. "Maps Showing Relation of Land and Submarine Topography, Nova Scotia to Florida." *United States Geological Survey*, Miscellaneous Geological Investigations, Map I-451, (1965).

Uchupi, E. "Slumping of the Continental Margin Southeast of Long Island, New York." *Deep-Sea Research* **14** (1967): 635–639.

Uchupi, E. "The Continental Margin South of Cape Hatteras, North Carolina: Shallow Structure." *Southeastern Geology* **8** (1967): 155–177.

Vacquier, V., Raff, A. D., and Warren, R. E., "Horizontal Displacements in the Floor of the Northeastern Pacific Ocean." *Geological Society of America Bulletin* **72** (1961): 1251–1258.

Vening Meinesz, F. A. "Gravity Expeditions at Sea." Waltman, Delft, Vol. 1, 1932.

von Arx, W. S. *An Introduction to Physical Oceanography*. Reading, Mass.: Addison-Wesley, 1962.

Warren, B. "Oceanic Circulation." In *Encyclopedia of Oceanography*, edited by R. W. Fairbridge. New York: Reinhold, 1966.

Wattenberg, H. "Über die Titrationsalkalinität und den Kalziumkarbonatgehalt des Meerwassens, Deusche Atlantische Exped. METEOR 1925–1927," Wiss. Erg., Bd., 8, 2 Teil (1933): 122–231.

Weeks, L. G. "The Gas, Oil, and Sulfur Potentials of the Sea." *Ocean Industry* (June, 1968): 43–51.

Wegener, A. "Die Entstehung der Kontinente." *Geolica Rundschau* **3** (1912): 276–292.

Wells, J. W. "Coral Growth and Geochrometry." *Nature* **197** (1963): 948–950.

Whitmore, F. C., Jr., Emery, K. O., Cooke, H. B. S., and Swift, D. J. P. "Elephant Teeth from the Atlantic Continental Shelf." *Science* **156** (1967): 1477–1481.

Wiegel, R. L. "Waves, Tides, Currents and Beaches: Glossary of Terms and List of Standard Symbols." *Council on Wave Research*, University of California, 1953.

Wilkerson, J. W. "Airborne Oceanography." *Geo-Marine Technology* **5** (1966): 287–293.

Worzel, J. L. "Extensive Deep-Sea Sub Bottom Reflectors Identified as White Ash." *Proceedings of the National Academy of Sciences* **45,** No. 3 (1959): 349–355.

Wüst, G., Brogmus, W., and Noodt, E. N. "Die zonale Verteilung von Salzgehalt, Niederschlag, Verfunstung, Temperatur und Diche an der Oberfläche der Ozeans." *Kieler Meeresforschung* **10** (1954): 137–161.

Zarudski, E. F. K. "Swordfish Rams the *Alvin*." *Oceanus* **4** (1967): 14–18.

PAPERBACK BOOKS ON OCEANOGRAPHY

This list was kindly provided by Professor Bernard Gordon of Northeastern University. Additional material was supplied by Lynn Forbes.

Abbott, R. T. *How to Know American Marine Shells*. New York: Signet (KT375).

Abbott, R. T. *A Guide to Field Identification, Seashells of North America*. New York: Golden Press, 1968.

Bascom, W. *Waves and Beaches*. New York: Doubleday, Anchor Science Study Series, 1964.

Behrman, A. S. *Water is Everybody's Business*. New York: Doubleday, Anchor (AMC4), 1968.

Blanchard, D. C. *From Raindrops to Volcanoes, Adventures With Sea Surface Meteorology*. New York: Doubleday, Anchor (S50), 1967.

Boolootian, R. A. *Marine Biology, A Study of Life in the Sea*. New York: Holt, 1968.

Burke, W. T. *Ocean Sciences, Technology and the Future International Law of the Sea*. Columbus, Ohio: Ohio State University Press, 1966.

Carrington, R. A. *Guide to Earth History*. New York: Signet (MT335).

Carson, R. *The Edge of the Sea*. New York: Signet (P2360).

Carson, R. *The Sea Around Us*. New York: Signet (P2361).

Carson, R. *Under the Sea Wind*. New York: Signet (P2339).

Carson, R. *Silent Spring*. New York: Fawcett Publications.

Carson, R. *Life Under the Sea*. New York: Golden Press, 1969.

Chapman, V. J. *Coastal Vegetation*. New York: Pergamon.

Clark, J. *Fish and Man, Conflict in the Atlantic Estuaries*. Highlands, New Jersey: Special Publication No. 5, American Littoral Society, 1967.

Clarke, A. C. *The Challenge of the Sea* (Introduction by Wernher von Braun). New York: Dell (#1159).

Clarke, A. C., with Wilson, M. *The Treasure of the Great Reef*. New York: Harper & Row, Perennial Library (P25).

Coates, C. W. *Tropical Fish as Pets*. New York: Collier Books (AS177).

Coker, R. E. *This Great and Wide Sea*. New York: Harper Torchbook (TB551), 1962.

Cousteau, J. Y. *The Silent World*. New York: Pocket Books (GC119).

Cowen, R. C. *Frontiers of the Sea*. New York: Bantam Books (HP29), 1963.

Daniel, H., and Minot, F. *The Inexhaustible Sea*. New York: Collier Books (AS9K).

Darwin, C. *The Structure and Distribution of Coral Reefs*. Berkeley: University of California Press, 1962.

Darwin, G. H. *The Tides*. San Francisco: Freeman.

Dawson, E. Y. *How to Know the Seaweed*. Dubuque, Iowa: W. C. Brown, 1956.

Defant, A. *Ebb and Flow: The Tides of Earth, Air and Water*. Ann Arbor, Michigan: University of Michigan Press (AAS506), 1958.

Dibner, B. *The Atlantic Cable*. Waltham, Mass.: Blaisdel (BP15).

Dowdeswell, W. *Animal Ecology*. New York: Harper Torchbook (TB543).

Eddy, S. *How to Know the Fresh-Water Fishes*. Dubuque, Iowa: W. C. Brown, 1957.

Forbes, L., compiler. *Oceanography in Print*. Falmouth, Mass.: Oceanographic Education Center, 1968.

Galtsoff, P. S. *The American Oyster*. U.S.F.W.S. Fishery Bulletin Vd. 64. U.S Government Printing Office, Washington, D.C., 1964.

Gordon, B. L. *Handbook for Advisers to Junior American Littoral Society*. Highlands, New Jersey: American Littoral Society.

Gross, M. G. *Oceanography*. Columbus, Ohio: C. E. Merrill Books, 1967.

Guberlet, M. L. *Seaweeds at Ebb Tide*. Seattle, Washington: University of Washington Press, 1956.

Gullion, E. A., ed. *Uses of the Seas*. Englewood Cliffs, New Jersey: Prentice-Hall, Spectrum, 1966.

Heyerdahl, T. *Kon Tiki*. New York: Pocket Books.

Hirsch, P., ed. *Underwater*. New York: Pyramid, 1966.

Johnson, M. E., and Snook, H. J. *Seashore Animals of the Pacific Coast*. New York: Dover Publications, Inc., 1967. (Reprint of 1927 edition.)

Keen, M. J. *An Introduction to Marine Geology*. New York: Pergamon Press, 1968.

Kuenen, P. H. *Realms of Water*. New York: Wiley, 1963.

Lane, F. W. *Kingdom of the Octopus*. New York: Pyramid, 1963.

Lawrence, L. G. *Electronics in Oceanography*. Indianapolis, Indiana: Bobbs-Merrill, 1967.

Lewis, W. M. *Man and Dolphin*. New York: Pyramid, 1963.

Lilly, J. C. *The Mind of the Dolphin*. New York: Avon Discussion Books, 1969

Long, E. J. *New Worlds of Oceanography*. New York: Pyramid, 1965.

Mager, N. H. *A Guide to Tropical Fish*. New York: Washington Square Press.

Morton, J. E. *Mollusca*. New York: Harper Torchbook.

Newell, G. E., and Newell, R. C. *Marine Plankton: A Practical Guide*. London: Hutchinson Educational, 1963.

North, W. J. *Golden Guide to Scuba Diving, Handbook of Underwater Activities*. Washington, D.C.: Smithsonian Institution, 1965.

Peterson, M. *History Under the Sea: A Handbook of Underwater Exploration*. Washington, D.C.: Smithsonian Institution, 1965.

Pickard, G. L. *Descriptive Physical Oceanography*. Oxford: Pergamon Press, 1963.

Prescott, G. W. *How to Know the Fresh-Water Algae*. Dubuque, Iowa: Wm. Brown.

Rapport, S. *The Crust of the Earth*. New York: Signet.

Reid, G. K., and others. *Pond Life. A Guide to Common Plants and Animals of N. American Ponds and Lakes*. New York: Golden Press, 1967.

Scott, W. B. *Freshwater Fishes of Eastern Canada*. University of Toronto Press.

Shepard, F. P. *The Earth Beneath the Sea*. New York: Atheneum, 1964.

Smith, R. F., Swartz, A. H., and Massmanon, W. H., eds. *A Symposium on Estuarine Fisheries*. Washington, D.C.: American Fisheries Society Special Publication No. 3, 1966.

Spar, J. *Earth, Sea and Air*. Reading, Mass.: Addison-Wesley.

Stewart, H. *The Global Sea*. New York: Van Nostrand, 1963.

Tucker, D. G., and Gazey, B. K. *Applied Underwater Acoustics*. New York: Pergamon Press, 1966.

Turekian, K. K. *The Oceans*. Englewood Cliffs, New Jersey: Prentice Hall, 1968.

University Curricula in the Marine Sciences and Related Fields. Marine Sciences Affairs Staff, Office of the Oceanography of the Navy. Academic years 1969–1970 and 1970–1971, U.S. Government Printing Office, Washington, D.C.

Wickstead, J. H. *An Introduction to the Study of Tropical Plankton*. London: Hutchinson, 1965.

Yasso, W. E. *Oceanography: A Study of Inner Space*. New York: Holt, 1965.

Younge, C. M. *The Seashore*. New York: Atheneum, 1963.

GLOSSARY OF OCEANOGRAPHIC TERMS

abyssal Referring to that part of the ocean between a depth of about 2,000 to 6,000 m.

abyssal hills Small irregular hills, rising to a height of 30 to 1,000 m, that cover large areas of the ocean floor. They are especially common in the Pacific Ocean.

abyssal plain A very flat portion of the ocean floor underlain by sediments. The slope of this feature is less than 1:1000.

acidic solution A liquid whose hydrogen ion concentration is greater than its hydroxyl ion concentration, or whose pH is less than 7.0.

alkaline solution A liquid whose hydroxyl ion concentration is greater than its hydrogen ion concentration, or whose pH is greater than 7.0. Sea water is slightly alkaline, having a pH between 7.5 and 8.4

anaerobic A condition where oxygen is absent. The Black Sea is an example.

anion A negatively charged ion. Examples are chlorine, Cl^-, and oxygen, $O^=$.

aphotic zone That part of the ocean where not enough light is present for photosynthesis by plants.

aquaculture Farming of the ocean, whereby organisms such as fish, algae, and shellfish are grown under controlled conditions. At present this technique is only used in nearshore areas.

atoll A circular-shaped coral reef surrounding a lagoon.

atom The smallest component of an element that has all the properties of the element. An atom consists of protons, electrons, and neutrons.

atomic weight The relative weight of an atom on the basis that the oxygen atom has a weight of 16. The atomic weight is essentially equal to the number of protons in the atom.

authigenic deposits Deposits that have formed in place before the sediment is buried. They usually have precipitated directly from the sea water.

autotrophic bacteria Bacteria that produce their own food from inorganic compounds.

basalt An igneous rock, commonly found on the sea floor, mainly composed of feldspar and pyroxene minerals. Basalt rocks are thought to underlie most of the ocean basin.

bathyal Referring to that part of the ocean between depths of about 200 to 2,000 m.

bathymetry The measuring of the depth of the ocean.

bathy-thermograph An instrument used to measure temperature in the ocean.

benthic or benthonic The area of the ocean bottom inhabited by marine organisms.

benthos Organisms that live on or in close contact (such as certain fish) with the ocean bottom.

berm Flat portion of a beach formed by wave action.

bioluminescence The production of light by living organisms as a result of a chemical reaction.

biomass The amount of living organisms in grams per unit area or unit volume.

biosphere A collective term for the area of habitat of the organisms of the earth.

biotope An area where the principal habitat conditions and the living forms adapted to the conditions are uniform.

boiling point The temperature at which a liquid starts to boil. For pure water this temperature is 100° C or 212° F at normal pressure.

Carbon-14 A radioactive isotope that can be used for dating. This isotope is especially useful in dating material that was once alive, since all living matter contains carbon. The half-life of Carbon-14 is 5,570 years.

catastrophic waves Large waves, resulting from intense storms or submarine slumping, that can cause immense damage and loss of life.

cation A positively charged ion. Examples are hydrogen, H^+, and sodium, Na^+.

centrifugal force A force due to rotation which causes motion away or out from the rotating object.

chlorophyll A group of green pigments, found in plants, that are essential for photosynthesis.

colligative properties Those properties that vary with the number of chemical elements in a solution and not with the composition of the elements. In sea water with increasing salinity, boiling point and osmotic pressure increase, and freezing point and vapor pressure decrease.

colloidal particles Very small particles, usually smaller than 0.00024 mm.

community An integrated group of organisms inhabiting a common area. These organisms may be dependent on each other or possibly upon the environment. The community may be defined by its habitat or by the composition of the organisms.

compensation depth The depth at which the oxygen produced by a plant during photosynthesis equals the amount the plant needs for respiration (during a 24 hr period).

conservative elements Elements in sea water whose ratio to other conservative elements remains constant. Examples are chlorine, sodium, and magnesium.

continental margin That portion of the ocean adjacent to the continent and separating it from the deep sea. The continental margin includes the continental shelf, continental slope, and continental rise.

continental rise An area of gentle slope (usually less than half a degree or 1:100) at the base of the continental slope.

continental shelf The shallow part of the sea floor immediately adjacent to the continent. It generally has a smooth seaward slope and terminates seaward at an abrupt change in slope beginning the continental slope.

continental slope A declivity averaging about 4° that extends from the seaward edge of the continental shelf down to the continental rise or deep-sea floor.

convection currents Motion within a fluid due to differences in density or temperature.

Coriolis force An apparent force due to the earth's rotation. This force causes moving objects to turn to the right in the northern hemisphere and to the left in the southern hemisphere.

covalent bond The bond or linkage between two atoms in a molecule, formed by the sharing of electrons.

dead reckoning A type of navigation that uses only the speed and direction of the ship to estimate its position.

decibar A measure of pressure equal to 1/10 normal atmospheric pressure and approximately equal to the pressure change of one meter depth in sea water.

deep-scattering layer A sound-reflecting layer caused by the presence of certain organisms in the water. The layer, or layers, which may be 100 m thick, usually rises towards the surface at night and descends when the sun rises.

Deep-Sea Drilling Project A large-scale scientific project whose main aim is to drill numerous deep holes into the sediments on the ocean floor.

density Weight per unit volume.

desalination A variety of processes whereby the salts are removed from sea water resulting in water that can be used for human consumption.

detrital deposits Sedimentary deposits resulting from the erosion and weathering of rocks.

diurnal Referring to tides, one low and one high tide within one lunar day (about 24 hr and 50 min).

divergence The flow of water in different directions away from a particular area or zone; often associated with areas of upwelling.

earthquake A sudden motion of the earth caused by faulting or volcanic activity. Earthquakes can occur in the near surface rocks or down to as deep as 700 km below the surface. The actual area of the earthquake is called the focus; the point on the earth's surface above the focus is called the epicenter.

echo sounding A method of determining the depth of the ocean by measuring the time interval between the emission of an acoustic signal and its return or echo from the sea floor. The returning signal is usually printed to give a visual picture of the topography of the sea floor. The instrument used in this method is called an echo sounder.

electrical conductivity A measure of the ability that a material has for conducting electricity.

epicenter See earthquake.

erosion A term that describes the physical and chemical breakdown of a rock and the movement of these broken or dissolved particles from one place to another.

estuary A semienclosed coastal body of water having a free connection with the open sea and within which sea water is diluted by fresh water derived from land drainage.

euphotic zone That part of the water which receives sufficient sunlight for plants to be able to photosynthesize.

fathom A common unit measure of depth equal to 6 ft (1.83 m).

fault A fracture of rock along which the opposite sides have been relatively displaced.

fetch The distance over the sea surface that the wind blows, in the area where seas are generated.

fish-protein concentrate An odorless, tasteless protein concentrate that can be made from almost any kind of fish. This product is thought by many to be a partial solution to some of the world's food problems.

focus See earthquake.

food chain A complex system that involves many different organisms, each of which is the food for an organism higher up in the chain or sequence.

fracture zone A large linear and irregular area of the sea floor, characterized by ridges and seamounts. These features are commonly associated with the median ridge common to most ocean basins.

fractionation The separation or division into different components that occurs with some isotopes in the marine environment.

freezing point The temperature at which a liquid freezes or solidifies at normal pressure. For fresh water this temperature is O° C or 32° F; for normal sea water (salinity about $35^0/_{00}$) the freezing temperature is −1.9° C or about 28° F.

frequency The number of cycles or events in a given period of time.

geomorphology The study of the shape of the earth's surface, and the processes that control and modify these features.

geostrophic current A current where the horizontal pressure gradient is balanced by the Coriolis force. These currents can be calculated by careful measurement of temperature and salinity at closely spaced localities.

geosyncline A long linear basin that contains large (a thousand or more meters) accumulations of sediments. These basins may be uplifted, folded, and faulted, eventually forming a mountain range.

granite A coarse-grained igneous rock consisting mainly of quartz and alkali feldspar.

gravimeter A device used to measure differences in the earth's gravitational field.

gravity The force of attraction which causes objects on earth to fall toward the center of the earth. The universal law of gravity as first given by Newton states that every particle in the universe attracts every other particle with a force that is proportional to the product of their masses and inversely proportional to the square of the distances between the particles.

grazing The feeding by zooplankton upon phytoplankton.

gross production The amount of organic matter photosynthesized by plants over a certain period and within a certain area or volume.

guyot A flat-topped seamount.

hadal The deepest parts of the ocean; that part below a depth of 6,000 m.

half-life The time it takes for one-half the atoms of a radioactive isotope to decay into another isotope. The half-life is different for each radioactive element.

halocline A zone, usually 50 to 100 m below the surface and extending to perhaps 1,000 m, where the salinity changes rapidly. The salinity change is greater in the halocline than in the water above or below it.

heat capacity A ratio of the amount of heat absorbed or released by an object to the change in temperature of the object. In other words, how much heat is necessary to raise the temperature of the object.

herbivores Organisms that eat plants.

heterotrophic bacteria Bacteria that use organic material, produced by other organisms, for their food.

Holocene See Pleistocene.

holoplankton Organisms that spend their entire life as plankton.

hydrological cycle The system whereby the water is removed from the ocean by evaporation into the atmosphere and eventually returns to the ocean either directly as precipitation or indirectly by rivers.

interface The boundaries or surfaces between two different materials; the major interfaces in the ocean are the water-atmosphere, water-biosphere, and water-sediment.

igneous rocks Rocks formed by the solidification of molten magma. Magma is composed of numerous minerals (mainly silicates) and gases derived from the earth's crust and mantle, and is in a melted state.

ion An atom or group of atoms having an electrical charge. Most of the atoms in sea water are in the ionic form. An ion having a positive charge is called a cation; one having a negative charge is called an anion.

isotope Different forms of the same element, differing mainly in their atomic weights.

JOIDES Joint Oceanographic Institutions Deep Earth Sampling—a program that initially drilled six holes into the sediments on the continental shelf and slope off eastern Florida. The second phase of the program, The Deep-Sea Drilling Project, has resulted in numerous holes drilled into the Atlantic and Pacific Oceans.

kilometer A metric measure of distance equal to 1,000 m, 0.62 statute miles, or 0.54 nautical miles.

knot A unit of velocity equal to one nautical mile (6,080 ft) per hour. It is approximately equal to 50 cm/sec or 1.69 ft/sec.

lagoon A shallow pond or lake separated from the sea by a shallow bar or bank.

latent heat The amount of heat absorbed or released by a substance during a change of state, under conditions of constant temperature and pressure. The latent heat of evaporation relates to the amount of heat necessary to go from the liquid to the gaseous state.

lava Liquid rock which comes to the surface, usually from a volcano or a fissure.

leeward The direction toward which the wind is blowing.

littoral The benthic zone between high tides out to a depth of about 200 m.

longshore currents Currents in the nearshore region that run essentially parallel to the coast.

magma Molten rock material derived from the earth's crust and mantle. When it is extruded and flows on the earth's surface (above or below water) it is called lava.

magnetic anomaly A departure of the regular pattern of the earth's magnetic pattern. The departure may be due to the concentration of magnetic minerals, or to a buried (or exposed) igneous rock.

magnetometer An instrument used to measure the direction and intensity of the earth's magnetic field.

meroplankton Animals that spend only a portion of their life as plankton, ultimately becoming nekton or benthos.

metabolism The process which includes the formation of protoplasm by organisms from food or photosynthesis, the eventual breakdown of the protoplasm, and the release of waste products and energy.

metamorphic rocks
Rocks that have undergone large changes in temperature, pressure, or chemical environment. These metamorphic rocks were already rocks prior to these large changes.

micro-temperature structure
Small scale, in terms of vertical or horizontal dimensions, changes in temperature.

mixing processes
Any process or condition that causes mixing of the sea water.

Mohorovičić discontinuity
The sharp change in seismic velocity occurring at about 11 km depth in the ocean and 35 km depth under land, that defines the top of the earth's mantle. This discontinuity, commonly called the Moho, may represent either a chemical or a phase change in the layering of the earth.

monsoon
A term for seasonal winds, usually applied to the changing wind patterns in the Indian Ocean.

neap tide
Low tides which occur about every two weeks when the moon is in its quarter positions.

nekton
Animals that are able to swim, independent of current action.

neritic
The part of the pelagic environment that extends from the nearshore zone out to a depth of about 200 m; in other words, the waters overlying the continental shelf.

nutrients
Compounds or ions that plants need for the production of organic matter.

ocean basin
That portion of the ocean seaward of the continental margin which includes the deep-sea floor.

oceanographic station
Oceanographic observations made while the research vessel is stopped.

osmosis
The movement of dissolved ions or molecules through a semipermeable membrane. An osmotic pressure will result when a difference in concentration exists on either side of the membrane. The greater the difference the higher the osmotic pressure; the flow will be toward the more concentrated solution.

outcrop
An exposure of rocks at the earth's surface.

oxidation
The process whereby an element or compound combines with oxygen, or whereby electrons are removed from an ion or atom.

oxygen-minimum zone
A layer below the surface where the oxygen content is very low or zero.

paleomagnetism The study of variations in the earth's magnetic field as recorded in ancient rocks.

peat A brownish sediment composed of partially decomposed plant tissue.

pelagic A division of the marine environment, including the entire mass of water. The pelagic environment can be divided into a neritic (water that overlies the continental shelf) province and an oceanic (the water of the deep sea) province.

pelagic sediments Sediments deposited in the deep sea that have little or no coarse-grained terrigenous material.

pH A measure of the alkalinity or salinity of a solution. pH is the logarithm of the reciprocal of the hydrogen ion concentration, or $pH = \log 1/H^+$. A pH value of 7.0 indicates a neutral solution, lower than 7.0 is acidic, and higher is alkaline.

photosynthesis The production of organic matter by plants using water and carbon dioxide in the presence of chlorophyll and light; oxygen is released in the reaction.

photosynthetic zone That part of the ocean where photosynthesis is possible, usually defined by the availability of light. In the open ocean this zone usually extends from the surface to about 100 m.

phytoplankton Those plankton that are plants.

pinger An acoustic device used to determine distance of instruments above the bottom.

plankton Floating or weakly swimming organisms that are carried by the ocean currents. The plankton range in size from microscopic plants to large jellyfish.

plankton bloom A large concentration of plankton within an area, due to a rapid growth of the organisms. The large numbers of plankton can color the water, causing in some instances a red tide.

Pleistocene A geological epoch that ended about 10,000 years ago and lasted about 1 to 2 million years. This epoch has been subdivided into four glacial stages and three interglacial stages. The last of the Pleistocene glacial stages is called the Wisconsin stage. The period we are now in, the Holocene Epoch, is not part of the Pleistocene and may be an interglacial stage.

polymorphism Organisms that can occur in several different forms, independent of sexual differences.

pressure The force per unit area upon an object.

primary shorelines Shorelines where the coastal region has been mainly formed by terrestrial agents, such as rivers, glaciers, deltas, volcanoes, folding, and faulting.

primordial Pertaining to the beginning or initial times of the earth's history.

productivity The production of organic material.

protoplanets The early planets which preceded and developed (according to the condensation theory of the origin of the planets) into the present planets.

pycnocline A zone where the water density rapidly increases. The increase is greater than that in the water above or below it. The density change, or pycnocline, is due to changes in temperature and salinity.

radioactive elements Those elements that are capable of changing into other elements by the emission of charged particles from their nuclei.

rare gases Those gases (such as krypton, xenon, and argon) that are present in the earth's atmosphere in very small quantities.

relict sediments Sediments whose character does not represent present-day conditions, but a past environment.

residence time The residence time of an element in sea water is defined as the total amount of the element in the ocean divided by the rate of introduction of the element or the rate of its precipitation to the sediments.

respiration An oxidation process whereby organic matter is used by plants and animals and converted to energy. Oxygen is used in this process and carbon dioxide and water are liberated.

rip current A narrow seaward-flowing current that results from breaking of waves and subsequent accumulation of water in the nearshore zone.

rock weathering The chemical and physical processes that cause rocks to decay and eventually form soil.

salinity The total amount of dissolved material in sea water. It is measured in parts per thousand by weight in one kilogram of sea water.

SCUBA Self-Contained Underwater Breathing Apparatus.

sea Waves within their area of generation; usually they are irregular without a definite pattern.

seamounts   Isolated elevations, usually higher than 1,000 m, on the sea floor. Usually they resemble an inverted cone in shape.

secondary shorelines   Secondary shorelines are those where the coastal region has been mainly formed by marine or biological agents, like coral reefs, barrier beaches, and marshes.

sedimentary rocks   Rocks that have formed from the accumulation of particles (sediment) in water or from the air.

seiche   See stationary wave.

seismicity   Relates to earth movements or earthquakes; an area of high seismicity has numerous earthquakes.

shoal   A submerged but shallow bank or ridge which can be dangerous to ships.

sextant   An instrument for measuring angles.

shelf break   The sharp break in slope which marks the edge of the continental shelf and beginning of the continental slope.

shoreline   The place where land and water meet.

sill   A ridge separating one partially closed ocean basin from the ocean or another basin.

slumping   The sliding or moving of sediments down a submarine slope.

solubility   The degree with which a substance mixes with another substance.

sound channel   A sound channel can occur where the sound velocity reaches a minimum value. Sound in this zone is refracted upward or downward back into the zone, with little energy loss. Thus the sound traveling in this channel can be transmitted over distances of many thousands of kilometers.

sounding   The determination of the depth of the ocean. It can be done by lowering a line to the bottom or, electronically, by noting how long sound takes to travel to the bottom and return.

specific heat   The amount of heat required to raise or lower a unit mass of a substance to a certain temperature.

spontaneous liquefaction   When water-saturated sediments are subjected to a sudden shock, shear, or increase in pore water pressure, the internal grain-to-grain contacts within the sediment may change. If this happens, the entire sediment mass may move or flow, similar to an avalanche.

spring tides   High tides that occur about every two weeks, when the moon is full or new.

standing crop   See biomass.

stationary wave   A type of wave where the wave form does not move forward but the surface moves up and down. At certain fixed points, called nodes, the water surface will remain stationary.

storm surges   Abnormally high water levels due to strong winds blowing on the water surface.

surf   Surf is a term for breaking waves in a coastal area.

swell   Waves that have traveled away from their generating area. These waves have a more regular pattern than sea waves.

synoptic measurements   Numerous measurements taken simultaneously over a large area.

taxonomic classification   A systematic method of classifying animals and plants.

telemetry   A method, usually electronic, of measuring something and then transmitting the measurement to a receiving station.

terrigenous sediments   Sediments composed of material derived from the land. Usually these deposits are found close to land.

thermistor   A heat-sensitive device that can be used to measure temperature.

thermocline   A zone where the water temperature decreases more rapidly than the water above or below it. This zone usually starts from 10 to 500 m below the surface and can extend to over 1,500 m in depth.

tidal bore   A large wave of tidal origin that will travel up some rivers and estuaries.

tidal currents   Currents due to tides.

tides   The regular rising and falling of sea level, mainly caused by the gravitational attraction of the moon and sun on the earth.

topography   The study or description of the physical features of the earth's surface.

tsunami   A long period wave caused by a submarine earthquake, slumping, or volcanic eruptions. Tsunamis, sometimes called tidal waves, have heights of only a few centimeters in deep water, but can reach several tens of meters before they break on the beach.

turbidite A generally coarse-grained sediment that is deposited from a turbidity current. These sediments are generally found interbedded with the fine-grained muds typical of the deep sea.

turbidity current A turbid, relatively dense current composed of water and sediment that flows downslope through less dense sea water. The sediment eventually settles out, forming a turbidite.

turbulence A flow of water in which the motion of individual particles appears irregular and confused.

upwelling The movement of water from depth to the surface.

velocity The rate of motion in a given time, that is, 50 km/hr.

volcanic rocks Rocks that have resulted from volcanic eruptions.

wave attenuation The decrease in the wave form or height with distance from its origin.

wave crest The highest part of a wave.

wavelength The horizontal distance between two wave crests (or similar points on the wave form) measured parallel to the direction of travel of the wave.

wave period The time required for successive wave crests to pass by a fixed point.

wave refraction The change in direction of waves which occurs when one portion of the wave reaches shallow water and is slowed down while the other portion is in deep water and moving relatively fast.

wave trough The lowest part of a wave between two successive crests.

wave velocity The velocity or speed at which the wave form proceeds. It is equal to the wavelength divided by the wave period.

zeolite A particular type of authigenic mineral.

zooplankton Those plankton that are of the animal kingdom.

INDEX

A boldface number indicates a page on which an illustration appears; a "g" indicates that the term is defined in the Glossary of Oceanographic Terms.